THE NEW NATURALIST

A SURVEY OF BRITISH NATURAL HISTORY

DARTMOOR

The aim of this series is to interest the general reader in the wild life of Britain by recapturing the inquiring spirit of the old naturalists. The Editors believe that the natural pride of the British public in the native fauna and flora, to which must be added concern for their conservation, is best fostered by maintaining a high standard of accuracy combined with clarity of exposition in presenting the results of modern scientific research. The plants and animals are described in relation to their homes and habitats and are portrayed in the full beauty of their natural colours, by the latest methods of colour photography and reproduction.

THE NEW NATURALIST

DARTMOOR

By

L. A. HARVEY

and

D. ST. LEGER-GORDON

WITH 17 COLOUR PHOTOGRAPHS
BY E. H. WARE
36 PHOTOGRAPHS IN BLACK AND WHITE
AND 3 MAPS OF THE AREA

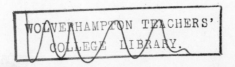
COLLINS
14 ST. JAMES'S PLACE, LONDON

First published 1953
Second edition 1962

CONTENTS

CONTENTS

Note: Chapters 11 and 12 are by D. St. Leger-Gordon; the rest by L. A. Harvey

PLATES IN COLOUR

It should be noted that throughout this book Plate numbers
in arabic figures refer to Colour Plates, while roman numerals
are used for Black-and-White Plates

PLATES IN BLACK AND WHITE

PLATES IN BLACK AND WHITE

EDITORS' PREFACE

In 1951 DARTMOOR was nominated as a National Park. This inevitable act has brought to particular public notice an unique "island" of upland England about which views are as strongly held as they are diverse.

The competing claims of national defence, water-supply, mineral working, afforestation, hill sheep-farming, public recreation and nature conservation which affect so many of the remoter parts of Britain are here all concentrated in one compact area in the heart of a single county. Should a television mast be allowed to rear its head in this domain of wild nature? Are man-made lakes a desecration or a desideratum? Do planted conifers destroy or enhance the landscape? All these are burning problems.

The romantic moorland-covered granite island of Dartmoor rises in the midst of the rolling sea of Devon's farmland. To some its open windy surfaces, sweeping upwards from sodden bogland to boulder-strewn tors are uninviting, even forbidding, and they may hurry across by one of the few main roads to seek the friendly shelter of one of the many villages which nestle around the moorland margin. Others will seek to stay and here attempt to wrest from Nature some of her closely-guarded secrets—the long-disputed origin of the valuable pockets of china clay or even of the granite itself; the relationship between the present vegetation and the remaining fragments of native woodland at the highest levels known in Britain. The heart of Dartmoor is a world of strange isolation, the domain of Dartmoor ponies, of Scottish black-faced sheep. Yet, in contrast with this lonely heartland is a fringe of lively villages, of human social life—villages like Widdi-combe, whose very name spells romance.

Exeter is the gateway to Dartmoor and it is fitting that the University College of the South-West should nourish a group of experts interested in Dartmoor's problems. No such group can be successful without skilled leadership and close collaboration. Such leadership is provided by Professor L. A. Harvey, and the close and careful integration of his text with the learned and well-written contributions of Mr. D. St. Leger-Gordon has made the work a balanced and consistent whole. The story of man's activities rises naturally from the study of the physical environment and background of natural history, and the Editors take pride in presenting this comprehensive regional synthesis in the *New Naturalist* series.

THE EDITORS

AUTHOR'S PREFACE

Many books have been written about Dartmoor, and the writer of
each has approached his task from his personal angle. I, too, have my
viewpoint, from which by training and inclination I look on my
surroundings. As an ecologist I observe and delight in the habits and
community relationships of plants and animals. Frankly, this, my
trade, is also my escape from the irksome burden of being human.
The reader therefore who shares the complaint expressed in his
Spectator review of the companion volume, *Snowdonia*, by Mr. Clough
Williams-Ellis, that Peacock was sacrificed to slugs and beetles, must
be prepared to witness similar immolations here. I am not reconciled
to the view of man as the centre about which the affairs of the world
revolve. The account I present of Dartmoor is therefore as objective
as I have been able to make it, relating directly to the plants and
animals which live there, and to the ways in which our human
arbitrariness may affect them.

Inevitably much of what I have included is not my own. No
individual can hope to present a portrait of a region without the aid
of innumerable friends and mentors. None but I may be held responsible for opinions I have expressed, though many have helped to
mould these, by letter, by conversation, by their published work. I am
particularly indebted to Lady Aileen Fox and the late Colonel Ransom
Pickard, without whose help the account of the archæology of the
region could not have been written. Colonel Pickard provided the
facts, Lady Fox invaluable criticisms and corrections of my manu-
script. Mr. H. G. Hurrell sent me much information about the birds
and mammals, and has been perpetually fertile in encouragement and
suggestion. Mr. C. A. Wilson, County Pests Officer, generously ran-
sacked his files to provide information about the spread of grey squirrels
in South Devon, while Mr. C. C. Whitley and Lt.-Col. W. G. Clarke,
Masters respectively of the South Devon Hunt and the Dartmoor

Foxhounds, responded generously to my inquiries about foxes seen in their country. Mrs. W. B. Yeats and Messrs. A. P. Watt & Sons have generously permitted me to quote the lines from 'Into the Twilight.' (*The Collected Poems of W. B. Yeats*) which appear on p. 3, to them my thanks. The Map of the Geology of South Devon was drawn by Miss Mary Stonehouse, while for that of the Dartmoor National Park I am indebted to Mr. Geoffrey Clark and the Devon County Council Planning Department. Mr. E. H. Ware's photographs speak for themselves. I must, however, express to him my deep gratitude for the many hours of patient care he expended on them. I might almost say that he is responsible for the completion of this book; for all too frequently it has been the thought of his contribution to it which has lifted me over the more difficult passages of my own. My thanks also to the Editorial Board, who, individually and collectively, have been so patient and encouraging, and to countless others who must remain unnamed only for lack of space. Finally, to Clare Harvey my warmest thanks, for her knowledge of botany and above all for the help and spiritual sustenance which only a wife can offer.

L. A. HARVEY

University College of the South-West,
Exeter
June 1950

CHAPTER I

APPROACH TO DARTMOOR

SPRING COMES EARLY in the warm west, and by March the wild Daffodils may be blooming at Steps Bridge and the Bracken shooting under its rusty pall of last year's withering. Soon the scrub oaks begin to unfold their buds, and then the copses and valley woods become a riotous patchwork of translucent colour: red, orange, yellow, bronze and every imaginable shade of green. The Bilberry flowers come, to hang like waxen pale lanterns, the Bracken and Oaks mature to a darker green, a deeper shade, and high summer is here. Asphodel and Cotton grass brighten the bogs, and, to the seeking eye, the paler delicacies of Sundews, Butterwort and Bog Pimpernel display their exquisiteness. Soon the moors begin to flower; first the deep purple of Bell Heather and the pale rose of Cross-leaved Heath, and then the great sweeps of the true Heather in its many tints of pink. The fruits ripen on the Bilberries till the plants look as if hung with little round sloes, each set stiffly on the wiry stems. On the Rowans at the stream-sides great flat bunches of berries turn bright red and the trees seem as if aflame.

Summer gives place imperceptibly to autumn. The fronds of Bracken and the leaves of the trees begin to turn yellow, then brown and russet, the Heather blooms fade and fall, Bilberries and Rowans are harvested by man and birds, and the only fruits now to be found are the blackberries at road and plantation side, and on the walls and hedges. And so the moor divests itself of its summer fripperies and once again the eye is free to appreciate the grandeur of its lines, the noble arcs of the hills, the towering, tumbling pinnacles of the tors, the texture of its fabric of rock and grass and heather, the swift fall of its ubiquitous amber waters.

Whatever the season, whatever the weather, Dartmoor casts its spell. It is a place apart, differentiated from the surrounding country by its height and wildness and the peace to be found in its solitudes. The climate is different, the air noticeably fresher and softer, and the limpid light associated with hill country softens and yet enhances all its colours. One must recognise, however, that attraction is a personal thing, conditioned by the observer's background, interests and preferences. Moreover, because of the strength of charm exercised by familiar things, it is difficult to write with considered judgment about scenes well known and loved. For my part, I never approach Dartmoor without a lightening of heart and a sure knowledge that I am entering country which is a delight to all my senses. There I shall find pleasure in the great whalebacks of the hills, in the honey-scent of the Heather, the spring of its wiry stems underfoot and the light dusting of pollen from its prodigal flowers as I brush past. My ear will be alert for the mew of a Buzzard, the cronk of passing Ravens, although, alas, I am now deaf to the nearer, smaller chirrup of grasshoppers.

Or, in another mood, at another season, I walk in a wet, quiet world. It's a "soft day" and a fine rain is gentling down from clouds which hang low enough to trail their hems across the hilltops and shut them momentarily from view. The brown leaves of autumn litter the floor of the woods and give off a rare scent as I scuff them up. Rich and delicately-coloured toadstools grow among and above them, and the greens of ferns and ivy, moss and lichens on the tree-trunks seem the brighter for their contrast with the sombreness of the dying year. On the moor above, every shoot of Heather and Bilberry gleams softly wet, and the trailing tips of the hair-fine grasses carry each a glistening droplet of water. Nothing stirs but the quietly grazing sheep and ponies, or Buzzard, Raven and Crows overhead. The smaller birds stay in cover, while such insects as remain from the earlier season's wealth stay close in the drier bottom of the herbage. Only here and there the big black slugs display the elegance of their shining rugosity. But in this quiet world one need not travel far to hear the sound of water. The small brooks flow with a swifter vigour and a deeper speech, and the rivers, murky now with sediment, boil over and among their rocks in turbulent violence, a foot and more above the white marks left by summer's drought.

So the Moor rests, and yet changes, with the seasons, from day to day, from hour to hour, always beautiful although not always clement. Here,

E. H. Ware

Plate 1. Looking north-west from King Tor

" where hill is heaped upon hill;
For there the mystical brotherhood
Of sun and moon and hollow and wood
And river and stream work out their will."

Those, and they are many, who are not yet so civilised that they no longer appreciate such communion, will find fresh delight whenever they visit it, and I am content if the pages which follow stimulate only a few to go and seek their pleasure there.

Dartmoor is situated in the heart of South Devon, forming the skeletal core of the peninsula which projects seawards between Exeter and Plymouth and culminates in the famous headland of Start Point. To the south of the Moor lie the warm, lush farmlands of the South Hams; eastwards stretch the red soils which give so much colour and character to vast acreages of Devon. The western and northern borders are lapped by the sandstones and shales of the Upper Devonian and Culm Measures; shallow, rather poor soils which support for the most part wet pastures, and the conifer plantations of the Forestry Commission. It matters little from whence the approach to Dartmoor is made. It towers above the surrounding country in granite solidity, the sweep of its rolling uplands, crowned here and there by spectacular tors, contrasting sharply with the flatter, lower farmlands about it, and yet blending into a landscape at all times eminently satisfying.

If I were asked at what time of year Dartmoor is at its best I should have difficulty in finding an answer. So much depends on the individual preference, so much on the mood of the moment. To those who love wild places I would say, " See it at all seasons. You will always find pleasure there." In winter the sweeping hillsides are mottled in shades of russet, brown and black, intensified here by cloud shadows, or lightened there by the grey of granite and lichen on the tors. The vivid green of Sphagnum in the bogs never fails to startle, and yet relieve, the eye by its freshness. Or sometimes the whole lies under snow, its whiteness broken by the tors and copses and plantations, and laced by the dark ribbons of the streams which everywhere dissect the landscape.

The best way to see Dartmoor is on foot. By no other means, unless it be on horseback, can one approach the heart of its wild places, and happily, in R. H. Crossing's *Guide to Dartmoor*, there exists

D

B

a most comprehensive description of its tracks and contours. First published by the *Western Morning News* as five separate parts in 1914, no recent issue is available, and it is not readily obtainable. A number of other excellent, although less detailed, descriptions of the region have however been published. The traveller with an eye to country will appreciate in particular the pen-sketches of contours and landmarks with which its text is embellished. But the National Park of Dartmoor embraces much country which lies outside the scope of these guides, and some brief description of the region is necessary before we begin to discuss its features in more detail.

The boundaries of the National Park were drawn partly with an eye to the necessity of using easily defined features such as roads, rivers and the like, and partly in order to include within the area the very beautiful and interesting " in-country " which fringes the Moor proper and constitutes a logical part of the total complex from the points of view of its geological, topographical and biological structure. Thus, as may be seen from the map on page 10, the southern boundary follows the main Exeter to Plymouth road from Chudleigh Knighton through Ashburton, Buckfastleigh and South Brent to Ivybridge, and thence across country through Cornwood to Bere Ferrers on the River Tavy. From here the river is followed as far as Tavistock, north of which town the border is extended a mile or two westwards in order to include Brentor, with its famous little church, and Lydford Gorge. Returning eastwards the boundary follows the road to Okehampton and thence towards Exeter as far as Crockernwell. On the eastern side by-roads are used as far as Dunsford, from which point the bank of the River Teign is used until it once more reaches the Exeter to Plymouth road just west of Chudleigh. Thus, in addition to the Forest and its Commons, there are included, at the south-west, the very beautiful woods of the Tavy and Walkham valleys, and, to the east, the extremely interesting outlier of mixed farm-, wood- and moor-lands lying roughly between the River Teign and the road from Bovey Tracey to South Zeal.

The visitor may choose from among a wide selection of small communities the point from which to explore Dartmoor. Of the comparatively few lying actually within the boundary, the larger are Princetown, Bovey Tracey, Moretonhampstead and Chagford. The smaller villages and hamlets include Holne, Buckland-in-the-Moor, Lustleigh, Manaton, North Bovey, Widecombe, Postbridge, Throwleigh, Gidleigh, Peter and Mary Tavy, Yelverton and Horrabridge. For the most part the only approach is by road. But a single-track branch railway winds up the 1,200-foot climb from Plymouth to Princetown, while a similar single line extends from Newton Abbot to serve Bovey Tracey, Lustleigh and Moretonhampstead.[1] Four Youth Hostels are situated at Steps Bridge, Gidleigh, Postbridge and South Brent respectively, and there are comfortable inns and hotels in most of the townships as well as at a number of more isolated spots on the roads between. And, of course, as is the case throughout the south-west, there is no lack of accommodation to be found in private houses and farms. For those not active enough to walk, all the better-known localities may be easily reached by car, or by the coach trips which run throughout the season from Exeter, Plymouth, Torquay and Totnes and other towns in the vicinity, visiting Dartmeet, Holne Chase, Princetown, Haytor, Manaton, Becky Falls and Widecombe, to mention only the better known of Dartmoor's noted places.

Most of the Dartmoor towns and villages have a long history, the course of which it is left to Gordon to trace in a later chapter (p. 152), and which has left its impress on their architecture and customs. For the most part the local granite has been used in the construction of the larger buildings, and this confers on them an attractively rugged forthrightness. The churches in particular, with their heavily-buttressed walls and stout square towers, seem to express for the community its determination to abide come rain come shine, and the survival of Saxon and Norman features in their architecture betokens the enduring age of many. To-day the main activities are agriculture and catering for visitors. But in the past tin and wool have been staple industries, and then the stannary towns of Ashburton, Tavistock and Chagford, together with Lydford of evil fame, must have been very busy places. The woollen industry, probably introduced by the Cistercians at Buckfast Abbey during the twelfth century, spread along the southern side of the Moor, but continued to be centred on the mills at Buckfastleigh and Ashburton. Mills still operating here are now supplemented by the output of the modern plant established to the south at Dartington, but all are small and specialised in their products by contrast with the huge concerns of Yorkshire. The other industries of the region include paper-making at Ivybridge and Buckfastleigh and quarrying for stone, baryta and iron ores. China clay working is most active to the south-west, at Lee Moor, but valuable clay also occurs in the Bovey basin,

[1] Both these branch lines have recently been closed down by British Railways.

the products being some of them exported out of the area and some used in local potteries and for the making of the famous Devon grates.

As will be shown later (p. 60) the Bovey beds have an interesting geological history. They consist of seams, often intricately interbedded, of pottery clay and lignite. The lignite workings have had a chequered history which is described in a privately printed booklet by C. W. Parish, *The Creation of an Industry* (1947). Before the advent of the railway in 1868 lignite was extensively used as a low-grade fuel in cottagers' fires and in the potters' kilns. The railway brought cheap coal to the doorstep and the lignite then became virtually worthless and its extraction unprofitable. But in Germany the presence of immense deposits of " braunkohle " and of a cadre of world-renowned industrial chemists led to the development of a number of uses for the products of their mines. Crude lignite is of a low thermal value, but after treatment it was made up into briquettes which were able to compete with coal as fuel for many purposes. But a more important product, not to be found in all lignites, is Montan Wax, the uses of which have developed tremendously under modern demands. It forms an important ingredient of inks, glues, polishes and paints, as also in such widely different things as insulators, cosmetics, confectionery, soaps, sealing-wax, insecticides and fungicides. Fortunately, the Bovey deposits resemble those of Germany in possessing a high content of this wax. Indeed, in 1913, the Germans were exploring the possibility of importing raw material from Devon to supplement their own sources of supply. To-day, as a result of these preliminary investigations, followed during the last war by the efforts of our own Fuel Research Board and finally by the establishment of modern plant for extraction and treatment of the crude material, the Bovey lignite deposits promise to become a source of new wealth to both Devon and Britain.

Happily, these industries do little to spoil the amenities of Dartmoor. With the exception of the china clay-workings, which inevitably intrude their white dust and pits and spoil-heaps into the Lee Moor region, the factories and workings are situated on the fringes of the in-country close to the main roads and the railway. Their traffic merges into that of these already busy trunks, and at a distance of a mile or less their influence becomes negligible as far as the visitor is concerned. There is little of the grime or densely packed housing which has come to be such a feature of the industrial north, and the rural character of the

Plate I. Raven, *Corvus corax*, at nest in Rowan tree, with young

Plate II a.   Bellever Tor, seen over one of Dartmoor's stone walls

   b.   Old plough headlands and furrows, near Grimspound

countryside remains dominant and unspoiled. Of the other towns little need be said at this juncture. Each has its particular characteristics derived from activities associated with it. Princetown is dominated by its associated Dartmoor Prison, Okehampton by the military camps established in connection with the artillery ranges to the immediate south, while Tavistock, Moretonhampstead and Chagford serve their quiet functions as market towns, coming to vigorous life periodically for the carnival or fair. These, of which Widecombe Fair and Tavistock Goosey Fair are well known and celebrated in song, have usually a long tradition behind them. Nowadays the inhabitants for the most part look forward to them as brilliant spectacles and social events rather than for the opportunity of commercial exchange which was their original function, and for those who have not witnessed carnival time in Devon such a fair is well worth visiting.

One most pleasant feature of the towns and villages is their compact structure. Within five minutes' walk from the centre of most of them one has passed the last house and is between loose stone walls covered with Maidenhair Spleenwort, Wall Pennywort and Herb Robert, with intimate views over them of the small, steep green pastures into which the land is divided. Or the way may climb between high banks crowned with hazels and brambles and draped with many a fern; at some point, almost inevitably, the road will run alongside a small brown river, its course larded with moss-grown boulders, its banks clothed with Alders and Oaks. With the inevitable right-angle turn the road crosses the stream by a narrow, high-arched granite bridge and is off again, climbing and winding through coppiced woodland until it has breasted the valleyside and is once again quietly meandering on its leisurely course. There must be hundreds of miles of such lanes intersecting the in-country around Dartmoor, and on them you can dawdle or stride along, it hardly matters whither. Sooner or later they intersect with another track, or terminate in a stony farmyard, or debouch on to open moorland. Unless you really want to go somewhere one is as beguiling as another. Nevertheless, with a good one-inch map, it is possible to chart a course through them and arrive at a specified objective, having walked all day without passing more than an occasional farm-cart or tractor or exchanging more than a word or two with a hedger or shepherd.

The hub of all this, and the reason for it being as it is, is the great central core of granite, Dartmoor, with its vast stretches of bog and moor. It is surprising, therefore, neither that all roads lead eventually out on to the moors, nor that this country is included within the boundary of the National Park. It constitutes an integral part of a countryside the character of which I must try to analyse in subsequent chapters.

CHAPTER 2

DARTMOOR AS A NATIONAL PARK

IT SEEMS GOOD at this early stage of the book to devote some pages to a consideration as to why Dartmoor was chosen as a National Park. It is the more appropriate in that the National Parks Bill has so recently (1949) received the Royal assent and Dartmoor has (1951) become the fourth of our National Parks. Thus the years of careful argument and examination, which began with the appointment of the first National Parks Commission under Dr. Addison in 1929, have at last borne fruit. Let us hope that the seed of this fruit, germinating more rapidly than that of the parent stock, may produce, by careful management, something worthy of the efforts and aspirations of the many people and organisations who have contributed to its cultivation.

John Dower's conception of a National Park (Cmd. 6628, 1945) caught the imagination, and we cannot do better than examine Dartmoor in its light. He defined a National Park as, " an extensive area of beautiful and relatively wild country in which, for the nation's benefit and by appropriate national decision and action: (a) the characteristic landscape beauty is strictly preserved; (b) access and facilities for public open-air enjoyment are amply provided; (c) wild life and buildings and places of architectural and historic interest are suitably protected, while (d) established farming use is effectively maintained."

It is not surprising that the National Parks Committee (England and Wales) in their report (Cmd. 7121, 1947) grouped Dartmoor, together with the Lake District, North Wales and the Peak District, as regions recommended for first consideration. As an extensive area of beautiful and relatively wild country it is unrivalled in southern England, although small by comparison with either the Lakes or

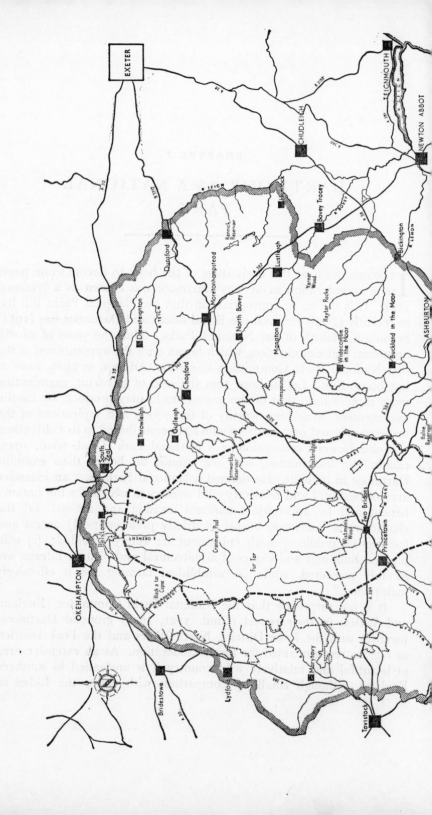

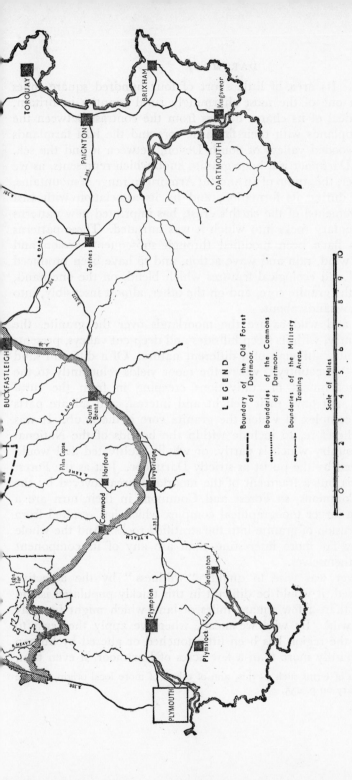

DARTMOOR NATIONAL PARK

LEGEND

Boundary of the Old Forest
of Dartmoor.

Boundaries of the Commons
of Dartmoor.

Boundaries of the Military
Training Areas.

Scale of Miles

0 1 2 3 4 5 6 7 8 9 10

TORQUAY

BRIXHAM

PAIGNTON

Kingswear

DARTMOUTH

Totnes

BUCKFASTLEIGH

South
Brent

Piles Copse

Harford

Cornwood

Ivybridge

Yealmpton

Plympton

Plymouth

PLYMOUTH

North Wales. Its area of little short of four hundred square miles stands within one of the most charmingly rural counties in Britain, and a great deal of its charm derives from the contrast between the bare rolling uplands with their fantastic tors and the lush farmlands and thickly wooded valleys of South Devon, between it and the sea. The heart of Dartmoor is a huge granite knob which represents, as we shall show later, the stump of an ancient Armorican range of mountains. The granite, during its formation, and by its association with vast orogenic movements[1] of the earth's crust, has imprinted new patterns on the sedimentary rocks into which it was intruded. These patterns in their turn have been modified through subsequent erosion and moulding by wind, rain and wave action, and so have been produced topographical and ecological features which blend, on the one hand, into those of the granite core, and on the other, almost insensibly, into those of the lowlands about.

Beautiful and wild as are the moorlands over the granite, the marginal country, with its steep hillsides and deep-cut valleys, presents an equal beauty, although of a different nature. Of a different kind again, is the " in-country," where the moor yields reluctantly to the insistent encroachment of cultivations creeping in from the rural surroundings. All have their delight and interest, and all are parts of one great complex of which the granite core is the knub. It was but logical, therefore, to include within the bounds of the National Park much country which is partly, or wholly, cultivated and would not be regarded by the purist as strictly Dartmoor. Just as the Forest of Dartmoor is but a fragment of the moorland area covered by the Forest and Commons, so Forest and Commons in their turn are a part only of a larger topographical complex which has resulted from the initial intrusion of granite into the stratified rocks. And the whole complex is by far more interesting than are any of its component elements by themselves.

John Dower was wise to qualify " wildness " by the adjective relative. Indeed, it would be difficult in this thickly populated island to find more than a few square miles of land which might be truly described as wild. By wild we mean, when we apply the term to country, that the region has been little touched or altered by human activity. Of hardly more than a few acres of Dartmoor, if even that,

[1] Elucidation of terms such as this, and of others of more local origin, will be found in a glossary on p. 255.

may this be said. We can only infer from their remains what effects prehistoric civilisations have had on Dartmoor. But these remains, as will be amply demonstrated in later chapters, are exceedingly numerous, and they betoken the existence of a population which must have been dense by comparison with much of a then sparsely settled island. We know that the growing civilisations of western Europe became deeply interested in sources of tin and copper, and there is ample evidence that from these times right up until the beginning of the present century ores of these metals were extracted by a variety of methods from the deposits in which Dartmoor and its in-country are richly endowed. By panning the streams and mining the lodes, this long line of activities has altered the face of the country. River beds, deepened in one place or dammed in another, have been induced to shift. Open-cast workings have scoured deep gullies in the hillsides, and the spoil-heaps thrown aside have consolidated into hummocks and mounds. The mere fact that people were living there, quite apart from their means of livelihood, has altered the terrain. From a very early date men made their dwellings and pounds with the granite blocks so liberally scattered beneath the tors, and the tumbledown remains of these houses and walls have outlived their creators by many centuries, as have also the monoliths, stone-rows and circles which were prominent cultural implements of some of the earliest races.

The archaeologist can read traces of lynchet and terrace cultivations dating back, some, maybe, to the Bronze Age, some to Saxon times. During the period of recorded history other cultivations have been made in association with the " ancient tenements " and " in-takes " and " new-takes," and many of these, with their walled fields, are still in use. Moreover, it is not so very long ago, during the times of the Napoleonic wars, that quite large stretches of now-open moorland were under the plough, and Plate II, p. 7, shows the lines of ridge and furrow which may still be seen at one of these sites.

From very early times the moorland communities must have had their highways, linking one settlement with another, and all with the tin ports on the coast through which passed the trade with France and the Mediterranean countries. Many of these tracks crossed the wildest moorlands, and constant treading through the centuries has left indelible marks on the land and on the plants growing there. Moreover, it is inconceivable that men lived on these uplands without domestic animals. These, by their grazing, began the processes of change in the vegetation which are so ruthlessly hastened to-day by the modern hill-grazier with his burning, cutting and heavy stocking. In addition, the defence of himself and his herds forced man into constant warfare against the larger carnivores, possibly wolf and bear, until these have become long extinct throughout Britain. Trees, peat and turf have been used in quantity as fuel, either for domestic dwellings or in the blowing houses where tin and copper were smelted. Even remote copses, like Black Tor Beare, have been hacked or felled, and it is unlikely that much accessible woodland has remained undisturbed.

Wildness is then indeed a relative term in Britain, even on these remotest hills, and on Dartmoor we can find the true wilderness only in the remote fastnesses of the bogs overlying the highest watershed in the north, around Cut Hill and Fur Tor. Even here we cannot be sure. We know that the peat has been regressing, probably for centuries, but whether this may be attributable to a natural climax and recession, to climatic change, or to human interference with the water-courses lower down is a question to which no full answer may at present be found. The ground is, however, too waterlogged, unstable and uneven for human habitation, or to attract grazing animals; tin and other minerals, if they are there, are buried deep beneath the peat; even the peat itself is not accessible except near the margins, because the soft, uncertain ground makes it difficult or impossible to cart it away. Consequently, this region alone of Dartmoor has hardly been changed by human artefact until the artillerymen from Okehampton began their practice firing across it, and drove metalled roads up to its very margins. Even so, it remains for the most part wrapped in lonely and quiet integrity.

For all this, however, Dartmoor is as nearly wild country as we may expect to find in Britain, and the communities of plants and animals which live there comprise many species which cannot tolerate, or be tolerated in, the farmlands below. The lists of fauna and flora which are appended at the end of the book, incomplete as they are, present pictures of communities such as may only be found in places remote from the intensive changes which are associated with cultivation or industry. The botanist will note the rich contribution to the populations made by mosses, liverworts and lichens. The abundance of these lowly plants may be attributed to various causes. Many are encouraged by the mild, damp climate, others by the acidity of rock surfaces or peat, or by the boggy conditions or standing water. Over

Oliver Pike

Plate III a.   Long-tailed Field Mouse, *Apodemus sylvaticus*

b.   Bank vole, *Clethrionomys glareolus*

A. R. Thompson

Humphrey & Vera Joel

Plate IV a. Hay Tor

     b. Fernworthy Reservoir and plantations

E. H. Ware

large areas, such as the big blanket bogs, the relatively low pressure of competition from flowering plants permits the development of a crypto-gamic flora, which elsewhere is reduced or excluded by the cover of a more familiar vegetation. In short, the mosses and lichens are alone in being able to tolerate, and even thrive in, the rigours of the acid soil and the bitter winds of winter on the high moors. As a consequence, conditions come to resemble those of the vast tundra areas which cover a wide belt of northern Europe.

The flora of the moors contains a number of unusual plants, derived from various sources during the history of the region. Some of these plants are characteristic of Northern Europe, for instance the very rare little Bog Orchis, *Hammarbya paludosa*, the Crowberry, *Empetrum nigrum*, the Cowberry, *Vaccinium vitis-idaea*, the Cranberry, *Oxycoccus quadripetalus*, the Club-moss, *Lycopodium selago* and the two Cotton-grasses, *Eriophorum angustifolium* and *E. vaginatum*. As Harris (1938) has suggested, such plants are best interpreted as relics of a more northern flora which in earlier periods must have possessed a very different distribution. In recent years the work of Dr. Godwin and his collaborators, on pollen and other plant remains in peat and similar deposits, has provided us with a picture of the general changes in the vegetation of our islands since the Ice Ages. In particular, the studies (Godwin et al, 1950) on deposits on Bodmin Moor, not far from Dartmoor, have revealed that the Late-Glacial flora of that region at the close of the last Ice Age contained plants of Arctic distribution today, such as the Mountain Avens, *Dryas octopetala*, the dwarf Willow, *Salix herbacea*, and the dwarf Birch, *Betula nana*, with others of a more general northern distribution, such as the Crowberry, *Empetrum*, still to be found, although very rarely, as relics on these south-western moors. Incidentally it must be added that some of the species, in particular those of *Vaccinium*, *Empetrum*, *Oxycoccus* and *Lycopodium*, are by no means common and it requires more than a casual search to discover them. The little Bog Orchis, for instance, has only been seen twice in the last 85 years, although in part this apparent rarity may be due to its extremely inconspicuous size and colour, and to its habit of growing in dense sphagnum.

An interesting element of the flora is that provided by the Lusitanian plants. These are species typical of Spain, Portugal and southern and western France, but just extend to the western and especially the south-western parts of Britain. The Pale Butterwort, *Pinguicula lusitanica*, is one of these, occurring in S. W. England, in one restricted area of west Wales, in W. Scotland, and in Ireland. On Dartmoor it completely replaces the Common Butterwort of the bogs of more easterly and northerly Britain. Of other Lusitanian species, Cornish Heath, *Erica vagans*, does not occur, except at one locality where it was introduced in 1930 by Miss Boggis, at Lydford. But a vigorous colony of Dorset Heath, *Erica ciliaris*, now covers a patch of hillside on Soussons Down, and is now the only known stand of the plant between its two main British stations at the Lizard and on Wareham Heath in Dorset. This is a beautiful, brilliantly coloured heath, and one which acquires new beauty after its flowers die, when the rich carmine of the bells turns to an almost equally brilliant light chestnut, and the dead flowers remain on the stems. Small wonder that, like its Cornish cousin, it has given rise to a galaxy of garden plants of great merit. The origin of this particular colony is unknown. The *Devon Flora* tells us that it was first recorded in 1911, and states that it seems neither to increase nor to decrease. The latter is, however, no longer true. I first saw the colony in 1936, when it consisted of no more than a few score of plants occupying at most some twenty square yards. By 1948, however, when I last saw it, despite having been burned over at least once during the preceding twelve years, it was much more vigorous. Satellite outliers from the parent colony had appeared, and the whole then comprised several thousands of plants and covered some hundreds of square yards.

Unhappily the colony has become included within the Forestry Commission's plantation on Soussons Downs, and indeed planting furrows had been run through it and young conifers, on their upturned sods, were already established over and among the heather plants. It is a significant sign of the vigour of the plants that they were already beginning to sprout through the overlying peat, and there is little doubt that the colony will survive. For the Commission agreed, with promptitude and kindly co-operation, to preserve the stand. An area of about three-quarters of an acre around it has been demarcated and all the young trees within it uprooted. The plants will, therefore, remain unshaded by the trees as they begin to grow tall, and they will have every chance to survive. One cannot help regretting that the colony will thus be converted into something of a museum piece, but the regret is mingled with satisfaction that so interesting a species will be given every opportunity to maintain itself, and it is always possible that, from a vigorous colony, it may eventually be able to spread more widely on to the open moors.

Two other species require mention. Cornish Moneywort, *Sibthorpia europaea*, is an inconspicuous little plant the trailing stems of which twine among those of other plants. The small rounded leaves and tiny pink flowers are not very obvious in such a situation, and they must be sought in moist shady places by the banks of streams, in the sides of wells and in similar stations. Marsh St. John's Wort, *Hypericum elodes*, on the other hand, is one of the most characteristic plants of the bogs and indeed it is more widely spread in England and on the Continent than most of the other members of the group, although it is not always easy to recognise it as an *Hypericum*, if one is not familiar with it. Its grey-green, very hairy leaves are not unlike those of some of the mints, and they often acquire that same intensely silvery appearance from the innumerable tiny drops of water which accumulate on them from the moist atmosphere. The small yellow flowers are less often seen open than as tightly rolled little yellow spikes, of which it is rare to find more than one at a time on a stem. It is a very attractive species, and perhaps the one which comes to mind first when one is thinking of a Dartmoor bog or marshy stream.

The lists of birds and mammals contain comparatively few rare species, apart from casual migrants and wanderers among the birds. But, as the reader will discover, the countryside is sufficiently wild and diverse in character to encourage the larger predators and scavengers which we have left in our British fauna. Badger, *Meles meles*, and Otter, *Lutra lutra*, may be seen by those prepared to spend the necessary time and patience. Foxes, *Vulpes vulpes*, are numerous despite trapping and shooting and the attentions of several hunts. It is common to flush them from where they are lying out among heather or deep bracken, and many good views may be had as they bound away over the rough ground. Rabbits, *Oryctolagus cuniculus*, are numerous, although none of the warrens in which they were formerly farmed is now maintained.[1] They are, like the Foxes, particularly addicted to the clitters, where the roughly tumbled boulders provide ideal cover for their buries. Hares, *Lepus europaeus*, occur, but only in small numbers, and during many years of walking over the moors I personally have never seen one. There is little information about the smaller mammals, beyond the fact that they occur, particularly commonly in the deep cover provided

[1] The attack of myxomatosis was somewhat local and less severe than elsewhere, and a considerable population still flourishes.

by young conifer plantations. Some idea of their relative abundance in the in-country is provided by a sample one hundred caught in break-back traps during December 1947 to January 1948 by Mr. H. G. Hurrell at Wrangaton. This included:

Bank-Vole, *Clethrionomys glareolus*	47
Long-tailed Field-Mouse, *Apodemus sylvaticus*	30
Short-tailed Vole, *Microtus agrestis*	3
Common Shrew, *Sorex araneus*	17
Pigmy Shrew, *Sorex minutus*	2
Water-Shrew, *Neomys fodiens*	1
TOTAL	100

It is not clear why the Hare should be so scarce on Dartmoor. Possibly the ground cover is unsuitable, or the frequent burning of the Heather may seriously interfere with breeding.

During the last few years a very promising investigation has been commenced of the bats of some parts of the county. The work is being undertaken by the members of the Devon Spelaeological Society, and, through the courtesy of the Society, I am able to summarise the more important results which have been obtained from banding experiments. The bats are found, mostly during the winter months, at roosts, in caves at Buckfastleigh and Pridhamsleigh, in the Bulkamore iron mine, the Virtuous Lady copper mine and Penn Recca slate quarries, as also elsewhere in South Devon in caves at Chudleigh, Afton, Ogwell, Yealmpton and Brixham. Between September 1948 and February 1950 just over 670 bats have been banded, the data being tabled below:

Species	Male	Female	Indeter-minate	Total
Greater Horse-shoe, *Rhinolophus ferrum-equinum*	293	228	—	521
Lesser Horse-shoe, *R. hipposideros*	64	64	2	130
Natterer's, *Myotis nattereri*	7	3	—	10
Long-eared, *Plecotus auritus*	2	2	—	4
Pipistrelle, *Pipistrellus pipstrellus*	2	6	—	8
TOTAL				673

A number of interesting pieces of information are accruing as a

E. H. Ware

Plate 2. Autumn at Merivale

result of the work, mostly, as may be expected, referring to the Greater Horseshoe, which is by far the commonest species. A very high rate of recovery of marked bats is maintained, no less than 299, or 57.4 per cent, of *R. ferrum-equinum* having been taken again, while recoveries of *R. hipposideros* total 35, or 26.9 per cent. One bat has been recovered no less than twelve times. We may infer from this that the local population does not change very much, except at the breeding season, there being little evidence of immigration from elsewhere.

The winter work has gone far to disprove the idea of deep winter sleep in bats. Both the Horseshoes have been found to undertake extensive cross-country flights during the period. While some local movement might be expected to result from the inevitable disturbance of the animals during weighing, measuring and ringing, there seems no reason why this should induce them to undertake flights of ten miles or so. Moreover, it has been observed that, in some instances at least, the bats were alert before any actual disturbance and handling began. The movements noted may be summarised as follows:

Distance of flight in miles	Total number of flights	Total number of winter flights
1–2	129	70
2–3	36	17
6–10	5	—
10–16.7	4	1

Unfortunately the summer haunts have yet to become fully known. The winter roosts are normally deserted between April and September or October, and only two relatively small " nursing colonies " have hitherto been discovered in summer. It is interesting to note, however, that even in these groups of pregnant and nursing females some males are tolerated. In the winter there seems to be little segregation of the sexes. The bats sleep, sometimes in solitude, at other times in clusters of up to as many as one hundred, but on the average between twenty and twenty-five. No cluster has been observed comprised of one sex only, and there may be a predominance of either sex up to proportions of one to four, or the numbers of each sex may be equal.[1]

[1] Since writing this further results have been published (J. H. D. Hooper, 1951). Up to April 1951 over a thousand bats have been banded, and the high rate of recovery of the two Horseshoes has been maintained. Many flights of up to as much as seventeen miles have been recorded and the lightness of winter sleep, particularly of the Greater Horseshoe Bat has been confirmed by observations of quite extensive winter movements.

The outstanding large birds of the region are Buzzards, *Buteo buteo*, Ravens, *Corvus corax*, and Carrion-Crows, *Corvus corone*, all of which are resident and may be met during the course of any day's walking over either the moors or the in-country. The Buzzard has increased in numbers steadily during the last twenty or twenty-five years. It breeds more frequently in the taller trees of the marginal valleys than on the tors of the moor; indeed, it is an extraordinary feature of the species on Dartmoor that it prefers a tree site rather than the rock ledges to which it is more normally accustomed around the coasts of Britain. Recently an almost pure white male, bred from a pale female, has been flying in the southern confines of the Moor. Raven and Carrion-Crow are now both abundant, but have not always been so. Indeed, the fortunes of the Corvidae have fluctuated considerably in the region, as Mr. Hurrell has shown in a summary of the reports provided by competent observers since the days of Polwhele, which is stated in the table on page 21:

Of most of the Accipitridae other than the Buzzard it is possible only to make passing references, as they can most of them no longer be regarded as more than casual members of the fauna. The lists are indeed melancholy reading, with items such as:

Rough-legged Buzzard, *Buteo lagopus*	Occasional. D'Urban says used to occur every autumn.
Marsh-Harrier, *Circus aeruginosus*	Occasional. Formerly abundant, now rare.
Hen-Harrier, *Circus cyaneus*	Occasional. Used to nest, now occasional in winter.
Kite, *Milvus milvus*	Occasional. Formerly bred Holne Chase.
Honey-Buzzard, *Pernis apivorus*	Occasional. One 1848.
Osprey, *Pandion haliaetus*	Occasional. 1, Goodmeavy, in Plymouth Museum.

But, to set against these, both Hobby, *Falco subbuteo*, and Merlin, *Falco columbarius*, are known to nest occasionally, while that beautiful bird, Montagu's Harrier, *Circus pygargus*, has recently begun to breed again after the lapse of half a century. There is, at the time of writing, 1949, little evidence that the species is increasing, or indeed that it is firmly established, and all who value so fine a species will concur in the necessity not to divulge the neighbourhood in which it nests. For, not only may the nest be robbed by anti-social people, but the adults

	POLWHELE 1797	MATHEW and D'URBAN 1892	ROWE 1896	MATHEW 1906	HURRELL 1916-1946	ROBINSON 1944-1945 POSTBRIDGE ONLY
Raven *Corvus corax*	Not mentioned	Numerous up to 1850. Only occasionally seen 1892. A few pairs breed	Now scarce but still breeds in some unfrequented parts of moor	Increasing	Big increase to about 1941. Flocks seen 13, in '21, '31, 50, in '36, '41. Possible decline since '41	Believed increasing
Carrion-Crow *Corvus corone*	Not common	Common in south	Frequent	Still numerous but decreasing	Common. Esp. abundant in early 20's	Abundant
Magpie *Pica pica*	—	Generally distributed and common	Common	Still plentiful	Common. Esp. during 30's	Common. Increasing
Jay *Garrulus glandarius*	Sometimes in large flocks	Still common in woods	Becoming scarce	Has decreased but still breeds in suitable wooded parts	Common in suitable habitats	Absent, Postbridge
Jackdaw *Corvus monedula*	Met with on cliffs. (Implies not general)	Very numerous	Common	Numerous and increasing	Very common Roosts in woods well into moor	Common.
Rook *Corvus frugilegus*	?	Very abundant	Common	Abundant and increasing	Abundant. Often penetrate into moor	Resident, believed decreasing; due to felling?

21

may be so much disturbed by overeager watchers that they may desert the locality. Suffice it that the birds have now nested for two or three years within the four hundred square miles of the prospective National Park, and there is every hope that it may be able to establish itself firmly once more.[1] One other interesting record is the almost yearly passage across Dartmoor of immature White-tailed Eagles, *Haliaeëtus albicilla*, mostly during winter or early spring.

A feature of the bird-life of the region which may strike the visitor from the north is the scarcity of game birds. Dartmoor has never been preserved, and although Red Grouse, *Lagopus scoticus*, have been introduced they have never thriven, possibly on account of the abundance of foxes. A few birds may occasionally be seen, the stock being just able to maintain itself, but a covey of eight is a rarity worth recording, and it is possible to walk the moors for days without seeing a single bird. Black Game, *Lyrurus tetrix*, are also scarce, except in a few favoured localities, usually on the edges of conifer plantations, while Pheasant, *Phasianus colchicus*, and Partridge, *Perdix perdix*, are not infrequent in the in-country.

A group of birds, the status of which is changing markedly, and for the better, is that of the ducks and associated waterfowl. Until recently the only reservoirs have been at Burrator, Holne and Hennock, and most of the records of waterfowl have come from Burrator. But now that Fernworthy Reservoir has been completed it is proving very attractive, probably because of the excellent cover and quietude provided by the extensive plantations which fringe its margins. Comparative figures obtained by Miss P. B. Lind in 1949 for Fernworthy and Hennock are recorded in tabular form, on the next page, to indicate the sort of populations which may be expected on the two reservoirs during the winter.

The many other interesting features of the bird life of the region may better be discussed in relation to the various special types of habitat which Dartmoor exhibits. Mention of them is therefore deferred to subsequent chapters.

The characteristic reptiles of Dartmoor are the Common Lizard, *Lacerta vivipara*, and the Adder, *Vipera berus*. The Slow-worm, *Anguis fragilis*, occurs less frequently, while the Grass-Snake, *Natrix natrix*, is usually confined to scrub and woodland, where the cover is coarse and dense, and it is by no means a common reptile here. Lizards are almost ubiquitous on the heather and bilberry moors, but Adders tend

[1] The birds have continued to breed in small numbers, but show no sign of building up their numbers beyond a few pairs. 1960.

Plate 3. Tavy Cleave: a typical water-cut higher reach

Date	FERNWORTHY 1.1 29.1 5.3 26.3 25.9 23.10 20.11							HENNOCK 1.1 29.1 5.3 26.3 25.9 23.10 20.11						
Mallard .. *Anas platyrhyncha*	39	13	6	6	14	14	36	65	74	40	9	—	29	79
Teal .. .. *Anas crecca*	22	15	17	11	—	16	30	—	—	—	—	—	—	—
Wigeon .. *Anas penelope*	—	2	—	—	1	—	—	—	2	—	—	—	—	—
Pochard .. *Aythya ferina*	10	—	—	—	24	—	—	20	30	—	—	—	—	15
Tufted Duck .. *Aythya fuligula*	—	—	—	—	—	—	—	4	4	—	2	—	—	—
Goosander *Mergus merganser*	—	—	—	—	—	—	1	—	—	—	—	—	—	—

to be more localised, preferring the sunnier hillsides and particularly those covered by clitters or where there is an ample supply of loose boulders on which they may bask, and beneath which find cover. Mr. E. E. Lowe, writing of the species in the *Victoria County History* (1906), says, " Both blackish and red forms occur as well as the type, and Mr. Hearder says of the first that those he has caught (about half a dozen) have always been distinctly aggressive." Whether this is so or not I have no first-hand information. But in general it may be said that the viper is never aggressive unless very suddenly disturbed. In fact, so retiring are they that it is possible never to see one on Dartmoor, unless one searches actively and quietly. On the other hand, one lady of my acquaintance invariably wears wellington boots for cross-country walking on the Moor because of her peculiar horror, which she shares with many people, of this, to my mind, very attractive reptile.

Dr. Julian Huxley has drawn my attention to a common belief, the existence of which is confirmed by my wife, who spent her youth in Moretonhampstead. This is that where one finds the Wood-Ant, *Formica rufa*, there Adders are absent. Many natives of Dartmoor who will not pick Whortleberries on the open moors lest they encounter an Adder will cheerfully go picking in the woods where these ants abound. Whether this negative correlation results from antagonism between the two species or is due to the animals requiring different surroundings may be worth investigation. Certainly Adders are scarce in such valley woods as those of the Teign between Steps and Fingle Bridges, although both Grass-Snakes and Slow-worms are to be found. Moreover, Wistman's Wood, in which the Wood-Ant is not at all common, is believed locally to be swarming with Adders. It must be confessed, however, that although I have paid a number of visits to this copse the only Adders I have seen have been in the Gorse and Heather of the surrounding moor.

This brief sketch, covering as it does only a few salient features of the diverse wild life of the region, and deferring all reference to the insects and other invertebrates to the more detailed expositions which follow, is sufficient to establish the case for conservation of the natural features of Dartmoor. The parallel case for the preservation of buildings and places of architectural and historic interest is not so immediately apparent. There are few such in the region, with the notable exceptions of the relics of Bronze and Iron Age civilisations, in which Dartmoor is peculiarly rich, and the Ancient Tenements, which are held by copy of Court Roll and are of great antiquity. All these are, however, to be discussed in some detail in the sections of the book concerned with history and prehistory, and it is only necessary here to draw attention to their existence and importance.

Presumably on account of its extreme isolation until the days of steam and metalled roads and the modern car, and also on account of the poverty of its soils and the rigour of its climate, Dartmoor is embellished with few large houses. The main interest of the student of architecture will, therefore, be directed towards the farmhouses and cottages, many of which have their own dignity and beauty, as may be seen from Plate XXIII, p. 194. The best-known large buildings are notorious rather than well-famed. The now ruined Lydford Castle is known principally for its association with the savage " Lydford Law " of the Stannary Court which was held there. Dartmoor Prison, built by Thomas Tyrwhitt to house French prisoners during the Napoleonic wars, has become the most dreaded of H.M. criminal prisons, and certainly contributes little towards the amenities of the Moor. The several great religious houses lay on the southern and western margins, at Buckland in the Moor, Buckfastleigh and Tavistock. Only Buckfast Abbey remains in active being, but even this is a new fabric, built in recent years.

Brent Tor, on the westernmost margins of the National Park, has a long history. The tor itself is not of granite, but of true volcanic trap, a fact which accounts for its steep-sided abruptness. The top of the hill is crowned by ancient earthworks and the tiny church of St. Michael.

The church was dedicated to the saint by Bishop Stapledon in 1319, but in a twelfth-century document Walter Giffard states that his father built it and gave it with some land round it to the Abbey of Tavistock; its date is therefore about 1130 to 1140 A.D. The history of the building is enlivened by two rival legends. The one, a widely spread legend about hill-top churches, says that it was originally intended to build at the foot of the tor, but the Devil carried the stones nightly to the top of the hill, until the builders wearied of their fruitless labours and agreed to let the Devil have his way. The other relates that it represents the fulfilment of a vow made by a merchant when his ship was stormbound in the Channel. In the words of Carrington's inimitable but not deathless verse:

> " *Then*
> *As bent the timbers of his stout-ribb'd bark*
> *To the huge ocean-shock, and wave on wave*
> *Dash'd on the staggering deck; the sufferer vow'd*
> *In silent agony, that if the ear*
> *Of Heaven would listen, and its arm be strong*
> *To save;—upon the first dear spot of earth*
> *Propitious morning shew'd, he would erect*
> *A temple to the Highest. It was heard,—*
> *(Thus swains relate) the anguish'd vow was heard—*
> *Propitious broke the dawn. The winds no more*
> *Swept o'er the madden'd waters, and the voice*
> *Of the great sea-wave died away; scarce heard*
> *Save where the billow chafed the sand and made*
> *Sweet music with the rocks. The welcome Sun*
> *Chasing the tempest, in the brightening East*
> *Victorious rose, and through the scatter'd haze*
> *Brent Tor uplifted his magnific brow,*
> *With shouts tumultuous hail'd!* "

It seems a pity to cast doubt upon a story told with such fervour, but the fact remains that Brent Tor is just under 1,000 feet high and well inland, and it would indeed be remarkable if it were " the first dear spot of earth propitious morning shew'd " to a ship at sea. The dedication to St. Michael is significant in relation to the ancient earthwork on the hilltop, St. Michael, the killer of devils, being made the patron saint of many religious buildings erected on the site of older pagan edifices.

For the rest, we are concerned with the history of a sturdy and independent yeomanry whose buildings have the beauty of fitting their purposes, lowly though these may be. It is, perhaps, the more important that these farm and dwelling houses, small churches, mills and cottages should be preserved in our National Parks, since their claims to preservation tend to be overruled elsewhere in the interests of worldly progress. There is, moreover, nothing in this which is incongruous with the postulate that established farm use shall be effectively maintained.

Doubts begin to arise, however, when we come to consider the preservation of the characteristic landscape beauty and the provision of access and facilities for open-air enjoyment. The beauties of Dartmoor are diverse and enduring, and they can hardly be spoiled save by a deliberate vandalism which can only be conceived in relation to war. The great rolling uplands of Purple Moor Grass, Bog Cottons, Heather and Bilberry, which, according to the mood, fill one's mind with inconsolable loneliness or with peace, are so vast that they can never be totally destroyed by conceivable human actions. The tors, which have withstood centuries of slow attrition by weather, will still be here millenniums hence, when man is known only by his bones and the crumbling ruins of his civilisations. The rivers will continue to pour their bright-brown waters through cascade and pool. These things cannot be lost to the world. But we live in a time when men are particularly prone to do terrible things to their surroundings. All the world's our oyster, and we swallow it down with little thought that we may leave posterity with only a midden of shells. On Dartmoor the already over-stocked pasturage is indiscriminately burned, the Heather being weakened and Bracken encouraged. Economic and military considerations being paramont in our minds, huge conifer plantations are created, which not only restrict access to large areas, but also seriously distract the eye from the lovely sweeping lines of the hills. Water undertakings flood large basins and submerge many unique features. The military occupy nearly half the area of the moors, firing over and on to them, thereby excluding from them both grazing stock and public. This takes us a long way from our conception of a National Park, and it is well to dwell for a moment on some of these activities and consider whether they can continue to be practised in the light of John Dower's postulates.

The activities of the Forestry Commission and other afforestation schemes on Dartmoor have been the subject of considerable controversy in the local press, and discussion of some aspects of this will be reserved for a later chapter (see p. 114). The major objections which have been offered are, first, that the plantations are not in harmony with the Dartmoor scene, secondly, that many areas which have been planted are on such poor soil that the stand will be a permanent slum, and thirdly, that in the initial stages the ridges and furrows, and in later stages the densely growing young trees, impede the choice of the walker to go where he will. The first objection is only partially valid, and is, of course, a matter of opinion rather than of fact. Those who detest the serried ranks of plantations of single species which have hitherto been the normal plantings, will find it difficult to find beauty in them, wherever they may be sited. There are, however, situations in which the close growth of the trees and the sweeping boughs along the margins of the stands confer a tenderness which would be lacking in their absence. Such a quality many may find at Fernworthy, where the beauty of the water is framed and enhanced by the trees about it. On the other hand, it is difficult to find delight in the gloomy regimentation of the half-grown trees of the Dartington Hall plantations in the Teign valley at Clifford Bridge. There the eye is too close, and one sees, not the green of the cover, but the dead brown and darkness of the undercover, the mathematical regularity of the stems being broken only by the litter of ragged twigs which have died on the trunks as the light was excluded from above. It is regrettable indeed that the scrub oaks in these beautiful valleys, with their varied light and shade, and irregular growth, are no longer regarded as profitable. One can only hope that economic necessities will not overweight our scale of values to the point where all these gorges are given over to the relatively greater returns of conifer crops.

Another deplorable setting for conifers is that at Bellever. Bellever Tor (Pl. II, p. 7) is one of the most charming hills of Dartmoor. It has none of the awesomeness of the larger tors, being crowned only by a low outcrop of granite, but it rose in beautiful symmetry from the plateau between the East and West Darts. And now so much of its clean sweeping lines is submerged beneath an irregular cover of spiked conifers. One suspects that the minds which conceived of the plantings here were concerned so closely with the economics of the problem as to be quite blind to the lines of the countryside. The answer which is frequently made to complaints of this nature is that we have yet to see matured plantings, and that, in the absence of clear felling, the groups which will be left of mature trees will enhance the view rather than detract from it. There is probably much truth in this argument, and for my part, I am content to await confirmation of it, in many places. But I cannot believe that the Bellever trees will ever be anything but irrelevancies. The landscape was the frame for the tor; the new frame of trees obscures the picture. The fact that much of the ground in which the trees are planted appears to be quite unsuited to them, and that as a result the trees are making irregular and poor growth, is an additional rub to the sore. Mistakes are bound to arise in the course of undertakings so large, varied and experimental as those of afforestation in this country. But it is no consolation that the Bellever site should be one of these errors. Irretrievable damage has been done to the natural beauty, and we have acquired a slum, the sole use of which, to mix metaphors, is to beat the dog of the Commission.

It is another matter again when we look at the Soussons Down plantations. These cover a wide acreage of open moorland, which was never of outstanding beauty or interest, apart from the colony, already mentioned, of the Dorset Heath. Moreover, the eastern margins of the plantings cover one of the least inspiring of the old tin-mining areas at Vitifer and Birch Tor. The scene of dereliction here in the West Webburn valley is more reminiscent than anywhere else on Dartmoor of the decaying buildings and spoil-heaps which mar so many Cornish headlands. The Commission is to be congratulated on its attempts to clothe some at least of this under the healing cover of trees, and the sole reservation I would make is that, in doing so, they should not disturb the small colony of Ring-Ouzels, *Turdus torquatus*, which breeds here. The pair portrayed in Pl. 6, p. 46 was one of several from the region, and, although the bird occurs elsewhere on Dartmoor, it would be a pity to lose this site.

The problem of access is a serious one, as becomes only too clear when one tries to traverse a modern plantation. The walker will find that the young trees are planted in the upturned sods which have been ploughed out of long furrows and turned on to the ridges between. Three methods of progression are open to the walker here. He may proceed along a furrow or a ridge, being in either case forced to follow its line over long distances. He may walk across the ridges and take his own line across country. But by either method the going is laborious and exhausting, for the ground is very uneven and full of snags and stones, and such care must be taken to watch for foothold or to avoid treading the young trees that it is impossible to enjoy the experience. The majority of people find themselves confined to the third process, of keeping to the fire rides and service roads, and being thereby the more strictly canalised in direction. Once the young trees have begun to cover the ground it is inevitable that only the made ways can be used. Restrictions of this kind are most undesirable in a National Park; for much of the delight of walking resides in one's ability to follow the inclination of the moment, and set paths should therefore be restricted only to ground where established agricultural use makes this imperative. This being so in the forestry plantations, it follows that, if Dartmoor is to achieve its maximum success as a park, then no more extensive plantings should be contemplated here.

One further point, which appears only rarely to be pressed, is that of the fate of the land after the crop of timber has been taken. This presents serious problems which I do not believe have been adequately faced. The felling of the trees, whether clear or partial, must leave a large acreage of ground covered with tree-stumps. It may be presumed that the surface litter will be cleared, but what is to happen to the land? Will it be left to regenerate as it may, the stumps slowly to rot away and an untidy scrub to grow among them? Or will the stumps be uprooted and the land cultivated and sown down to grass? Or will it be cleared and replanted with trees? It is one thing to break the natural sequence of communities of plants, but another problem altogether to restore the plant cover after the crop has been taken. It must be a cardinal policy in a National Park, indeed, in any part of our countryside, to plan not merely for twenty, thirty or fifty years ahead, but in perpetuity.

The influence of water undertakings on scenery and access is as drastic as that of afforestation, but arouses less antagonism. The demand for piped water is one which touches nearer home than does that for timber; and the existing reservoirs, with the possible exception of Holne, which is rather bare, have created new beauty and interest in a region which would otherwise possess no lakes. The mirrored surface of the water, and the trees which usually fringe its margins rest and refresh the eye. The ornithologist finds interest in the waterfowl which are attracted, some as winter visitors, others as breeding birds. The nostalgic may lament the loss of beauties submerged beneath the water, while finally, the most serious aspect of water conservation, which will be treated at greater length in a subsequent chapter, is the heavy extraction of water at the sources of the streams, which thereby restricts their volume, detracts from their grandeur, and may in some cases seriously deplete their capacity to support fish.

The gravest threat to the amenity of Dartmoor has been deferred until last. This is the extent to which the military have begun to use it. Since the end of the last century there has been an artillery range on the moors to the south of Okehampton. This initial excursion did not pass without opposition, and there is no doubt foundation for the story of the implacable lady who sat herself beneath a striped sunshade in the middle of the range one day, and rejected all persuasion to move. As firing days were then strictly limited, this must have been peculiarly galling to the units concerned. The urgencies of two wars, coupled with advances in gun design and explosive power, have combined to force, not only a much more frequent use of the ranges, but also an extension of the area used. During the last war, for instance, almost the whole of the country between Okehampton and Tavistock over to the Moretonhampstead to Princetown road as far east as Merripit Hill was used daily and all day long. In addition, modern armoured warfare has demanded extensive areas for training purposes, with or without live ammunition, and as agricultural land was not available, except in the most extreme cases, the brunt of this has fallen on just those wild, marginal lands which naturally are looked upon as the nuclei of the National Parks.

These incursions were accepted during war, as part of the price to be paid for survival, and in the expectation that they would cease once this had been achieved. As we know only too well, such a retraction was not seriously contemplated by the military authorities until public opinion forced it upon them. It was only after a series of inquiries at local and national levels that the necessity to restrict military exercises to much smaller areas was accepted. Even so, it is difficult to reconcile the minimum military demands for land on Dartmoor, in so far as these are known, with the idea of it as a National Park. On the map, p. 10, are delineated the known boundaries and proposed uses of the army's zones, slightly modified from the pattern as agreed after the public inquiry at Exeter in 1947. In area alone they occupy an excessive proportion of the present National Park, while in quality they take some of the best and wildest parts of the moor. When it is added

Plate 4. The Teign valley above Dunsford: a characteristic, deeply-
cut secondary valley, heavily wooded with scrub oak

that it transpired only at the actual inquiry that the military authorities were not prepared to discuss the situation on the southern moors, below the Moretonhampstead-Princetown road, which were then used, and still are being so used, by the Royal Marines for live exercises, it will be realised how fugitive are dreams of a real Dartmoor National Park unless these activities are drastically curtailed, or preferably stopped. Few will be persuaded that such things as artillery shelling and firing of live ammunition, covering nearly half its area, can be compatible with such cardinal principles of maintenance in a National Park as ample provision of access and facilities for public open-air enjoyment, suitable protection of wild life and buildings of architectural and historic interest, and effective maintenance of established farming use.

The stock answer, which is given in response to all protests against military use of land, is that the condition of international relations being what it is, and having now standing military forces with annual accessions of conscript recruits, it is essential to maintain these forces in a state of preparedness and to train the new drafts as they are recruited, and where else can this be done except over wild, marginal land of this kind? And I have heard responsible people from all walks of life gravely assenting to this. My own view is that it is time the view be challenged before it is too late and it has acquired the weight of an axiom. We are becoming so used to hearing the terms " military expediency " and " economic necessity " that we become dulled to them and are apt to forget our spiritual needs, or at best to place them, as has a past Prime Minister, low down in our scale of values. I cite the words of his White Paper, *Needs of the Armed Forces for Land for Training and other Purposes* (Cmd. 7278) presented to Parliament in December 1947. The following statements may be found under the heading, " The Choice of Training Areas within Great Britain ": " It is obviously essential to avoid, if at all possible, the use of good agricultural land or that reserved for forestry, as well as catchment areas for water supply," and, " It must be borne in mind, however, that the only type of land the use of which for Service purposes would not be open to objection on the grounds mentioned above is, broadly speaking, that found in areas of high amenity value. This, and not any disregard by the Services of the need for preserving them, is the reason in many cases why training is proposed in National Park areas." In other words, we must destroy now, much of the beauty of our wild places, in order that Britain may be protected and its people fed.

Indeed, we live in a mean age when a proposition such as this is allowed to go unchallenged.

It may be answered that the beauty will not be destroyed, that only a minute proportion of the countryside will be touched, and that in any case the public will only be excluded during actual firing or live exercises. But this surely ignores the profound truth that beauty lies in the eye of the beholder. For the impress of what the eye sees is deeply modified by the state of the mind which receives its impulses. It is difficult indeed to appreciate the beauty of lonely places, and to gather rest and refreshment from this, when the sight of them is conditioned by the thud of guns or the rattle of small arms; or when access to them is only to be gained past a notice warning that danger exists beyond when a red flag is flying at such and such a point, and concluding with the statement, " It is dangerous to handle shell found on the moor." The man who can put such things out of his mind and enjoy beauty and peace is lucky indeed, and there are many who, rather than face the dangers, imaginary or real, prefer to forgo such dobutful pleasure.

I am convinced that military exercises are not compatible with the idea of a National Park, and that any attempt to arrive at a compromise is worthless. Indeed, I would go so far as to postulate that the armed forces should be permanently excluded, as such, from such areas. In this connection I suggest it has still to be demonstrated that the objections to using less crucial land in parts of Scotland, Germany or Canada, are valid on grounds of state rather than military policy. For the conception of the parks is a noble one, which recognises that the human mind has a need to get away from mundane matters periodically. I shall no doubt be labelled as totally impractical for holding such a view. But it is legitimate to ask such critics whether it is the more hopeful for our human future to work for something which may bring tranquillity to the mind, something which may eventually become universally understood and respected, than to accept that we must be prepared for another war. Economically neither we nor any other nation can afford the luxury of another war, and I am daily more sickened and humiliated at the manner in which Twentieth-Century man is accepting its possibility, I had almost written probability. That way lies hate and mistrust, and at the end, either a third war which inevitably must bring to ruin a civilisation already nearly bankrupted by the struggles of the first half of the century, or a life of fear, dominated for ever by the rattling sabres and the posturings of rival ideologies. The one way offers at least a chance of something better, but I cannot see anything worth a snap of the fingers in the other.

It must not be thought that I believe in National Parks as a panacea for the ills of the world. To those who have followed my argument it will, I hope, be apparent that my concern is with a frame of mind, a standard of values, of which the ability to conceive of military exercises within the parks is an example. For my part, I do not share this state of mind, nor do I accept the standard, and I believe it to be a decisive, and fatal, step on to the Gadarene slope to recognise such practices as a normal feature of our lives.

In conclusion then it may be said that Dartmoor conforms to the criteria of a National Park, provided that no further rein is given to the Forestry Commission, or to private individuals, to plant a larger acreage than is now afforested, in 1949, and that the demands for water catchment are not allowed to take too heavy a toll of water from the streams. But, and this is indeed critical, it is essential for the peace of the region, and to ensure to the public full access to, and enjoyment of, its beauty, that military exercises should be excluded. If we are not prepared to face this then I do not believe that we can have any park worthy of the name.

CHAPTER 3

THE PHYSICAL PATTERN OF
THE COUNTRY

THERE ARE THREE areas which we may usefully consider as Dartmoor. The original Forest of Dartmoor, the Dartmoor of the Devonians, which is the Forest plus the many commons associated with it, and the National Park of Dartmoor.

The Forest of Dartmoor was defined by Perambulation in A.D. 1240. By the Charter of the Forest granted by King John and dated 18 May 1204, all Devon is purported to be disafforested " up to the metes of the ancient regards of Dartmoor and Exmoor, as those regards were in the time of King Henry I." But little effect was given to this charter until, in 1240, King Henry III bestowed the Forest on his brother Richard, and the bounds were then perambulated by twelve knights summoned by the Sheriff of Devon. The bounds set forth were, " Hogan de Cossdone—Parva Hundetorre—Thurlstone—Wotesbroke-lakesfote—Heighestone—Langestone—Turbarium de Alberysheved— Wallebroke—Furnum Regis—Wallebrokeshede—Wallebroke usque cadit in Dertam—per Dertam usque ad aliam Dertam—per aliam Dertam ascendendo usque Okebrokesfote—ascendendo. Okebroke usque ad la Dryeworke—Dryfeld Ford—Battyshull—Caput de Wester Wellabroke—Wester Wellabroke usque cadit in Avenam—Ester Whyte-burghe—Redelake—Grymsgrove—Elysburghe—Crucem Sywardi— Ysfother—aliam Ysfother—Mystor—Mewyburghe—Lullingesfote— Rakernes brokysfote—la Westsolle—Ernestorre—vadum proximum in orientalis parte capelle Sancti Michaelis de Halgestoke—Hogam de Cossdone." Nearly four hundred years later, under King James I, a similar survey of the bounds was made by twenty-five jurors, and was presented at a Survey Court at Okehampton in 1609. To-day the bounds recognised by the Duchy of Cornwall agree closely with the original per-

34

ambulation, and run, in modern terminology, from the foot of Cosdon, where Smallbrook falls into the Taw, over Metherall Hill to White Moor Stone, and thence to Little Hound Tor—Wild Tor Well—Thurlestone, or Hew Thorn Clitter—Manga Rock—across the north Teign—along Hurston Ridge to King's Oven—Walla Brook Head (near the Warren House Inn)—down the Walla Brook to the East Dart—down the Dart to Dartmeet—up the West Dart to Wo Brook Foot—up the Wo Brook to Drylakes—up Drylakes and across the hill to Corfield Ford—Knattleborough on Ryder's Hill—West Wella Brook Head—down the West Wella Brook to the Avon—a short distance up the Avon, thence up the hill to Western Whiteburrow—thence to Redlake Mires and down Redlake to the Erme—up the Erme to Erme Head—Boundary Stone—Broad Rock—Plym Head—a short distance down the Plym, and thence to the cairn on Eylesbarrow—Siward's, or Nun's, Cross— South Hisworthy Tor—North Hisworthy Tor—Rundle Stone—Great Mis Tor—across the Walkham under Grenna Ball—Dead Lake Head —White Barrow—Higher Pile of Lynch Tor—Homer, or Wester Red Lake, a short distance below its source—down Red Lake to the Tavy —down the Tavy to Rattle Brook Foot—up the Rattle Brook to its source—Stinka Tor—Sandy Ford—across Dinger Plain to Curtory Clitters—across the Blackaven under Row Tor—then down by the right bank of that stream to Crovenor Steps—up the hill to the summit of Belstone Ridge, to a point just north of Winter Tor—down the further side, and across Taw Plain to the starting point at the confluence of the Taw and Small Brook. Inspection of the map on p. 10 will show how much of the region this boundary encloses. Along all its course the Forest edge marches with various common lands. Where some natural feature, such as a river or a tor, is used, no trouble arises. But at some points this is not possible; for instance, " across Dinger Plain to Curtory Clitters." Every man tends to take his own line across country, and endless disputes have arisen between the Duchy of Cornwall, to which the Forest belongs, and the commoners, whose natural tendency is to encroach on the Duchy lands wherever such indeterminate bounds allow. Sometimes, as also between neighbouring commons, the line is demarcated by a stone wall. But often only certain landmarks, and artificially placed bond-stones, are used, and the boundary is maintained by a periodic beating of their bounds by the commoners. This is done, at varying intervals usually of about seven years, and is the occasion of some ceremonial, and sometimes acrimony,

D.   D

when disputes arise over the line taken relative to neighbouring lands. It is traditional to encourage the younger members of the community to accompany the elders, so that a visual memory of the common boundaries may be carried to succeeding generations.

While they are of profound significance to the lives of the commoners, these boundaries mean little to the biologist (except where they follow some natural feature), for they do not demarcate natural communities from one another. It is only when we come to consider the peripheral boundaries of the commons, where the moorland begins to give place to cultivated farmlands, that we find significant change in the plant and animal communities. This is one reason why it was so important that the boundaries of the National Park of Dartmoor should lie for the most part outside those of the Forest and its commons.

When we consider the topography of the region we find that it comprises, firstly, a high central area of true moor, or blanket bog, overlying granite except where the rock protrudes through its covering of peat and is exposed on the tops of the hills as the famous tors. The blanket bogs extend over many square miles of country, between Okehampton to the north and the road between Princetown and Moretonhampstead to the south, and again, south of this road, in the lower-lying bogs of the Red Lake and Plym Head area. Surrounding this on all sides is a girdle of heather and bilberry moorlands, lying only slightly lower than the blanket bog, and this is the part of Dartmoor which is most visited by tourists. It is more accessible than the bogs and, except to the adventurous, more attractive by the colour and variety of its scenery. Outside it again is a belt of land, the depth of which varies between one place and another, and which is in various states of use and cultivation. Great tongues of common may project into an otherwise farmed countryside; deep-cut valleys thrust outwards from the moor, their steep sides clothed with oak woods. And the character of the whole changes almost imperceptibly as one passes outwards across the " in-country " to the lower-lying plains of rural Devon.

The different features of the land, and of the communities living on it, take their beginnings out of the past history of this part of the world, and they are maintained in part by the conditions of soil, elevation and climate which reign here, but also in part as a result of human interference with the natural conditions. First we must consider the early history of the region, in so far as it may be deduced from our knowledge of changes in the earth's surface. Leaving a discussion of the geological structure until the next chapter, we may say that Dartmoor, in common with a number of other granite exposures in the south-west of England, the Scilly Isles, Land's End, Carnmenellis, and Bodmin Moor, represents the stump of an old mountain range. The overlying thousands of feet of rock which constituted these mountains have become worn away by sub-aerial and submarine erosion, until nearly all the sedimentary rocks have been pared off and the granite core is now exposed at their base. Subsequently to this, further erosion has operated differentially on rocks of different degrees of hardness. The central core of hard granite has been worn down very slowly, and so to-day it stands much higher than the surrounding country, rising at Yes Tor and High Willhayes to just over 2,000 feet. Around this core is a metamorphic aureole, in which the original sedimentary rocks have been baked and hardened by the heat radiated from the molten magma as it cooled and crystallised into what we now see as the granite. Outside this again are the original sedimentary series of Devonian and Carboniferous rocks, often buckled and distorted by the forces generated during the great mountain building movements of the earth's crust. But apart from this the rocks remain relatively soft and unchanged.

It appears that much of the erosion which took place, although by no means all of it, was submarine, and that the height of the land above sea-level changed several times. For there is evidence on Dartmoor, and in the neighbouring valleys, of no less than three, and possibly four, erosion platforms, or raised beaches, at heights to-day of respectively, 400, 800 and 1,000 feet, the fourth being possibly at about 2,000 feet. The rivers reflect this history. During each period of stability their valleys tended to flatten out into a flood plain near sea-level. But each uplift rejuvenated them, giving them an extra two to four hundred vertical feet to fall before they reached the sea. As a consequence they have cut steadily back through the soft sedimentary rocks, with the result that each stream passes through three well-defined phases within the moor area. The upper reaches may be comparatively sedate, the brown peaty waters tumbling through a series of low cascades with long shallow pools between them. This part of the valley is wide and shallow, and as it approaches the 1,000-foot platform it often flattens out into a waterlogged plain, as, for instance, at Taw Marsh (Pl. IX, p. 70). Below this the streams fall rapidly, almost headlong, into deep gorges, due in part to the softer character of the rocks, which are therefore the more easily cut away than is the granite. But much is also due to the rejuvenation of the streams below the odd shore line, as a result of the aforementioned uplift of the land during post-Pliocene times. Comparison of Plates 8, p. 66 and 4, p. 30, showing respectively the upper reaches of the Avon and the gorge section of the Teign, will indicate how marked is the difference in character of the river valleys at these two levels.

One of the most striking characters of Dartmoor is a negative one. The only large stretches of water are the reservoirs, all of which have been created artificially by damming valleys, as at Kennick (Pl. 16, p. 174), Burrator, Holne and Fernworthy (Pl. IV, p. 15) and the recently completed Avon Reservoir. There are no natural lakes or sheets of water of any size in the whole neighbourhood. Dartmoor is almost the only extensive area of highland in Britain of which this may be said, and the reason is not far to seek. Devon lay south of the great ice sheets which covered all the remainder of highland Britain during the Glacial Periods. Dartmoor, therefore, escaped the scouring action of the glaciers which produced the characteristic valleys of North Wales and the Lake District and the Pennines. Moreover, there were no terminal moraines dropped by the melting ice as the glaciers retreated, to block the ends of the valleys. As a result, the water, having cut its own paths downwards, drains off without hindrance, except where occasionally a valley flattens out as we have seen at the 1,000-foot platform, and so tends to become waterlogged and choked with peat. There is no doubt that Dartmoor, during each glacial period, wore a snowcap for long periods of each year at least, and the presence of this thick cover has left its mark on the distribution of the rocks split off by frost from the tors above, in a manner which will shortly be discussed. But there is no sound evidence, either from topographical form, or from errant or scored boulders, of the existence of the solid streams of ice which flowed over much of the rest of these islands.

Perhaps the most familiar, certainly the most famous, features of Dartmoor are the tors, and associated with them the clitters, or clatters. The tors usually crown the hill-tops and are outcrops of granite, exposed by erosion and carved by these same processes into dominating, often fantastic elements of the landscape, as may be seen in Pl. IV, V, pp. 15, 54. It must not be supposed that Dartmoor is a continuous solid mass of granite covered, except at the tors, by a skin

Plate 5. Maidenhair Spleenwort, *Asplenium trichomanes*, on a stone wall

of peat. Over wide stretches of the region the superficial rock has become rotted by percolating water and has decomposed, giving at first a loose gravelly mass, which ultimately breaks down completely to a fine clay in which are embedded the insoluble quartz and mica which are universal components of the mother rock. The processes involved, and the products which result, will be more exhaustively discussed in the succeeding chapter of the geology of the area. It may be mentioned here, however, that it is the glistening fragments of quartz and mica which confer their white brilliance on the spoil-heaps of the china clay works which dot the south-west corner of the moor, at Lee Moor. Fortunately, clay working is confined to a comparatively small area here, and Dartmoor as a whole has escaped the disfigurement which mars the St. Austell Moors in Cornwall.

Returning to the tors, they represent as it were islands of sound rock which stand up on the ridges and hilltops. Often the face of the tor gives an appearance as if it were bedded like a sedimentary rock. But this, as again will be discussed later (p. 52) is a false inference, the rock being of purely igneous origin. It is not surprising that many of the patterns assumed by the tors have suggested fanciful resemblances to animals or human beings, and names such as Hound Tor, Bowerman's Nose and the like have resulted from such imaginations.

Below many tors the hillside is strewn with a clitter. This is a loose jumble of boulders weighing anything up to several tons. The rocks are scattered haphazard over the ground, sometimes half-buried, at other places perched upon one another, where they have fallen from the tor above. For this is the debris which has resulted from the splitting action of frost, driving wedge-like into the crevices of the jointed tor. Frequently, in the opinion of the authors of the *Geological Survey, Dartmoor Memoir*, these clitters lie farther distant from the foot of the tor than may be expected. They suggest, therefore, that most of the falls occurred during glacial periods, when the ground below was covered several feet deep with ice and snow. This in itself would tend to project the fall farther outwards relative to the pitch of the slope, and in addition the smoothed contours and polished surface of the ice-covered ground would have facilitated a degree of sliding which could not have occurred had the rocks fallen directly to the ground.

Such jumbles of rocks as the clitters provide rather special ecological niches in the region. The Badger, *Meles meles*, for instance, although he often traverses the moor, is rarely found living there, except when on rare occasions a sett is excavated in a clitter. Rabbits find excellent cover here, as may also Adders. It has also been suggested, and the view will be discussed in more detail later (p. 107), that the wind-shelter provided in the hollows among the boulders has enabled young trees to obtain a firm root-hold and strength to meet winter gales, which would otherwise destroy them in the absence of such cover. Certainly the three most interesting oak copses on Dartmoor, Wistman's Wood, Black Tor Beare and Piles Copse, are so situated. Elsewhere the clitters are strewn over the open hillsides and the same vegetation which covers the moor around penetrates among the boulders, except where these are heaped so closely as to exclude the light from the underlying soil. An occasional Rowan, *Sorbus aucuparia*, may grow from a protecting crevice, many ferns take advantage of their high shade tolerance to colonise the deep pockets and clefts, mosses, such as the common *Rhacomitrium lanuginosum*, spread in great sheets up the rocks to mingle with the innumerable lichens which often, as on the tors above, are so thickly spread as to render invisible the underlying granite surface.

The granite of Dartmoor, as elsewhere, is rich in metalliferous deposits. Some are of primary origin, having been present in the magma out of which the rock solidified. Others have infiltrated later as a result of secondary changes, and these tend to be localised in particular regions in which such processes have altered the granite. Of a great variety of metals found, that which has been most extensively worked is tin. Despite its significance to a bronze-working culture there is no evidence that the tin of Dartmoor was worked until much later than the Bronze Age; in fact, not until approaching Norman times was there any serious attempt to win the metal. The social aspects of tin working are discussed in sections of the book later. But it is necessary here to refer to the changes in topography which tin mining and streaming have wrought, and to the changes which have resulted in the habitat as a consequence. Two methods of obtaining tin have been extensively used on Dartmoor. Firstly, as it is probably the earlier method, streaming or panning, and secondly, mining. The tin streamers took advantage of the fact that the heavy tin-bearing stone tends to be deposited in river beds wherever the gradient slackens and the slower movement of the water reduces its powers of rolling stones along the bottom. They, therefore, usually entered a stream at some point where a sill occurred to slacken the current and worked up the bed from there, scooping out the gravel from the bottom, winnowing away the lighter, non-metalliferous particles, and extracting the ore from the residue. The waste was thrown out on to the banks, where it still remains as irregular hummocks dotted along the stream-side. Sometimes where the valleys have flattened out into old flood plains, and the streams pursue devious and often variable courses through deep peat, this peat has been excavated, used as a sieve in the winnowing process, and then thrown aside and the rejected gravel heaped upon it.

Fortunately for the amenities of Dartmoor, mining has been restricted to the more highly productive veins. It calls for more permanent plant to produce the final metal, than do the stream deposits, which by their nature demand a mobile working method. It has only paid, therefore, to work areas where there is enough ore to keep the smelting plant active over periods of years. Being concerned here with the effects of mining operations on the scenery, we may defer a detailed discussion of the deposits found to a later chapter (p. 156). As might be expected, many of the sixty or more mines listed in the Dartmoor area by the Geological Survey in 1912, are situated in the softer rocks of the metamorphic aureole, and here subterranean shafts and galleries have been cut to depths of over 200 fathoms in some cases. The main effects noticeable, apart from the engine-house, stamping plant and the like, are the unsightly spoil-heaps. But where tin has been worked in the granite itself an opencast system has usually been used. Huge gullies have been left deeply cut into the moor, their depth enhanced by the spoil which has been thrown out at the sides. This spoil, being already half-rotted granite, compacts into less jagged heaps than does the fire-hardened shale of the metamorphic aureole. Nevertheless, the combined effects of gully, often still with torn and crumbling sides, hummock and derelict buildings is unsightly and depressing. If confirmation of this is desired it is only necessary to walk through the area of the Birch Tor and Vitifer mines, immediately south of the Warren House Inn. Whatever may be one's opinions on the desirability or no of the Forestry Commission's activities on Dartmoor as a whole, there will be few who will raise serious objections to their attempts to screen some of this barrenness with trees. Not only did the old tin workers torture the landscape with their cuttings and waste. They also destroyed, or so we believe, much of the primitive woodland. This is not the place for a full discussion of the history of woods in the region, which may be reserved for a later chapter. It may be said, however, that, although there is nothing to support the view that Dartmoor was once completely clothed with trees, nevertheless, the frequent discovery of fragments of trees, principally Birch, *Betula* spp., and Hazel, *Corylus avellana*, in the peat bogs indicates that conditions in the past differed from those we see to-day. The tin smelters undoubtedly burned both wood and peat as fuel in their furnaces, and it is not unreasonable to suppose that they took the nearest available supplies. Without a far more extensive examination of the peat than has hitherto been attempted, it is impossible to say by how much the tinners have reduced the woodland. One might, however, hazard a guess that the valleys and many north-eastern slopes, where the winter force of the south-westerly gales is softened, may well have been wooded up to between 1,200 and 1,500 feet.

The people inhabiting Dartmoor in the Bronze Age have left many visible traces which add greatly to the interest of the moor, in the remains of their houses and villages and the great stone rows, monoliths and circles which they erected. The historical significance of these remains need not concern us here, but the lasting topographical effects of the tracks which linked one community with another and the whole region with the trading ports of the time deserve brief consideration. These tracks are to-day defined with varying clarity and by a variety of landmarks. The origin of many of them dates so far back that we can do no more than guess at the reasons underlying their making. One of the best defined of these is the so-called Central Trackway, and in the opinion of some archæologists at least this may have been the main road of the Bronze Age settlers. Other tracks, particularly those towards the south side of the moor, developed later, many of them carrying the traffic between the great religious houses there, Buckfast, Buckland and Tavistock Abbeys in particular. Of these tracks, probably the best known is the Abbot's Way, which links Buckfast with Buckland and Tavistock by way of the valleys of the Aune, or Avon, and Erme. Another track, the High Path, leads from the east side of Dartmoor, across the West Dart and the Cowsic and Walkham, to Lydford. This is a very ancient road along which the dead were carried to burial at Lydford from the early settlements in the east. Some idea of its

THE PHYSICAL PATTERN OF THE COUNTRY 43

antiquity may be gained from a document in the Exeter Episcopal
Registers, by which in A.D. 1260 Bishop Walter Bronescombe granted
permission to the inhabitants of the villages of Balbeny and Pushyll
(the "ancient tenements" of Babeny and Pizwell), on the Walla
Brook, to attend Widecombe Church instead of going to their parish
church at Lydford. An illuminating remark is made in this document,
"Et quod loca predicta a matrice ecclesia de Lideford sereno tempore per octo,
et tempestatibus exortis in circuitu per quindecim, distant miliaria." A striking
reflection on the depth and extent to which the rivers can flood during
rains, thereby forcing the traveller to detour and doubling the length
of his journey.

Space does not permit of a description of the courses of these various
tracks, nor is such a detailed discussion relevant to our subject. The
reader who is interested in them may well refer to William Crossing's
Guide to Dartmoor, published towards the end of the nineteenth century,
and of which a third edition dated 1914 may still be available. Before
leaving the tracks, however, it should be emphasised that only rarely
do they constitute continuous paths, the courses of which may be read
over long distances. In most instances they may only be traced with
certainty over the difficult parts of their length. This suggests that each
wayfarer chose his own path across dry, open country, being piloted
only at the few fords across streams or through the often narrow
passages over softer ground. Such points are often indicated by stone
crosses, particularly on the tracks which were extensively used by the
clerics.

The well-known "clapper" bridges by which some of the wider
streams are spanned (see Pl. VII, p. 62), that at Postbridge being a famous
example, lie for the most part on the line of pack-horse tracks, and
were probably built within historic times by the holders of the forest
tenements. Each is composed of huge slabs of native granite laid on
buttresses and piers of the same stone, and these rude structures have
stood the test of many centuries of use and of onset by the sudden and
turbulent floodings of the rivers over which they stand.

Modern roads are comparatively few. Fortunately, from the point
of view of both traveller and those who care for the quiet amenity of
Dartmoor, the main roads from Exeter to Plymouth and the West pass
on either side of the moor. Indeed, parts of both the Exeter-Plymouth
and the Exeter-Okehampton roads have been used as convenient
boundaries for the National Park. Two well-metalled roads actually

cross Dartmoor, the one from Exeter through Moretonhampstead to Princetown and on to Yelverton and Plymouth; the other from Ashburton throu ı Dartmeet to Tavistock. These are, however, narrow and poorly engineered by modern standards, and should be eschewed by the motorist who is in a hurry or is timorous with his gears. Where they cross the open moor long stretches of road occur on which gradients are mild and easy. But at some points, particularly where the descent is made from the granite plateau, the angle dips steeply and sometimes into a long, sheer descent, such as the hills at Merripit and Widecombe, or that from either side down to Dartmeet. Elsewhere the hills wind to a greater or lesser degree and hairpin bends, or double hairpins, like the Devil's Elbow just west of Princetown, are traps for the unwary.

Subsidiary roads approach or cross the moor at various points, as may be seen from the map, p. 10, or from the various Ordnance Survey sheets for the region. With due care a car may be taken along most of these, but the surface is often rough and in places only a single car's width is available. Moreover, the stone walls which edge many of them are sufficiently high effectively to cut off the view from the low-slung seat of a modern car. It cannot, therefore, be too strongly urged, in the interests of all, that cars should only be taken over such roads for very good reason, and then only with discretion and consideration for other users. Dartmoor is primarily a place to be enjoyed by the walker and horseman, and by those who can shake off, at least momentarily, the modern obsession that time saved in transporting oneself from one point to another has an intrinsic value. These roads have many charming features, and others which the more impatient may find exasperating. Although he does not refer specifically to Dartmoor, the Reverend John Marriott has summarised with wit and felicity the character of innumerable such lanes on the fringes of Dartmoor in a poem published in Samuel Rowe's *Perambulation of Dartmoor*, 1848, entitled, " The Devonshire Lane ":

In a Devonshire lane, as I trotted along
T'other day, much in want of a subject for song,
Thinks I to myself, I have hit on a strain,
Sure marriage is much like a Devonshire lane.

In the first place 'tis long, and when once you are in it
It holds you as fast as a cage does a linnet;

For howe'er rough and dirty, the road may be found,
Drive forward you must, there is no turning round.

But though 'tis so long, it is not very wide,
For two are the most that together can ride;
And e'en then 'tis a chance, but they get in a pother,
And jostle and cross and run foul of each other.

Oft Poverty greets them with mendicant looks,
And Care pushes by them, o'erladen with crooks:
And Strife's grazing wheels try between them to pass,
And Stubbornness blocks up the way on her ass.

Then the banks are so high, to the left hand and right,
That they shut up the beauties around them from sight,
And hence you'll allow 'tis an inference plain
That marriage is just like a Devonshire lane.

But thinks I too, these banks, within which we are pent,
With bud, blossom, and berry are richly besprent;
And the conjugal fence, which forbids us to roam,
Looks lovely, when decked with the comforts of home.

In the rock's gloomy crevice, the bright holly grows;
The ivy waves fresh o'er the withering rose,
And the evergreen love of a virtuous wife
Soothes the roughness of care,—cheers the winter of life.

Then long be the journey, and narrow the way,
I'll rejoice that I've seldom a turnpike to pay:
And whate'er others say, be the last to complain,
Though marriage is just like a Devonshire lane.

The modern townsman may find it hard to understand the idiosyncrasies of these narrow tracks, now sunk between earth banks or stone walls, now fringed by Hazel and Thorn scrub, sometimes closely over-arched with Oaks. Often a bright, foot-wide stream bubbles placidly alongside, or may lose itself in a marshy roadside waste of Meadow-sweet, *Filipendula ulmaria*, Hemp Agrimony, *Eupatorium cannabinum*, Marsh Thistle, *Cirsium palustre*, and Rushes. When it reaches the bottom of a hollow the chances are that its bed crosses the road, providing a water-splash to the delight of the very oldest of children. And always the lane twists and winds, until it reaches open moor or common, where it runs straight enough. For these have been made by and for local use; for the pack-horses of the old wool trade; for the small day-to-day traffic of the farmer and his neighbours, going about the fields on pleasure or business, to and from nearby houses, to and from village and small market town. They were made for people who were in no great hurry, whose eyes were set on the slow, orderly march of the farming year and had no far-distant objective. Their vehicles were horse-drawn, or they rode on stout ponies culled from the semi-wild moorland stock. If they walked, they were not particularly concerned that the underfoot was muddy. As a consequence, a system of intersecting lanes came into being, linking farmhouse with farmhouse and village, and stretching out beyond on to the common lands of the moor where each man had his rights of grazing, turbary and so forth. They are, therefore, an indelible record of the history of the rural civilisation associated with the moor.

The population of the region is sparse, as is only to be expected where living is so hard won. Few villages and towns are situated on the moor itself, they being distributed in a peripheral manner about its flanks. Princetown is the only place of any size within the moor, although several other small towns lie within the boundaries proposed for the National Park. Princetown derives its vitality from the artificial circumstance that the Dartmoor Prison has been located there. Although now, the local rural population has gravitated into the town, there can be no denying that the major interests are associated with the prison officers and their families, and with the crowds of visitors drawn to Princetown in summer, some by morbid curiosity, others by the fact that it lies on the route of the only direct east-to-west road which crosses Dartmoor. The other peripheral communities are mostly situated on, or close to, the arterial roads which cross the fringes of the area. The largest of these is Okehampton, in the north. This, like Princetown, has become secondarily enlarged and its character changed, in this case by its close proximity to the big military camps of the artillery ranges. For the rest we find small aggregates of from 1,000 to 3,000 inhabitants in Moretonhampstead, Chagford, Bovey Tracey, Buckfastleigh, Ashburton, South Brent, Ivybridge, Lydford and Yelverton. Smaller villages and hamlets include North Bovey, Manaton, Lustleigh, Holne, Widecombe, Peter and Mary Tavy,

Plate 6. Ring Ouzels, *Turdus torquatus*, male and female with young
at a nest in old tin-workings

Plate 7. Larva of Emperor Moth, *Saturnia pavonia*, on heather

CHAPTER 4

THE GEOLOGY OF THE REGION

D ARTMOOR, like its more westerly counterparts, Bodmin Moor, St. Austell Moor, Carnmenellis, Land's End and the Scilly Isles, is fundamentally a great knub of granite intruded into ancient sedimentary rocks which comprise the neighbouring country. The area of the Forest and its commons, and even more so of the proposed National Park of Dartmoor, extends far beyond the granite, and includes some of the country overlying the sedimentary strata. The whole is welded into one great complex, partly as a result of the initial intrusion of the granite magma, and partly by changes which succeeded this and resulting from submarine and aerial erosion.

A perusal of a geological map of South Devon (see p. 58) shows a series of Palaeozoic rocks succeeding one another from south to north in more or less latitudinal bands. The younger, Mesozoic rocks are confined, except for a few small outliers, to the east of the River Exe, and by far the greater area of the county is composed of the sandstones and shales with occasional limestone of the Devonian and Carboniferous periods. Briefly, the final geological pattern of the south-western peninsula results from two great periods of convulsion of the earth's crust. At the close of the Silurian period a series of folds appeared in this crust, running mostly in a direction from north-east to south-west and to these may possibly be attributed the general lie of the peninsula as a whole, though this is by no means certain. This Caledonian system remained stable for many millions of years, being subjected to weathering, and to deposition on it of the sedimentary rocks of the Devonian and Carboniferous ages. Towards the end of the last period, when the Culm Measures of the Carboniferous were being laid down, there occurred the second set of convulsions, and these threw up the

Armorican, or Hercynian, Mountains. This time the thrust was initiated from the south northwards, and the existing rocks were folded against the Caledonian girder and the massif of what is now Wales. As a consequence these Armorican mountains trend mostly from east to west, in a series of synclines and anticlines. The Culm Measures, which stretch right across Devon, from the northern fringes of Dartmoor to Exmoor and the neighbourhood of Bideford in the north, represent to-day the remains of one great compound syncline, passing into another complex anticline at its southern edge, where the older, Devonian rocks are exposed between Dartmoor and the south coast.

As a result of the enormous thrusts developed against the resistant massifs to the north and west, the sedimentary rocks became folded, compressed, and overthrust on one another. It is probable that, deep down in the weakening crust, small masses of molten magma were intruded at quite an early stage into the crests of the folds, where they began to cool and to crystallise. Following this came the main intrusions, spreading from the south northwards and extending on either side, to form what may be regarded as an enormous blister, the roof of which was the original country rock. This roof remained intact and there was no actual surface eruption. As a result of this the magma cooled under pressure and as it solidified so its upper surface became moulded against the lower surface of the overlying strata. Professor Brammall, to whom we owe the most modern study and interpretation of the Dartmoor granites, suggests that the pattern of the high watershed, extending from Red Lake and Lee Moor in the south, north-eastwards as far as Cut Hill or beyond, reflects this moulding. The direction of bedding and jointing planes in the exposed tors, moreover, suggests that they represent remains of the original upper surface moulding. At deeper levels the bedding planes tend to assume a general horizontal direction, such as might be expected as the great underground lake of molten rock cooled steadily from the surface downwards.

In the eastern half of the region, however, later disturbances have tended to crack the original granite block. Fresh magma was thrust through these cracks, further fragmenting the rock and even remelting it in some places. The final rock of this region therefore contains a variety of contaminating islands derived, some from the roof of country rock, some from the original minor intrusions into the crests of the folds, and some from the main intrusion of magma. In addition, a variety of secondary sills and veins of the last granite intrusion occur within the rocks derived from the main block. Some of the best examples of these may be seen at Rippon Tor, Wind Tor, Archerton and Holne Moor.

The intense heat from the molten magma, slowly dissipating through the superficial roof, profoundly modified the country rock in the immediate neighbourhood, baking it, and filling its cracks with minerals which condensed from the gases emanating from it. Because of the changes wrought in these sedimentary rocks by the processes which have been outlined, they constitute what is known as the metamorphic aureole to-day. The reader who has followed this description will realise that, immediately after the completion of this process what we know to-day as Dartmoor then consisted of a huge block of granite, the parts of which had originated from three different sources, and at three stages in the evolution of the system. The whole lay deep in the roots of a range of mountains which had been thrown up by the folding of the sedimentary rocks originally covering the earth's surface here, and in the immediate neighbourhood of the granite, extending to a distance of approximately three-quarters of a mile outwards on all sides, these rocks were baked and altered owing to the heat given off by the cooling of the magma.

The subsequent history of the region has been one of prolonged erosion of the surface, partly submarine, partly sub-aerial, coupled, at least in its later stages, with local rotting and modification of the granite itself. Eventually, the whole of the overlying mountains have become denuded, and as a result the hard granite centre now lies exposed on the surface, as the core of this old Armorican range. Incidentally, much of the rubbish which resulted from the denudation of the mountains has accumulated over east Devon as the breccias and red sandstones of the Permian rocks, which give so much brilliance of colour to the scenery of central and south-east Devon, and have earned for the county its soubriquet of " Red Devon."

The processes of erosion do not, of course, move at a uniform rate over such huge and varied complexes as these mountains were. Their forces will differ according to the angle at which they impinge on one part and another, or according as one part is shielded or exposed. And the materials on which they operate will be of different types and hardnesses and will therefore wear away at different rates. In particular, the region was subjected to a considerable degree of submergence below sea-level during Cretaceous times. By the time it was lifted up again the granite core was exposed, and now, under sub-aerial erosion, the depressions of its surface which were parts of the original pattern moulded on the granite when it cooled, became the natural drainage channels for rain water, and hence evolved naturally as the major river valleys by which the water was drained to the sea.

Before we analyse the history of the region further, it may be well to understand something of the structure of the granite itself. Granite is an igneous rock which, as we have seen, has cooled and crystallised under great pressure and at considerable depth below the earth's surface. The molten magma from which it originated consisted of a complex mixture of chemical compounds which, although it may be regarded in bulk as homogeneous, yet behaves much like a watery solution of mixed salts on drying and crystallising. That is to say, the individual compounds separate out into crystals which grow by accretion of more and more material to themselves. As a result the solid rock which results is a mosaic of crystals each of which may be defined from the remainder by its chemical composition, structure, shape and colour. The final pattern assumed by the rock depends on the constituents present in the original magma and their relative proportions, as also on the amount of pressure exerted on the cooling mass, and the rate at which it cooled. Sometimes, also, convection and eddy currents may occur while the mixture is still fluid, and these may align crystals into various patterns, as may also slow-flowing movements of the whole mass.

The materials which constitute something like 95 per cent of all granites are quartz, felspars (orthoclase and plagioclase) and dark mica or biotite. The remaining five per cent comprises variable amounts of many different minerals, the proportion of none of which usually attains to one per cent, except in the later stages of alteration of the rock. Some of these minerals, however, although rare in the total mass, may occur in local crystals or aggregates of significant size. Iron pyrites, for instance, sometimes confers a dark grey cloudiness on quite large pieces of rock, while the purple-black crystals of tourmaline may give a notable character to some granites.

The cessation of magmatic intrusion has left a considerable mixture of granites on Dartmoor, differing both in origin and in the proportions of their various constituents. In particular, the relative amounts of biotite, and so the depth of colour of the rock, vary between one type

Plate V. Hound Tor rocks, showing jointing and weathering

Plate VI. Old tin workings, West Webburn valley

E. H. Ware

and another. Those granites which are rich in biotite are darker than others in which quartz and felspars predominate. There can be no doubt that the cooling of such a complex system set up a variety of stresses which influenced the structure of the rock. Lines and planes of weakness were set up which are now manifested in the bedding and jointing of the granite, and these are clearly shown, under the influence of weathering, in the outcrops and tors (see Pl. IV, V, pp. 15, 24). Others gave rise to definite cracks and fissures through which rose thermal waters and gaseous emanations of magmatic origin and containing an abundance of silica, fluoboric acid and the like. As erosion proceeded, so also surface water, rich in humic and carbonic acids, began to percolate downwards, and this would naturally be forced to follow these same fissures. Probably also pneumatolytic changes were set in train in the granite itself. As a result of all these influences the structure and composition of the granite began to alter and the changes were particularly marked and rapid in the neighbourhood of such weaknesses as these. A comparatively early phase of such alteration may involve the deposition of tourmaline and haematite, producing the tourmalinised and red granites which are widely distributed over Dartmoor. At the same time the felspars may be turned cloudy, and they are eventually completely broken down into white mica, silica and kaolin. The biotite is converted into chlorite, which may stain the felspars green, and finally titanium oxide is released from it. The complete destruction of felspars and biotite by intense tourmalinisation converts the original granite into what is now known as schorl, in which secondarily added quartz is the dominant constituent.

The results of these processes are to be seen in many places. On the one hand, there occur in the rock metalliferous lodes, quartz veins and quartz schorl, all of which result from the accumulation of the products of pneumatolysis in the original fissures of the granite. On the other hand, the decay of the felspars leaves immense deposits of kaolin, representing the remains of the altered rock, the fissures in which have become filled as the aforementioned veins and lodes. It is probable that considerable areas of kaolin may exist beneath the peat in many parts of the moor. But, fortunately for the amenities of Dartmoor, it has only been extensively worked in the Lee Moor area, immediately north-east of Plymouth. Whiteworks, near Fox Tor Mire, and closer to the heart of the region, has been abandoned for many years now. The ruined engine house and the spoil-heap still, however, disfigure this lonely spot, while the bed of the old narrow-gauge railway by which its products were carried to Western Beacon, near Ivybridge, still scars the hillside over which it ran. The extraction of china clay from the kaolin deposits involves its separation from the other products of felspar decay, namely, quartz and mica. No adequate use has been found for these by-products, and they accumulate in the huge, glistening white spoil-heaps which are conspicuous at distances of twenty miles or more. In addition, the open pits from which the clay is dug are abandoned as they become worked out. Water accumulates in them and remains permanently turbid with a milky white suspension of clay particles. Finally, despite the most stringent precautions, which, incidentally, are not always exercised as carefully as they should be, a similarly turbid water drains off from the settling pits into the streams, the beds of which become coated with a white mud, while the water never runs with the limpid clarity which one has learned to expect of Dartmoor rivers.

The metalliferous lodes comprise those already mentioned as having developed within the granite, and also others which for the most part are situated in the metamorphic aureole. These result from the condensation in the fissures of the baked and contorted country rock of the more volatile constituents of the magma, and also from deposition of water soluble minerals, in a manner very similar to some of those responsible for filling the fissures in the granite. Their products include ores of tin, copper, zinc, arsenic and iron, together with smaller quantities of gold and silver, both of which incidentally occur as primary elements in the granite. The effects on the landscape of the various means used to extract these minerals have already been discussed (p. 40), and here we need only concern ourselves with the nature of the deposits themselves. Tin and copper are not now produced from Dartmoor, extraction being no longer profitable in the face of the much heavier output from other parts of the world, particularly Africa and Malaya. Between February 1920 and March 1921, for instance, the price of tin per ton fell from £407 to £153, and although it subsequently rose slightly, it was never again maintained at a figure at which it was economic to mine the ore in south-west Britain. A few of the Cornish mines struggled on, but in 1945, even after the restriction of imports imposed by war, only one Cornish mine was still open, while the Dartmoor mines had been closed for twenty years or more. The largest tin producers had been the mines at Birch Tor and Vitifer, and at Owlacombe, while a score of others, widely scattered in the region, have yielded in smaller quantities.

Early in the nineteenth century Cornwall and Devon between them contributed over half the world's supplies of copper, by far the richest of the Dartmoor mines being Wheal Friendship, Brookwood and South Devon United. But to-day the industry is dead beyond any prospect of revival. Lead and silver were extracted mostly at Wheal Betsy, while arsenic came mainly from Wheal Friendship and Owlacombe. To-day the only ore to be mined in any quantity is iron, which is found in beds of limonite and haematite in the Culm Measures at the Haytor and Ilsington and Smallacombe mines, or in similar deposits in Devonian limestone at the Devon and Cornwall United mine, near Ashburton. Umber, the oxide in which the iron occurs, is a valuable ingredient of paints and preservatives, and it seems likely that these works may continue in active production. The baryta which is worked at Christow has already been mentioned (see p. 49). Production of this mineral has risen by some 1,000 per cent during the last twenty-five years, and its use as a white pigment in paint, and also as a filling in paper and rubber suggests that the industry has a considerable future.

The metamorphic aureole presents a number of features of interest to the geologist. Calculations based on estimations of its horizontal width at various points, and the relation of this to the supposed, or observed, angle of dip of the granite, indicate that the approximate thickness of the aureole is about 3,500 feet. In parts, where it overlies the granite to the west and south, it may be upwards of a mile and a half across, falling to between a half and three-quarters of a mile where the granite dips more steeply to the east. The sedimentary rocks involved were the shales, grits, cherts and sandstones of the Culm and Devonian series, together with a certain amount of Devonian limestone in the south, particularly near Ashburton and Buckfastleigh. Each type of rock has responded in its own fashion to the heat and pressure to which it was subjected. The sandstones, grits and cherts were the least altered. Perhaps the most striking alteration of this type of rock is that shown by the radiolarian cherts of Standon Hill, where the rounded outlines of the minute fossil Radiolaria of which it was originally composed still remain visible, but polarised light shows that the whole rock has become recrystallised as a fine-grained quartzite. The shales and slates may often retain their apparent sedimentary

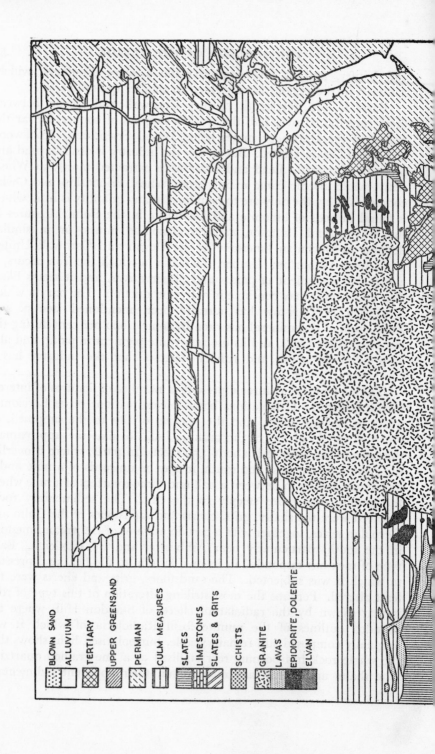

BLOWN SAND
ALLUVIUM
TERTIARY
UPPER GREENSAND
PERMIAN
CULM MEASURES
SLATES
LIMESTONES
SLATES & GRITS
SCHISTS
GRANITE
LAVAS
EPIDIORITE, DOLERITE
ELVAN

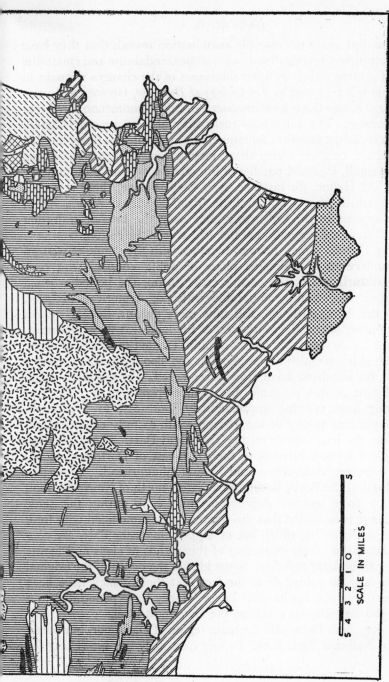

SCALE IN MILES

Fig. 2.—The Geology of South Devon.

lamination, but again microscopic examination reveals that they have become completely recrystallised as hornfelses, andalusite and chiastolite slates and spotted slates. A fuller discussion of the changes wrought in this aureole will be found in *The Geology of Dartmoor*, Geological Survey Memoir, 1912, and the reader interested in this phenomenon is referred to that volume. The calcareous rocks may also be strongly altered. These rarely consist purely of limestone, but more often as finely banded seams of shale, or more rarely chert, interspersed with calcite. These, often very small, localised patches of limestone may startle the unwary ecologist. At Heltor, for instance, near Steps Bridge, there is such a block, on which the beautiful little Pale Toadflax, *Linaria repens*, suddenly appears in the hedgerows after only the briefest transition from the more usual vegetation of the acid soils of the region.

During Tertiary times, Britain, together with the whole of western Europe underwent a prolonged phase of uplift, coupled with considerable disturbance of the earth's crust during the period when a great folding movement, comparable with the Armorican orogeny, threw up the Alps. Although this time more distant, the total effect of the two processes on the south-west of England was very important. On the one hand, successive phases of uplift created the series of raised beach-lines at levels which to-day stand at 400, 800, 1,000 and probably 2,000 feet, on which we have already remarked. On the other hand, the far-distant Alpine orogenic disturbances produced a pattern of faults along lines running approximately south-east to north-west, which is apparent to-day in the general south-easterly courses of rift valleys from the head-waters on the Teign and Dart. The parallelism of the valleys is most obvious to the south-east of Dartmoor, in the country between Ashburton and Moretonhampstead. Geologists believe also that the Bovey Basin, immediately north of Newton Abbot, represents a large tectonic depression which sank during this same period. There is no doubt that this depression became filled with fresh water, for the deposits, which are of Upper Oligocene date, are conclusively lacustrine, there consisting of thin bands of clays and lignite alternating irregularly together. Some idea of the depth of the original depression may be gained from the fact that shafts which have been sunk in search of the lignite near Bovey Tracey have penetrated to a depth of 500 feet without reaching the lowermost level.

The Bovey Beds lie outside the main region of Dartmoor, but partly within the National Park zone. In any case, they are interesting for the light which they throw on the flora of the south-eastern flanks of the mountains which, in Oligocene times, probably rose to about 3,000 feet. Clement Reid, who contributed to the *Newton Abbot* Memoir of the Geological Survey, 1913, a discussion of the deposits, has interpreted the conditions under which they must have been laid down. The Aquitanian stage, during which the lake existed, was one of warm, damp climate throughout Europe, and these conditions encouraged abundant growth of forest trees and climbers. The River Bovey, draining the Dartmoor mountains from the region in which Moretonhampstead and North Bovey are now situated, was a turbulent stream which must have fallen 650 feet at least, headlong, in the three and a half miles immediately before it emptied into the lake. Vast quantities of debris were swept along; soil and subsoil from the eroded banks, leaves and twigs falling from the streamside vegetation, and whole trunks and root systems of trees and shrubs undermined by the floods and swept downstream on the spates. Suddenly checked on reaching the lake, the water dropped its suspended matter, the coarser, heavier, materials first, the finer at a greater distance. The water must rarely have been free of a fine white turbidity from the kaolin derived from the decomposing granite; and the surface was dotted with rafts of decaying vegetation, trunks, branches, twigs and leaves agglomerated into loose masses which drifted over the water until, becoming waterlogged, they sank, to become petrified eventually as lignite. Remains of truly aquatic or marsh-dwelling organisms, whether plant or animal, are strikingly sparse, a fact which may be attributable to the turbidity of the water. Through the course of centuries the mountains to the north became steadily eroded down, and the lake filled with their debris. At its northern end a delta of coarse, heavy deposits steadily pushed southwards, while on the bottom layer after layer of finer sands and clays, intermingled with narrow bands of lignite, accumulated until at last the basin was full to the brim and the lake began to dry out. To-day the deposits are worked at Bovey Tracey for the lignite, from which waxes are extracted, and at Heathfield for the pottery and fire clays.

The lignite has yielded abundant evidence of the character of the forest flora of the valleys to the north of the lake. A very large proportion of it consists of twigs and trunks, cones and leaves of a comparatively small *Sequoia, S. couttsiae*, to which the Wellingtonias and Redwoods are related. There are, however, remains of many other plants, and the full list which is appended includes many species which are no longer indigenous, and many which to-day are confined to warmer climates than ours:

CRYPTOGAMIA
Goniopteris bunburyi
G. stiriaca
Lezeunea c. f. *minutissima*
Osmunda lignitum

Pteris (?) *hookeri*
Sclerotium cinnamoni
Sphaeria lignitum
S. socialis

GYMNOSPERMAE
Sequoia couttsiae
Taxodium distichum

Taxus baccata
T. (?) *nitens*

MONOCOTYLEDONES
Calla c.f. *palustris*
Cyperites deperditus
Palmacites daemonorops
Phragmites oeningensis

Poacites sp.
Potamogeton tenuicarpus
Sagittaria sp.
Stratiotes websteri

DICOTYLEDONES
Anona cyclosperma
A. (?) *devonica*
Calvarinus reticulatus
Carpolithes boveyanus
C. exaratus
C. scutellatus
Celastrus pseudo-ilex
Cinnamomum lanceolatum
C. rossmässleri
C. scheuchzeri
Cornus sp.
Daphnogene ungeri
Echitonium cuspidatum
Eucalyptus oceanica
Eugenia haeringiana
Ficus falconieri
F. pengellyi
Gardenia wetzleri

Leucothoe reticulata
L. vacciniifolia
Magnolia ludwigi
Myrica banksiaefolia
M. hakeaefolia
M. laevigata
Nyssa europaea
N. laevigata
N. microsperma
N. obovata
N. ornithobroma
N. striolata
N. vertumni
Nymphaea doris
Pterocarya denticulata
Quercus lyelli
Rubus microspermus
Vaccinium acheronticum

E. H. Ware

Plate VII a. The Great Ammil of 1947

   b. Clapper bridge over the Cowsic, above Two Bridges

E. H. Ware

Plate VIII a.   View looking southwards over Moretonhampstead. The passing rain-storm brings the 800-foot platform into prominence

    b.   Terraced hillside in the Challacombe valley

Laurus primigenia   *Vitis hookeri*
Leguminosites areolatus   *V. ludwigi*
          V. teutonica

The gardener will recognise several genera from among this list, species of which are now cultivated in gardens for their fruit or for decorative purposes. Most of them now have to be imported as aliens from abroad. They include, *Sequoia, Taxodium, Stratiotes, Celastrus, Cornus, Eucalyptus, Ficus, Gardenia, Laurus, Magnolia, Myrica, Nymphaea, Quercus* and *Vitis.* Even when a genus still occurs as a native, the species, except in rare instances, such as *Taxus baccata,* the Common Yew, differs from those which occurred in these valleys.

The only records of recent faunas are provided by remains found in caves, situated for the most part in Devonian limestone. Some of these are interesting for their stalactite and stalagmite formations, although these are rarely spectacular. So far only two have been found to contain animal remains. Of these the most famous is Kent's Cavern, near Torquay, but this lies too far to the south to merit consideration here. The caves in the Ashburton and Buckfastleigh district have, however, as it were, Dartmoor right on their doorsteps, and it is fortunate that an active group of speleologists is engaged in their exploration. The most interesting to be found so far, from our present point of view, has been the subject of preliminary excavation by Joint, Mitchell and Northey, between 1938 and 1941. Called, after its investigators, the Joint Mitnor Cave, it is a comparatively small hole into which it is believed the deposits of bones in its floor were swept by percolating water which fell through swallow-holes in the roof. No trace of human remains or activity were found, and although hyena bones were plentiful, there are no signs of gnawing of the bones, a fact which suggests that the bones were waterborne, after death. The most interesting feature of the finds is that they contained, besides the usual species, such as Lion, Wolf, Bear and Hyena, three other species not hitherto recorded in quantity in Devon. These are, Hippopotamus, *Hippopotamus amphibius,* Straight-tusked Elephant, *Elephas antiquus,* and Narrow-nosed Rhinoceros, *Rhinocerus leptorhinus.* Although these are widespread among remains of arctic species, both in cave deposits and in gravels, they are usually regarded as indicative of a warmer climate. This fauna therefore suggests the existence of a warm, interglacial period, of which the Kent's Cavern deposits give no hint. Possibly also the scarcity of horse bones, and the frequency of those of *Bos primigenius* may be accounted for by an abundance of forest in these warm conditions.

The only important deposit of recent date on Dartmoor, the peat, still awaits exploration. This, as we have seen, and shall have occasion to refer to frequently during the course of the book, forms two enormous sheets of blanket bog, covering the main watersheds of Dartmoor. Few borings or cuttings into it have been thoroughly examined, and we are therefore ignorant of anything it may have to tell of the history of the climate and vegetation. Such sections as are exposed, usually in the course of peat-cutting for domestic use, show that it is of relatively uniform fibrous consistency throughout, and there is no evidence microscopically of zonation, such as is shown by many peats in other parts of England and Wales. It is a matter for some concern, especially in view of the extent of military operations over it, that there is little evidence of active peat formation having occurred, possibly for some centuries, over most of the bogs. Indeed, there is considerable evidence that the peat is regressing slowly.

Most of the soils on the granite core of the region consist of peat, which may be several feet thick in many areas, especially over the bogs, but, particularly on the drier hillsides, may not be more than a few inches deep. Where this top layer has been broken up by cultivation, and the underlying rotted granite remains incorporated into the topsoil, a warm light soil is produced, as we have already seen (p. 48), and this may produce excellent crops of roots. Elsewhere, on the fringes, the soils are derived from the Devonian and Culm rocks, and are usually shallow. They vary from calcareous loams in the neighbourhood of limestone outcrops, to usually stiffish clays on the shales and grits. Being usually poorly drained they tend to be cold and unproductive.

CHAPTER 5

THE CLIMATE

THE ELEVATION of Dartmoor, coupled with its proximity to the western seaboard, is conducive towards a wet climate with both a high rate of actual precipitation and also a high degree of humidity in the air at all seasons. As may be seen on a rainfall map, the average annual rainfall over most of lowland Devon is not above 40 inches, and in the south-east of the county it may be well below 35 inches. The amount rises rapidly to an annual average of nearly 82 inches at Princetown. Unfortunately, owing to the sparsity of the population, there are few weather stations which are served regularly in the region, and it is scarcely possible to present comparative figures for different parts of the moor. It is believed, however, that Princetown and its environs constitute the wettest region, and that the fall declines steadily as one proceeds thence towards the outskirts of Dartmoor. At Okehampton, for instance, only fourteen miles distant from Princetown as the crow flies, the average fall for the year is only $55\frac{1}{2}$ inches.

The annual rainfall records have been published over a long period, for a number of scattered stations in the region, and are to be found in the *Transactions of the Devonshire Association*. A few of the relevant figures for the ten years from 1935 to 1944 are quoted in the following table, together with those for Exeter as exemplifying one of the driest stations in the county. It will be seen that not only is the rainfall comparatively high at all the Dartmoor stations, but also how much more violent may be the annual fluctuations.

The normally shallow Dartmoor streams rise very rapidly during rain, and may develop tremendous erosive power under such circumstances. I have still the most vivid recollections of crossing Dartmoor after three successive days of heavy rain, during the early years of the

TABLE: RAINFALL IN INCHES, DARTMOOR AND EXETER

Station	1935	1936	1937	1938	1939	1940	1941	1942	1943	1944
Cowsic Valley	98.85	83.26	80.86	88.40	88.00	71.05	64.30	75.73	75.18	78.15
Cranmere	84.50	80.80	84.90	80.40	87.20	75.60	65.90	77.80	83.95	86.55
Devil's Tor	80.55	76.65	79.21	78.50	84.10	68.11	62.36	73.10	70.39	73.64
Holne	69.17	73.04	72.51	74.68	74.47	66.67	56.00	64.08	66.22	65.54
Huccaby	64.92	69.24	74.55	64.41	64.82	57.00	55.39	58.18	61.95	57.56
Mary Tavy	63.94	58.07	58.35	64.31	64.30	53.60	46.64	57.59	59.88	58.50
Okehampton	61.14	58.31	58.38	55.23	61.53	56.61	46.39	47.98	55.02	53.08
Siward's Cross	69.80	59.45	62.75	60.32	71.05	60.22	49.70	70.69	75.94	78.76
Princetown	83.11	80.95	79.09	89.64	99.40	78.32	68.25	86.42	83.16	89.20
South Brent	74.48	73.70	74.10	75.66	83.18	70.62	68.40	68.19	70.60	71.07
Kennick	44.54	50.35	50.48	44.83	51.80	44.67	39.45	44.44	43.46	36.36
Exeter	34.95	35.01	38.19	29.63	36.90	32.94	28.30	29.24	32.42	26.83

nineteen-thirties. My wife and I crossed from Peter Tavy to Wide-combe, thus having to negotiate the crossing of several streams, including the Cowsic and West Dart. Normally, this presents little difficulty, and one can cross them dryshod on the stone sills which separate successive pools from one another. But on this occasion each river was a turbulent brown flood which topped all but the largest boulders, and the only possible crossings were by wading at the shallowest points we could find. Having no dry stitch on us by this time, we were not deterred by this prospect, but it was with peculiar thankfulness that we reached the farther banks. The Dart in particular was running waist-high, and at such speed that stones the size of a man's head were bowled away from beneath our feet as we stepped on them. It was no comfort to be told, on reaching the inn at Widecombe, that the Dart claims a heart a year.

Thunderstorms are comparatively rare over Dartmoor, although they may be very severe when they occur. In August of 1938, for instance, a series of such storms was generated over South Devon, and at one time three cloud masses were seen converging on the district of Chagford. At Newton Abbot, to the south, over six inches of rain fell in twenty-four hours and severe flooding occurred in the town, as also at Teignmouth, Exeter and many other places in the south of the county. Severe as they were in the lowlands, the effects on Dartmoor were even fiercer. On visiting the eastern moors on the following day, we found the streams still roaring torrents with their beds deeply scoured. The bogs were almost impassable, while on some of the lesser

Plate 8. The River Avon from Huntingdon Warren. The low mound
of one of the old warrens in the centre foreground

roads, such, for instance, as that which passes below Grimspound towards Widecombe, ruts a foot deep and eighteen inches wide had been torn in the metalled surface, and huge granite boulders were tossed aside as if by some gigantic schoolboys. Such phenomena are, however, rare, and a much more frequent, and potentially dangerous visitation is mist. As in all hilly districts mists may generate very rapidly and cause serious inconvenience to anyone on the more remote moors. The gently rolling terrain of the high moors, although offering little danger from precipices, at the same time may offer very little guidance to the lost. In the absence of a compass it is usually a safe procedure to find a stream and follow it downhill. There is usually some firm ground along the banks, and at the worst one may get wet feet, but eventually arrive at a road or habitation.

The mildness of climate of the south-western peninsula is mitigated to some extent on the high ground, where temperatures may be several degrees lower than average. Some comparative figures from Ilfracombe and Torquay, as representing conditions on the north and south coasts, Cullompton, in central east Devon and Okehampton and Princetown on Dartmoor will illustrate this:

Station	Altitude feet	Mean Ann. Temp. Degrees F.	Mean Diurnal Range Deg. F.	Mean Annual Range Deg. F.
Ilfracombe	25	51.6	8.4	8.4
Torquay	27	51.8	11	10–11
Cullompton	202	50	15.8	15.8
Okehampton	500	48–50	12–18	12–14
Princetown	1,430	47.8	10.5	10–11

Figures quoted from *Devon and Cornwall, A Preliminary Survey, 1947*

Snow, which comes rarely to the coastal belt, is normal to the Dartmoor winter, falling on an average of 15 to 20 days in the year, and often lying for long periods. It is by no means unknown for deep drifts to cut off outlying farms and hamlets for days at a time, and sheep and ponies suffer heavy losses during the severer weather, particularly under modern practice whereby the moors are dangerously overstocked. The implications of this are, however, discussed by Gordon towards the end of the book (p. 160) and will not be anticipated here. Beautiful as may be their effects, fantastically beautiful under an " ammil " such as that which again Gordon has described, snow and ice are not welcome to the moormen, and they generally leave in

D   F

their wake a trail of misery and destruction among the animals which are forced to endure their rigours.

The prevailing winds are south-westerly, and their force during winter gales is very great on the high, exposed moors. No records are available of actual wind speeds, but there is plenty of evidence of their direction and power in the misshapen forms of trees and bushes exposed to them. Menacing and bitter as they may be in winter, the winds are usually pleasant enough in summer, and the air feels light and gentle here when, all too frequently, lowland Devon is sweltering in a sultry, thunder-laden atmosphere.

It is not surprising that this climate, more rigorous than at lower altitudes, wetter, cooler, more windswept, and in which spring frosts occur later and autumn frosts come earlier, proves unkindly to agriculture. Hay and corn harvests are taken several weeks later than elsewhere in the county, and in many parts the shortness of the growing season, and wet climate, preclude the taking of any corn crop except oats. The principal type of farming is therefore grazing, and what arable fields there are exist primarily for raising a minimum of winter feed for the stock.

CHAPTER 6

THE MOORS AND TORS

F OR THE PURPOSES of this discussion the moor land plant communities of Dartmoor may be divided first into wet and dry moors. The wet moors are characterised by the fact of their growth on waterlogged peat at a high altitude. Purple Moor Grass, *Molinia caerulea*, Bog Cotton Grass, *Eriophorum* spp., and many other sedges are the characteristic species of the flora, together with Cross-leaved Heath, *Erica tetralix*, which tends to replace Ling, *Calluna vulgaris*, and Bell Heather, *Erica cinerea*, on wetter ground. These wet moors, however, fall more naturally into the category of bogs, and the area they cover constitutes the two great patches of blanket bog in the heart of the region. Consideration of their features will therefore be reserved to a later chapter, and we may confine ourselves here to the dry moors.

The term dry is relative, indicating merely that the ground on which the dry moors occur is drained, and does not remain water-logged for long periods. So humid is the climate that the soil is normally damp, and only in quite abnormal summers, like that which we had in 1949, do conditions ever approach those of a drought. Moreover, the drainage is rarely sharp, and the peaty soil is retentive of moisture, and small local bogs are frequent on the hillsides and in the valleys. While, therefore, it has been convenient to defer consideration of the bogs to a later chapter, it must be realised that these constitute a prominent feature of all parts of the moors, and the plants and animals associated with them contribute interest and variety to what would prove uniform, and to the casual glance, rather dull country. Frequent references must therefore be made to these local bogs during discussion of the moorland.

Moorlands are usually classified according to the species of plants which are common on them. Thus, Dartmoor has its grass moors, heather moors and bilberry moors. Some hillsides are dominated by low-growing hummocks of Western Furze, *Ulex gallii*, and are particularly painful to walk on; for the fine stems of the Gorse are everywhere, deep in the mat of vegetation, and the foot sinks anything from ankle- to knee-deep into the prickly bed at every step. Finally, Bracken, *Pteridium aquilinum*, is spreading over many Dartmoor hills at a rate which brings dismay to walker and grazier alike. Unfortunately, short of either deep cultivation or perpetual early cutting, no adequate control of this pest has been discovered. A great step towards checking its advance might, however, be taken if a more rational policy of " swaling," or moor burning, were adopted. At present swaling appears to be a quite haphazard process, undertaken at the caprice of any commoner. St. Leger Gordon discusses some of its social implications on a later page of the book (p. 169). As far as its biological results are concerned, it is becoming all too plain that too frequent and uncontrolled burning is steadily weakening the Heather and grasses; while the Bracken, the rhizomes of which lie too deep to be damaged, is encouraged, finding little cover to compete with when it comes up in the spring. As a consequence, large areas of formerly good Heather or grass grazing have become flooded with Bracken, and this, by the density of its shade, kills off almost all the other vegetation of the ground which it infests. It may be cut for litter, but no other use had been found for it, and it is detested by most users of the moors.

True grass moor is not really common on Dartmoor. The grass associations, apart from the *Molinia* moor of the blanket bogs, are more frequently heaths, in which a mixture of low-growing plants includes as prominent members:

Western Furze, *Ulex gallii*
Bell Heather, *Erica cinerea*
Whortleberry, *Vaccinium myrtillus*
Heath Bedstraw, *Galium saxatile*
Wood Sage, *Teucrium scorodonia*

Bracken, *Pteridium aquilinum*
Hard Fern, *Blechnum spicant*
Mat Grass, *Nardus stricta*
Heath Bent Grass, *Agrostis setacea*
Waved Hair Grass, *Deschampsia flexuosa*

Associated, but less prominent, members of the community are:

Tormentil, *Potentilla erecta*
Sweet Vernal Grass, *Anthoxanthum odoratum*

Sheep's Sorrel, *Rumex acetosella*

D. St. Leger-Gordon

Plate IX a. Highland cattle on Taw Marsh. Note the hummocks left by old tin streamers, right middle ground

     b. Wheatear carrying leather-jacket (Tipulid grub)

E. H. Ware

E. H. Ware

Plate X. Forestry Commission plantation. Trees and cover growing vigorously

Purple Moor Grass, *Molinia caerulea*, wherever, as often, damp conditions prevail

A variety of sedges

Eyebright, *Euphrasia officinalis*, especially where the vegetation is cropped short

Lady's Bedstraw, *Galium verum*, on the shales round the granite core, as, for instance, in the Plym valley, or that of the Taw at Belstone

Heath grades into grass moor over well-drained and relatively shallow peat. Here occurs a mixture of grasses such as Sweet Vernal, Sheep's Fescue, *Festuca ovina*, Fine Bent, *Agrostis tenuis*, and Brown Bent, *A. canina* var. *arida*, with Tormentil, Heath Bedstraw, Sorrel, Carnation Sedge, *Carex caryophyllea*, and Field Wood Rush, *Luzula campestris*. Lady's Bedstraw, again, may occur over shale, together with Thyme, *Thymus drucei*. Both here and on the heaths a rich thallophyte flora of mosses, leafy liverworts and lichens occurs, but except for the larger species, like some of the *Polytrichum* species, it usually must be sought for deep among the bases of the vascular plants. *Agrostis setacea* is a grass which is peculiarly associated with Dartmoor and the south-west of England, being confined in Britain to this region and Glamorgan. Like several other plants which occur here it is of Lusitanian distribution and provides one of the links between our British flora and that of Spain and Portugal.

The heather moors are extensive, being communities dominated by *Calluna vulgaris*. If left to itself this type of moor may become a cover as much as two feet high, the plants developing into tough, woody little shrubs. So dense is the canopy formed by the thickly growing uppermost twigs that little light can penetrate it, and beneath the upper inch or so of fine brownish green leaves is a miniature forest of twisted, dry, leafless twigs, standing over a litter of dry debris. Little else can compete here, and apart from lichens and an occasional plant of Tormentil, the thin stems of which thread among and over the canopy to reach the light, other species rarely occur. Such tough old plants are, however, rare, owing to the practice of swaling. The object of this periodic burning is to rid the ground of the woody twigs and stimulate a dense growth of tender young shoots, thereby improving the pasturage. When it is carried out with restraint, and with planned consideration of local conditions, this does indeed maintain the grazing qualities of heather moorland, and it is a normal and profitable procedure on the grouse moors of northern England and Scotland. But unhappily, on Dartmoor, swaling has become involved in local politics. The commoners regard it as a right which must be exercised, often regardless of whether or no it may be necessary or desirable for a particular moor. The result has been that the Heather is weakened, rather than stimulated, by too frequent burning, or by burning when the moor is too dry, so that the fierce heat engendered destroys the topsoil and, with it, the roots of the Heather. All too frequently, as we have already remarked, Bracken is encouraged, and completes the destruction of the pasturage started by this unwise incendiarism.

Not all the moors are so recklessly treated, and then an open, low-growing cover is formed, in which the Heather shoots grow long and slender. They are not only tender and nutritious, but also very floriferous, and it is moors such as these which provide the glowing sheets of late-summer colour, and incidentally a rich supply of heather honey for hive bees which may be brought up to the moor especially to harvest it. Here too the more open nature of the heather growth does not stifle other vegetation, and a more varied flora may be found. W. Watson in 1932 published a study of the plant communities of moorland, in which was included a heather moor near Widecombe. His list of plants is worth quoting in full, because it indicates so clearly the important contribution which the mosses, liverworts and lichens may make to these upland habitats. The plants are here grouped under their taxonomic categories, and within these in the order of abundance recorded (see pp. 73-76).

It must not be supposed that all the species in this list are distributed at random throughout the habitat, which itself is far from uniform. The soil moisture varies widely, from small boggy areas to dry, well-drained slopes; rocks and small granite stones are scattered over the ground; trodden paths and sheep tracks present a more compacted soil; and the pattern of the larger plants associated with these various conditions provides a series of micro-climates. As a result of the interaction of these, and other factors, the plant community presents a minute patchwork, and certain species are confined within particular elements of the pattern. Watson has added notes indicating the way in which many of the species are so restricted. Where soil moisture is the dominant factor this has been indicated in the list by either (moist) or (w), and notes on other habitats will be found in the flora lists in the appendix.

ABUNDANT	FREQUENT	OCCASIONAL	RARE	PRESENT
SPERMOPHYTA.	Seed plants			
Ulex gallii	*Polygala serpyllacea*	*Linum catharticum*		*Viola canina*
Potentilla erecta	*Ulex europaeus*	*Drosera anglica* (w)		*V. lactea*
Vaccinium myrtillus	*Drosera rotundifolia* (w)	*Veronica serpyllifolia*		*Sarothamnus scoparius*
Calluna vulgaris	*Galium saxatile*	*Betula alba*		*Betula pubescens*
Erica cinerea	*Anagallis tenella* (moist)	*Luzula multiflora*		
E. tetralix	*Pedicularis palustris* (moist)	*Eriophorum vaginatum* (w)		
Agrostis tenuis	*P. sylvatica*	*Rhynchospora alba* (w)		
Molinia coerulea	*Melampyrum pratense*	*Aira caryophyllea*		
Festuca ovina	*Rumex acetosella*	*Sieglingia decumbens*		
	Juncus bufonius			
	J. squarrosus			
	J. inflexus			
	J. effusus (w)			
	Luzula pilosa			
	Scirpus caespitosus			
	Eriophorum angustifolium (w)			
	Carex pulicaris			
	C. echinata			
	C. panicea			
	C. binervis			
	Anthoxanthum odoratum			
	Agrostis canina			
	Aira praecox			
	Deschampsia flexuosa			
	Nardus stricta			
PTERIDOPHYTA.	Ferns and Club mosses			
	Pteridium aquilinum	*Lycopodium selago*		
	Blechnum spicant			
	Lycopodium clavatum			

ABUNDANT MUSCI. Mosses	FREQUENT	OCCASIONAL	RARE	PRESENT
Polytrichum piliferum	Catharinea undulata	Tetraphis pellucida	Polytrichum alpinum	Dicranum bonjeani
P. juniperum	Polytrichum aloides	Polytrichum nanum	Campylopus brevipilus	Bryum pendulum
P. formosum	Campylopus flexuosus	P. urnigerum	Dicranum spurium	B. atropurpureum
P. commune (w)	C. pyriformis	P. strictum	Aulacomnium androgynum	B. erythrocarpum
			Mnium serratum	
Ceratodon purpurens	Rhacomitrium canescens	P. gracile	Hypnum imponens	
Dicranella heteromalla	R. heterostichum	Diphyscium foliosum		
Dicranum scoparium	Aulacomnium palustre (w)	Pleuridium subulatum		
Rhacomitrium lanuginosum	Bartramia pomiformis	Ditrichum homomallum		
Webera nutans	Philonotis fontana (w)	Dicranella cerviculata		
Brachythecium purum	Mnium undulatum	Campylopus fragilis		
Eurhynchium myosuroides	M. hornum	C. atrovirens		
Hypnum cupressiforme ericetorum	Thuidium tamariscium	leucobryum glaucum		
H. schreberi	Brachythecium rutabulum	Rhacomitrium fasciculare		
Hylocomnium splendens	B. velutinum	Fissidens adiantoides (moist)		
	Plagiothecium elegans	Leptodontium flexifolium		
	P. denticulatum	Funaria hygrometrica		
	P. undulatum	Bryum inclinatum		
	Drepanocladus fluitans (w)	B. pallens		
	Hypnum loreum	B. capillare		
	H. squarrosum	B. pseudotriquetrum (moist)		
	H. triquetrum	B. bimum (moist)		
		B. roseum		
		Mnium affine		
		M. cuspidatum		
		Climacium dendroides		
		Eurhynchium praelongum		
		Plagiothecium silvaticum		
		Drepanocladus exannulatus (w)		

ABUNDANT	FREQUENT	OCCASIONAL	RARE	PRESENT
		D. uncinatus		
		D. sendtneri		
		Hypnum cupressiforme		
		H. stramineum		
		H. cuspidatum		

HEPATICAE. Liverworts

ABUNDANT	FREQUENT	OCCASIONAL	RARE	PRESENT
	Pellia epiphylla (moist)	Marchantia polymorpha (most)	Pellia fabroniana (moist)	Allicularia geoscypha
	Alicularia scalaris	Aneura pinguis (moist)	Lophozia bicrenata	Sphlenolobus exsectiformis
	Gymnocolea inflata (bog)	Marsupella emarginata	L. floerkii	Leptoscyphus anomalus
	Lophozia ventricosa	Eucalyx hyalinus	L. attenuata	Cephalozia media
	Cephalozia bicuspidata	Aplozia crenulata		Cephaloziella bifida
	Cephaloziella starkii	Plagiochila asplenioides		Lepidozia setacea
	Calypogeia trichmanis	Lophocolea bidentata		
	Lepidozia reptans	Cephalozia connivens		
	Diplophyllum albicans	Calypogeia fissa		
	Frullania tamarisca	C. arguta		
		Ptilidium ciliare		
		Scapania compacta		
		S. curta		
		S. umbrosa		
		Odontoschisma sphagni		

LICHENES. Lichens

ABUNDANT	FREQUENT	OCCASIONAL	RARE	PRESENT
Biatora granulosa	Parmelia saxatilis	Alectoria chalybeiformis	Cladonia subsquamosa	Lecidia dicksonii
B. uliginosa	P. omphalodes	A. bicolor	C. caespiticia	L. sylvicola
Lecidia rivulosa	Hypogymnia physodes	Parmelia fuliginosa	Coniocybe furfuracea	Catillaria chalybeia
L. contigua	Lecanora polytropa	Cetraria aculeata hispida	Sphaerophorus melanocarpus	Bilimbia melaena
L. sorediza	Biatora coarctata	Psora demissa		Cladonia bellidiflora
Cladina sylvatica	Pertusaria dealbata	Lecidia lithophylla		C. bacillaris
C. uncialis	Candelariella vitellina	L. crustulata		Pycnothelia papillaria
Cladonia subcervicornis	Rhizocarpon geographicum	Acarospora fuscata		Peltidea aphthosa

ABUNDANT	FREQUENT	OCCASIONAL	RARE	PRESENT
C. floerkeana	*R. confervoides*	*Physcia hispida*		
	Gyrophora polyrrhiza	*Buellia microcarpa*		
	Cladonia pyxidata	*Rhizocarpon petraeum*		
	C. p. chlorophaea	*Bilimbia sabuletorum*		
	C. fimbriata	*B. lignaria*		
	C. gracilis	*Haematomma coccineum*		
	C. furcata	*H. ventosum*		
	C. squamosa	*Gyrophora polyphylla*		
	C. coccifera	*G. cylindrica*		
	Baeomyces rufus	*Cladina rangiferina*		
	Stereocaulon coralloides	*Cladonia foliacea*		
	S. denudatum	*C. ochrochlora*		
	Peltigera rufescens	*C. pityrea*		
	P. polydactyla	*C. degenerans*		
	Leptonium lacerum	*C. rangiformis*		
	Ephebe lanata	*C. macilenta*		
	Sphaerophorus globosus	*C. flabelliformis*		
	Botrydina vulgaris	*Baeomyces roseus*		
		Stereocaulon condensatum		
		Crocynea lanuginosa		
		Peltigera canina		
		Nephromium parile		
		Leptogium sinuatum		
		L. microscopicum		
		Ephebia hispidula		
		Polychidium muscicolum		
		Sphaerophorus fragilis		
		Verrucaria maculiformis		
		V. mutabilis		
		Porina chlorotica		
		Coriscium viride		

There are some two hundred and fifty species and varieties in the list of plants which has just been quoted. Yet, to a casual glance, heather moorland appears, as its name suggests, to be a rather uniform stand of one, or at most two or three, species. Heather may dominate the view over many acres of ground, sometimes with a sparse admixture of Bell Heather. Other plants are either low-growing, like the mosses, liverworts and lichens, or they may thread their thin stems among the wiry branches of the Heather, and, being supported so, never rise high enough above the general canopy to become conspicuous. For instance, Tormentil is a common plant on most moors, but its little yellow flowers tend to be overlooked, so low do they rest among the dark leaves of the heather. Yet other plants are confined to tufts and clumps, or, like most of the grasses, to the edges of trodden paths. Probably the most extensive breaks in the uniformity of the heather moors are those on the wetter ground, where Cross-leaved Heath, *Erica tetralix*, Purple Moor Grass, rushes and sedges replace the Heather.

The Club Mosses are never conspicuous plants on Dartmoor, as they may be on the Welsh hills. Two species have been recorded, *Lycopodium inundatum* and *L. clavatum*, but of these the only one which is likely to be found is the second. *L. inundatum* is extremely rare on the moor, and indeed elsewhere in the county. *L. clavatum*, however, is occasionally to be met with, although it usually has to be sought. The only circumstances of which I know in which it obtrudes itself to the observer are after burning of the Heather. Then the long creeping stems of the *Lycopodium* catch the eye by their chaffy colour and appearance as they twine among the blackened debris. It is interesting to find that this plant, with no woody stock and very shallow rooting, can survive swaling, and indeed recover vigorously long before the other plants of the community have made a new start.

One other plant of this community requires mention, because of the incongruity of its appearance here. This is the little Wood Sorrel, *Oxalis acetosella*, the normal habitat of which is indicated in its name. It occurs in the woods of the region, and one normally seeks it in such a situation. But, to my astonishment, I have found it apparently flourishing deep in the Heather among the stones of the encircling wall of Grimspound, and also at the bases of walls between here and the Warren House Inn. How it got here, and why it should live so happily in so unusual a situation, I cannot explain.

Whortleberry, *Vaccinium myrtillus*, is common in many situations on

Dartmoor, from the tops and chinks of the stone walls to the open ground of the hillsides, or the undercover of the oakwoods, where it is particularly vigorous in the coppices. On the moors it may occur in small patches or as single plants among Heather, and it appears to find itself particularly at home against the edges of stones and boulders, where, it grows into dense and very fertile little bushes. Sometimes, however, particularly on well-drained slopes, it becomes so abundant as to be the dominating, though not necessarily the dominant, plant of the community. Heather may then be sparse, and the ground between the Bilberry plants is usually clothed by fine-leaved grasses. The community of these whortleberry moors is therefore a more open one than that of the heather moors, a fact which may be attributable to the sparser growth and lower stature of the whortleberry plants in the open, thus allowing much more light to penetrate between them. The rich crop of berries produced is harvested by commoners, visitors, Wood Pigeons and possibly also Rooks.

In the past considerable acreages of what is now moorland have been farmed, and traces of these ancient cultivations remain at various places, particularly in the neighbourhood of Challacombe Down. The flanks of the Down are marked by prominent cultivation terraces, seen in Plate VIII, p. 63, the date of which is still unsettled, and this will be discussed at a later stage of the book (see p. 150). Higher up the valley, the flanks of Birch Tor may be seen to be seamed with headlands and furrows, as is clearly indicated in Plate II, p. 7, which shows the area as viewed from Shapley Common. This land was carrying crops of cereals up to the middle of the last century, but has now reverted to a rather stunted heather and grass moor. Many of the " newtakes " have also been let go back from grassland to moor, and on all these areas the natural communities have become to a greater or less extent modified. In particular, grasses such as Sheep's Fescue, *Festuca ovina*, and various Bents, *Agrostis* spp., are more prevalent. It cannot, however, be too strongly emphasised that, wild as the moors may be, none of their communities may be described as truly natural. All are managed to some degree or other, by swaling and by stocking with sheep, cattle and ponies. The stock, together with rabbits, graze the vegetation close, as may be seen with startling clarity when any part of the moor is fenced against rabbits and stock. The Forestry Commission lands are so fenced, and during the early years of growth of the young trees, when they are too small to shade the ground and

Plate XI. Weasel, *Mustela nivalis*

Plate XII a. Skylark, *Alauda arvensis*, at nest

Eric Hosking

b. Meadow Pipit, *Anthus pratensis*, at nest among heather and bilberry

E. H. Ware

so alter the ecological conditions, the indigenous vegetation grows out of all comparison with that of the open moorland about. Some indication of this may be seen in Pl. X, p. 71, which shows part of a young plantation at Bellever.

Rabbits were at one time carefully preserved as ground game, and artificial warrens were constructed and maintained for them. Names such as Warren House Inn, Headland Warren, Trowlesworthy Warren, Huntingdon Warren, Ditsworthy Warren, all relate to the existence of these structures, and of a house in which the warrener lived. Trowlesworthy Warren at least dates back to the thirteenth century, thus indicating the great age of the practice on Dartmoor. Although now long disused, the warrens remain distinct on the hillsides, as the illustration (Pl. 8, p. 66) of Huntingdon Warren indicates. They have the appearance of huge, low grave mounds, which are now demarcated as much by a change of the vegetation covering them as by their shape. Those at Huntingdon, for instance, are covered with dense mats of coarse bent grass, and this contrasts sharply in both colour and texture with the Sheep's Fescue and Waved Hair Grass of the moor on which they stand.

The right of turbary, which is still exercised by some commoners and forest tenants, allows the cutting of peat for firing. Although no longer so important as it was formerly, owing to the modern almost universal use of coal, peat is still burned on open hearths in some moorland farms and cottages, and some turf-ties, or pits, are still in use. In these it is required that the turf be replaced after the peat has been removed from below, so as to preserve the cover of herbage. But, particularly on some of the commons, where the peat may be very thin, the commoners have the right of cutting " vags." In the exercise of this right slabs of the turf itself are removed, overturned to dry, and used as fuel. This, of course, leaves patches of bare ground over which the plants of the surrounding moor slowly recolonise, and all degrees of this recovery may be found, from newly cut soil to what can only be distinguished from the untouched moor by its lower level and by the fact that usually the Heather upon it grows a little more thinly and of slightly lower stature. Such patches have their interest for the entomologist, for, during their early stages while the cover is still sparse, they provide a special niche for the Grasshopper, *Myrmeleotettix maculatus*. The common shorthorn grasshoppers of the grassy moors are *Chorthippus parallelus* and *C. bicolor*, but these seem to be almost entirely replaced on the turf cuttings by *M. maculatus*. This may be related to two factors in the ecology of the insects. Firstly, the mottled colour pattern of browns, greys and dark greens which normally characterise *Myrmeleotettix* renders it less conspicuous against the dappled browns of the recovering peat than is the more massive and usually lighter-coloured pattern of *Chorthippus*. In the second place, and this may well be indirectly related to the first factor, it has been pointed out by Clark (1948) that *Myrmeleotettix* favours a habitat in which plenty of bare ground occurs between the members of the plant community.

The insect fauna of the moors is not conspicuous for its variety, especially on the Heather. Probably the commonest lepidopteran is the Fox Moth, *Macrothylacia rubi*, the caterpillars of which are very conspicuous on grass tussocks and in low herbage. When young the hairs which clothe the body are comparatively sparse and short, and the annular pattern of dark brown and orange is very marked. The older larvae, however, are densely invested with long silky, fawn-coloured hairs, and the skin colours beneath tend to be obscured. A more spectacular caterpillar which, although quite frequent, must usually be sought for, is that of the Emperor Moth, *Saturnia pavonia*. This is a handsome insect, the segments of the body being a bright, deep green with black rings and markings, and a scattering of usually vivid orange warty knobs from each of which two or three short bristles protrude (Pl. 7, p. 51). It might be expected that such a pattern would make the larva very conspicuous. But normally it lives deep among the feathery fronds of the Heather, and there its pattern conceals it so well that, unless one searches very carefully, it may be easily overlooked. The cocoon is spun in the cover beneath the heather tops, and is an elaborate affair of closely woven brown silk and incorporating bits of heather twig and leaf. One end is left open for the emergence of the imago, but the opening is guarded by a *cheval de frise* of stiff silken points which converge outward to form a conical valve easily enough pushed aside from the interior but firmly closed to intruders from outside. The moths are very handsome, with a conspicuous-eyed pattern on the wing. They emerge during April and May and the males are particularly active, and are a common sight as they dash to and from over the Heather. The Oak Eggar Moth, *Lasiocampa quercus*, is another handsome species the larvae of which include Heather in their diet, but it is by no means so common as the Fox and Emperor. The large family of Noctuidae has many representatives: Grass Moths, Crambidae, are common on the grass moors, in the tussocks of which their larvae tunnel, while Plume Moths, Alucitidae, may occur, more commonly, however, in the Bracken. The commonest butterflies are the Meadow Brown, *Maniola jurtina*, Gatekeeper, *M. tithonus*, and Small Heath, *Coenonympha pamphilus*, the larvae of all of which are grass feeders. Small Copper, *Lycaena phlaeas*, and Common Blue, *Polyommatus icarus*, tend, especially the former, to be more local, although common; while the Grayling, *Eumenis semele*, tends still more to be restricted, to the drier hillsides. The rare Large Blue, *Maculinea arion*, has been reported on occasion, but its food plant, Thyme, is hardly common enough over most of Dartmoor for it to colonise the region in large numbers. Brown, Purple and Green Hairstreaks, *Thecla betulae*, *T. quercus* and *Callophrys rubi*, all occur, and sometimes may be quite common. The first two species are, however, rather definitely local in relation to the Blackthorn and Oak on which their larvae feed, but the green hairstreak may be more widespread, particularly over whortleberry moors. Fritillaries are not common on the open moor, but some species may wander long distances away from the woodlands they normally frequent. Silver-washed, *Argynnis paphia*, High Brown, *A. cydippe*, and Pearl-bordered, *A. euphrosyne*, may all be seen on occasion. Peacock, *Nymphalis io*, and Red Admiral, *Vanessa atalanta*, tend to occur more commonly about the cultivated lands, as does also the Small Tortoiseshell, *Aglais urticae*; but this species may be seen almost anywhere over the moors, like the Painted Lady, *Vanessa cardui*.

Beetles are plentiful in the thick undergrowth of the moorland plants, but few are conspicuous. Those most often seen are the Bumble Dors, *Geotrupes stercorarius*, usually either immobile or moving sluggishly on the grass by day. At dusk they become active and fly with a droning hum, seeking the dung on which they feed. In their turn they are eaten by both foxes and sheep; by the latter probably by accident in the course of grazing; their shards are often to be seen in the droppings of both these animals. Another conspicuous beetle, especially common where the ground cover is rather sparse, is the Common Tiger Beetle, *Cicindela campestris*, a beautiful, rose-spotted, green insect which is incessantly active by day, running and flying over rocks and soil during the early summer. Later in the year the neatly round openings of the tunnels in which its larvae live may be seen in bare soil, each with a little mounded rim of earth pellets thrown out by the burrowing grub. Like the adult, the grub is carnivorous, and it props itself in its tunnel with its massive jaws just at the opening, waiting to seize any passing prey.

The Hymenoptera, or Ants, Bees and Wasps, a sun-loving group, are less prominent on the moors than they may be in the surrounding lowlands, being deterred by the prevailing colder, wetter climate. Humble bees, Bombidae, are common, and include the handsome *Bombus lapponicus*, which is restricted to upland regions like this. Hive bees are usually numerous during the heather season, the few local hives then being supplemented by others transported to the moors from the lowlands about. Several species of ants are frequent on the drier moors, particularly where there are loose stones on the surface, beneath which some species habitually nest. But the big Wood Ant, *Formica rufa*, is not usually prominent here, except near woodland, from which its foraging lines may extend long distances into the Heather. It is, however, impossible to do justice to the group, and more especially to the section Parasitica, without reference to the lists, which even so are incomplete, in the Appendix on p. 244.

Birds, except for a few species, have to be sought for on the moors. Buzzards, Carrion-Crows and Ravens are almost ubiquitous, covering most parts daily from their nests, which are usually situated in trees (Pl. 13, p. 135) among the valley woods, or in the plantations. The Crows may select lower sites in isolated bushes, or in scrub woodland, far out on the moors; and occasionally, absence of well-grown trees may force Ravens into the same habit, although this often has disastrous consequences, the nests being more often robbed than not. More rarely an inaccessible coign may be selected on one of the tors, a situation which extraordinarily enough, as has already been remarked, is very rarely used by Buzzards. All three species range widely in search of food, performing in the main a useful function as scavengers, or, in the case of the Buzzard, in reducing rodents. Raven, Crow, Magpie, Herring-gull and, less often Great Black-backed Gull and Buzzard are all known to visit carcases on Dartmoor. The other common raptorial bird is the Kestrel, which nests frequently on the tors, or sometimes on a ledge of a disused quarry, such as that illustrated in Pl. 12, p. 98. Other birds of prey less frequently observed include Peregrines, which pursue the pigeons and Golden Plover, Merlins, feeding on Larks and Pipits, and which have been known to breed occasionally, particularly in the wild blanket bog areas. The Hobby is an occasional visitor, but

Plate 9. Hare Tor, with bog and stream in the foreground

like the Sparrow-hawk, is more a bird of the in-country, while, as has already been remarked, Montagu's Harrier, which feeds extensively on Lizards, has recently begun once again to breed in the region. The now very rare Kite, which last bred on Dartmoor at Holne Chase, has been seen on several occasions within the last few years, but unhappily the chances of its being able to re-establish itself here seem very remote.

Meadow-pipits and Skylarks are by far the commonest breeding birds. Indeed, Lack (1935) during sampling of 326 acres on various parts of Dartmoor, found 94 Meadow-pipits and 78 Skylarks, while of other species only a single Stonechat and one Cuckoo were recorded. The Cuckoo normally parasitises Meadow-pipits on these moors, and it may be seen and heard throughout the early summer months. Stone-chats and Whinchats are common, particularly on the rougher moor-lands with an admixture of Gorse. Wheatears are also common, nesting in the crevices of the walls, and manifesting themselves by their clacking calls and their short, brisk flights, or are conspicuous by their boldly upright stance on the boulders. Wrens are numerous and almost every gully holds its pair, while in a few valleys, where sufficient broken stony cover exists, Ring-Ouzels breed (Pl. 6, p. 46), and their rather flat, monotonous song threads the air throughout the day.

Snipe and Common Sandpiper are birds, respectively, of the bogs and river courses, rather than of the moors. They may, however, be flushed, as may also more rarely the Corncrake, during the course of a walk across country. Golden Plover occur regularly, sometimes in large flocks, during the winter. D'Urban and Mathew could find no evidence of the species having nested within many years of 1895, the date at which they were writing. It is interesting, therefore, to note the observation in the *21st Report* of the Devon Bird Watching and Preservation Society, of a pair of birds " much attached to one locality, breeding-ground mournful piping note ' tlee ' much used " in July 1948.[1] Curlew are present, breeding in small numbers, more frequently on the bogs than on the moorland; but in winter they are rarely seen, being then on the lower ground nearer the sea. Red Grouse and Partridge are scarce and very local, never having thriven despite attempts to establish them, while Black Game, which seem to have increased during recent years, are only usually to be found near plantations, although like grouse they feed on the Heather tips.

This small list exhausts the birds which are likely to be seen, or

[1] A brood of three young has since been reported in 1950.

which may reasonably be expected during the course of a normal year. Many other species occur as casual wanderers, or as passage migrants, but cannot be regarded as contributing to the animal communities of the moors. As such, they may be found in the appendix on page 229.

Mammals, other than ponies and farm stock, are rarely prominent. Rabbits occur in some numbers, particularly on the drier hillsides, or where a clitter gives them ideal cover, and, as we have seen, a number of ancient warrens remain as evidence of days when the animals were more highly prized than they are to-day. Hares occur in a few regions, but are not common, and it is a rare event to come across one during an ordinary day's walk. Of other rodents, Brown Rats frequent the settled lands, but there is little to encourage their spread elsewhere, and it is doubtful if they can find sustenance in open country during the winter. Mice and voles may be numerous, particularly in and near young plantations where the extra cover afforded by the lank undergrowth is available to them. Mr. Hurrell has seen tracks of the Long-tailed Field-mouse in snow among the rocks of a tor near Princetown, which indicates that they may remain active well out on the moors throughout the winter. They are preyed upon by Kestrels, of which bird they constitute the staple diet; they form a large part of the food of Adders, and are not despised by Fox and Badger.

Foxes are numerous, finding ample cover in the Heather and Bracken and retreating when pressed into impregnable fastnesses in the clitters. Several packs of hounds include parts of Dartmoor in their country, while the moormen may trap or shoot them. The animal's natural cunning, and the difficult nature of the terrain, however, enable the species easily to maintain its numbers. Probably on these remote hills Foxes perform a useful function. Rabbits and beetles constitute the bulk of their diet, the proportion of beetles fluctuating widely at different seasons of the year. In winter almost none appear to be taken, possibly more from their scarcity than from any preference on the part of the Fox. From spring onwards the proportion increases, until, in September, the droppings may consist almost entirely of shards, mostly of dung-beetles. Mice and voles are also eaten, particularly in the neighbourhood of forestry plantations, while the occasional presence of wool in the dung indicates that a sheep carcase may be visited if opportunity presents itself. Nests of ground birds such as Larks and Pipits may be raided, and it has been suggested that the inability of the Red Grouse to become established may be due largely to their vulnerability to Foxes. Reliable estimates place the density of the species at about three or four to the square mile, rising in some regions to as many as ten in March, at the early part of the season, but falling again, by loss and migration, by the end of the year. The average litter is between four and six, but as many as eight or nine cubs have been seen together. The Foxes of mountainous districts have been said to be larger, longer legged and darker than their lowland relatives, but this does not seem to apply to the Dartmoor stock. The colour is certainly more grey than elsewhere, but the average weight of the dog is about 16 pounds and well within the normal range. Colonel Clarke, Master of the Dartmoor Foxhounds, tells me in a letter that he has " never yet found any reference to it being possible to distinguish a Dartmoor Fox from any other Fox found in an ' in-country.' " On the other hand, Mr. C. C. Whitley, of the South Devon Hunt, writes, " There used to be a large greyhound type of Fox, but their numbers seem to have diminished." While, therefore, it is possible that large animals may occur in some parts of the region, there is no positive evidence that the hill Fox of Dartmoor is normally larger than those of the lowlands.

The Badger will require mention in connection with the woodlands in which it more usually excavates its sett. It is, however, active far out on the moors, even in snow, and rarely it may dig a sett in a clitter, the most remote of these being at Fur Tor. Occasionally one of the upland copses may be inhabited, and the animals have for instance been seen going out from Piles Copse. Their diet is even more varied than that of Foxes, as Neal has observed in his monograph (1949). It includes young Rabbits, mice and voles, wasps' nests, when these can be found on moorland, and a variety of small creatures, including even Earthworms. The latter are not, however, plentiful in the acid, often waterlogged soils of Dartmoor, a fact which may account for the sparsity of Moles, a species which is common in the lowland fields.

Stoats, *Mustela erminea*, and Weasels, *M. nivalis*, are common, particularly on rough ground and among the clitters. The Polecat, *M. putorius*, is almost certainly now extinct, although it used to occur. Brooking Rowe in 1862 stated that the animal was scarce at that time, two, however, having been seen together in the woods at Harford. But, some twenty-five years earlier, a small pack of hounds was kept at Two Bridges for the purpose of hunting Polecats, which were generally found among rocks and clitters in the valleys. During recent years no satisfactory records have been secured. A keeper at Shipley reported that his father had killed one between 1900 and 1910, and an animal which might have been a Polecat was seen by Mr. Hurrell's cousin crossing the Dart near Dartmeet on a fallen tree. Finally, in 1930, two fishermen are reported to have seen four creatures, larger than Stoats, playing among boulders near Bellever. It is, however, difficult to eliminate the possibility of Polecat-Ferrets from these recent records, none of which can be substantiated by critical data, and it is probably correct to regard the species as extinct in the region.

Lest the reader has received the impression that these moorlands are dull and monotonous, I must conclude by saying this is far from being so. It is true that many moors are dominated by one or two, or even a single species of plant, and this inevitably restricts the numbers and diversity of animals in the community and tends also to impress on the eye the colour and forms of a single pattern of vegetation. But the resident animals, interesting in themselves, are reinforced by others of widely ranging habits which cross or visit the moors; and the broad canvas of the plant cover is broken by countless local changes. Here a bog lends the bright green of its mosses, or the light tassels of its bog cottons, and, on closer examination, a whole galaxy of shining little plants. A group of standing stones, or a rocky outcrop lends a splash of contrasting colours in its grey stone encrusted with lichens in many vivid shades, and the moorland plants, surging against its base, grow in different forms and variety in the slightly altered ecological conditions they find there. Every change of gradient, every dip and rise, crest and valley, shows a different aspect of the covering herbage, and with this a different texture and colour. Moreover, the scene changes with fascinating speed, often dramatic suddenness, under the capricious Dartmoor sky. Valleys and hillsides now gay in sunlight, may be darkened to sepia and purple as a huge cloud shadow creeps over them; or long tongues of mist or rain may entirely obliterate the sight of them. And through the whole there threads the silver and limpidity of water. While, therefore, the moors may be placid and inviting, or cold and forbidding, or even occasionally terrifying, they are never, to the seeing eye, dull and monotonous.

Plate 10. Bog Asphodel, *Narthecium ossifragum*

THE TORS

The form and height of the tors vary between wide limits. Few show the symmetry and grace of Bellever (Pl. II, p. 7), where a conical hill rises with a sureness of line which leads the eye naturally and inevitably to the low rampart of rocks at its summit. On the other hand, only rarely do we see great lumps of rock like Haytor and Blackingstone Rock, which appear from a distance to have been turned with inconsequential incongruity from a child's sand bucket. These rocks stand some fifty or sixty feet above the downs on which they occur, as great domes of granite comparatively little broken by fissures and bedding planes. So little surface relief do they present indeed that, for the benefit of those who wish to enjoy the remarkably wide views to be had from their tops, an artificial stairway has been either cut in the rock, as at Haytor, or built against its face at Blackingstone. The former, with its iron handrail, aroused the righteous wrath of a Dr. Croker, who wrote in 1851 denouncing " the unsightly stair step to enable the enervated and pinguedinous scions of humanity of this wonderful nineteenth century to gain its summit." Although very impressive, and affording excellent prospects far and wide over Devon, for which they are justly famous, there is something to my mind almost artificial about them, as seen in a distant view. From a closer viewpoint both spring naturally and with some grace from the soil. But they do not compare with the wild fantasies of Great and Little Hound Tors, Bel, Mel and Honeybags, and many another scattered over the moor's extent. Here the granite is exposed, not in a solid lump, but as a jagged series of blocks divided and grooved into pillars and shelves, buttresses and battlements, by the age-long action of weathering on the joints and bedding planes in the rock. Small wonder that they have been named, here for a couchant beast, there for a pack of hounds in full cry, or after some giant of antiquity. And, for all their wild beauty, they have generally an endearing quality of intimacy. The stubborn granite is safe for foot or handhold; there are innumerable corners and platforms giving sitting room and shelter from wind or wet or sun. The pattern of the granite is rarely visible for the thick and varied coat of lichens encrusting it and softening what severity is in the rocky contours.

The damper crevices and surfaces may carry mosses and occasionally liverworts, and, where a little humus has accumulated in deep cracks, a few tufts of grass or a small colony of the Black Spleenwort, *Asplenium adiantum-nigrum*, may grow. Occasionally a few, rather stunted little clumps of either Heather or Whortleberry may struggle up into these crevices, but they usually stop short at the base of the rock. Sheep and ponies may take advantage of the leeside afforded by the tor in hard weather, and it is not unusual to find that, especially on the north-east side, a shallow depression has been trodden, sometimes down to bare ground, or more often covered by a mat of close-cropped grass. The base of the tor may also be used as a rubbing stone, as are suitable rocks and standing stones elsewhere on the moor, and in this case the granite is kept clear of lichens and its pattern of felspars, quartz and mica may be clearly shown.

The flat tops of some of the tors, as also of any large rocks elsewhere, may often be worn into shallow basins, known as " rock-basins " and formerly believed to be sacrificial altars. But geologists have found a logical natural explanation of the phenomenon (see *Dartmoor, Memoir*, H. M. Geol. Survey, 1912). The process involves a continual slow chipping of minute flakes of granite off the surface of the rock, under the alternating conditions of wet and dry, frost and thaw, during normal seasonal changes of weather. As a result of many repititions of the process during successive winters a shallow depression is carved into the surface of most of the broad flat rocks on which a film of moisture would originally have accumulated. The bottom of the depression is kept free of encrusting lichens or other plants owing to its instability under constant weathering of this nature, and, except during dry or very blustery periods, an inch or two of water may fill the cavity. This is so transient that it fails to support any animal life, other than a few species of rotifers, and by its presence it further inhibits growth of lichens. Moreover, once it reaches a certain depth, it stops the process of weathering, since it no longer freezes to the level of the underlying rock, and consequently the levering, chiselling action of the frosts is slowed and stopped.

So thin a plant cover supports few animals. Springtails, Pseudo-scorpions, beetles, spiders and the like may be found by sieving through the mosses and lichens; Woodlice, Earwigs, Centipedes and Millipedes, together with an occasional Slug or Snail, may be discovered in the crevices or beneath the more broadly peltate lichens. A few species of ants may nest in deeper cracks or beneath stones at the foot of the tor, and their foraging parties explore its whole surface; moths, flies and beetles from the moor round about bask or rest on the rocks, while midges and gnats may often be seen dancing in the upward current of warm air which rises from the heated surface of the rock after a hot day. Rabbits often burrow beneath the sheltering rock, where a jointing crevice allows, and occasionally an Adder may utilise holes so excavated. And, as we have already seen, Kestrels, Crows, Ravens, and more rarely Buzzards, may nest on the less accessible ledges.

The association of clitters with tors has already been discussed. They may be mere handfuls of small rocks, or huge jumbles of blocks of all sizes up to boulders weighing several tons and strewn over many acres of hillside. The flora and fauna of the rocks themselves are similar to those of the tors from which they are derived. But the loose nature of the formation and the fact that it is comprised of blocks resting on the soil, and not of living rock outcropping from the ground, render the clitter a much more favourable habitat for burrowing forms, and Rabbits, and even occasionally Foxes and Badgers may normally occur. But suffice it here to reiterate the intimate association of clitter and tor, and to defer discussion of the various influences exerted on the vegetation to the points in the dissertation at which they may more appropriately be examined.

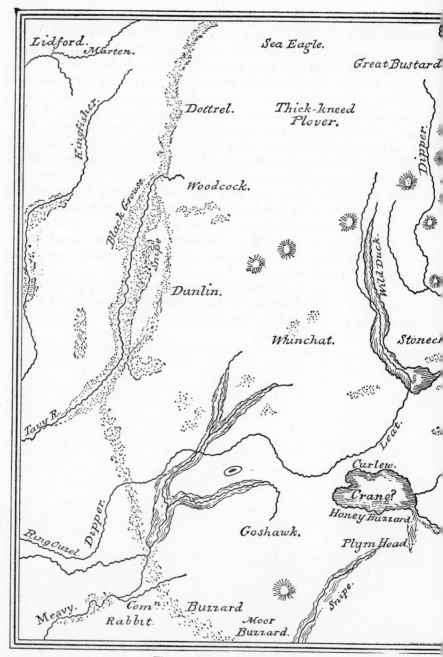

Fig. 3.—A Nineteenth Century record. Map of Dartmoo

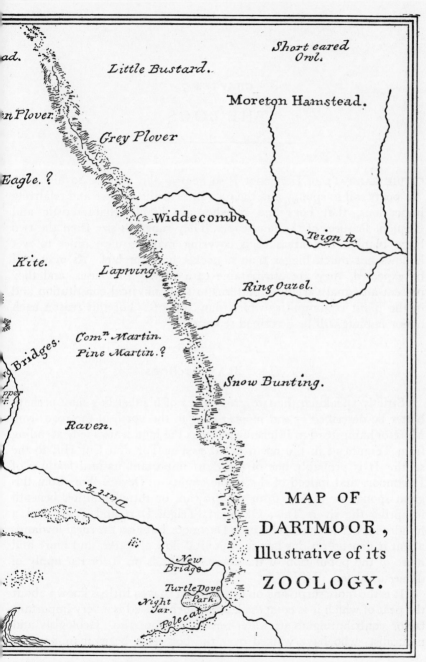

ad.

Little Bustard.

Short eared
Owl.

n Plover.

Moreton Hamstead.

Grey Plover

Eagle. ?

Widdecombe

Teign R.

Kite.

Lapwing

Ring Ouzel.

Comⁿ. Martin.
Pine Martin. ?

Snow Bunting.

o Bridges.

pper
:.

Raven.

Dart R.

MAP OF

DARTMOOR,

Illustrative of its

ZOOLOGY.

New
Bridge

TurtleDove
Park.

Night
Jar.

Polecat

C. Bellamy's *Natural History of South Devon*, 1839.

CHAPTER 7

THE BOGS

THE RAINFALL of Dartmoor is so heavy, the altitude so high, the peaty soil so spongy and the rock so near the surface and relatively impervious, that bogs and marshes are highly characteristic and frequent features of the landscape. They range in size from the two large blanket bog areas each covering many square miles to wet hollows not much bigger than a pocket handkerchief. As may well be expected, they are attributable to a variety of causes, and they present an equal variety of patterns in their physical constitution and in the plant communities which they support. For this reason each major habitat will be described separately.

THE BLANKET BOGS

Strictly speaking, the two great areas of blanket bog may perhaps better be described as wet moor. That to the north of the road from Moretonhampstead to Princetown covers the high watershed extending from Teignhead in the north as far as Fur Tor and Cut Hill to the south. It is probably one of the most important natural features of Dartmoor, and indeed of the whole county of Devon. For, from this great sponge or rather, from the growan, or rotted granite, beneath it, spring the rivers Taw, Okement, Teign, Dart and Tavy, and a hundred lesser streams. Not only Dartmoor but also the rural lowlands about it depend on this bog for the vital flow of water, and more and more of the population of the county depends on it for its supply of domestic water.

It is the more surprising on this account that so little is known about the peat of which it is composed, and which indeed is a very important factor contributing to its water-retaining properties. Geologists and naturalists who have walked over the bog have been unanimous in remarking on the sparsity of areas of active peat formation. In fact, all the evidence points to a steady retrogression which has been going on for a long time, and which is shown by the enormous cracks between the peat hags and the occasional rocks which provide a measure of the shrinkage of the deposits in the light-coloured band between former and present levels. But, beyond that it is very slow and is unlikely to have serious effects for generations yet, we know nothing of the rate of this recession, nor of the reasons underlying it.

But ignorance of the conditions necessary for the maintenance of the bog has not hitherto engendered any caution with respect to its use or misuse. Parts of the western half of the region have been incorporated for many years now in the artillery practice range based on Okehampton, and recent proposals from the military authorities to extend the firing eastwards, and to carry tracked vehicles over parts of it, met with opposition primarily from graziers and walkers rather than from water conservators. Moreover, until quite recent years peat was being cut on a commercial scale on the north side of the bog, near Cranmere Pool, and the practice ceased, not because of any qualms about its effects on the drainage from the region, but because of loss of financial support.

The surface of the bog at Cranmere Pool, as also at Cut Hill and Fur Tor, is particularly badly disintegrated, and isolated hags are left standing six feet or more above the level of a maze of bare peat channels and cracks. Cranmere Pool itself is merely an exaggerated expression of this condition, in which the hags have disappeared and the intervening channels have fused together and the level sunk so low that water stands on the surface except in the driest of seasons. Its position, so central in the northern half of Dartmoor, and so remote from road or track within its welter of quavering, oozing ground, has drawn innumerable walkers in the past to make an adventurous and often exhausting pilgrimage to sign the visitors' book and post a letter or postcard in the box there. To-day, most of the glamour has gone. A military track runs nearly to its margin and it is almost possible to go there by car. But the walker who attempts to cross the great bog, from Cranmere to Fur Tor, must be prepared for an arduous journey, and, unless the season has been very dry, he must not mind wet feet.

The flora of this " moorland " is very restricted. Heather and Cross-leaved Heath cover much of the ground, with the two Cotton

Grasses, *Eriophorum angustifolium* and *E. vaginatum* in the wetter hollows, *E. vaginatum* being the more localised of the two species. Several species of Rush occur commonly and *Hydrocotyle vulgaris* and Bog Asphodel, *Narthecium ossifragum*, are common wherever the ground is slightly wetter than the rest. *Potentilla erecta* twines about the Heathers, while rarer species include *Empetrum nigrum*, which is never conspicuous and must be sought for among the plants of *Calluna*, and *Sibthorpia europaea*, occurring for the most part along the banks of the streams. The cryptogamic species are numerous in what is a tundra flora, and include some liverworts and many mosses and lichens. These have been very extensively listed and studied by Tansley (1939) and Watson (1932) and the interested reader is referred to their works.

The wet acid soil and the low temperature and wind exposure at this altitude restrict not only the flora, but also, and perhaps to a greater extent, the fauna. Few but the smaller and more specialised animals can complete their lives here. The soil is too waterlogged to sustain burrowing species. Only here and there is rock exposed to give shelter to crevice haunting species. And the vegetation is too uniform and too niggard of blossom to attract many insects. Humble Bees and a few other pollen gatherers visit the scanty Heather bloom. Most of the other insects are either strongly flying forms, such as the passing migrant Lepidoptera, Dor Beetles and the like, or species whose larvae feed on one or other of the common plants, or are aquatic in habit, like the Dragonflies. The molluscs include the ubiquitous Black Slug, *Arion ater*, but few other species, the poor calcium content of the soil restricting Snails here, as elsewhere on Dartmoor. Few vertebrates occur. Frogs in the wetter places and Lizards in the drier Heather. But there is little to attract the Adders which may be common on the dry Heather slopes elsewhere, and, moreover, like the small rodents and shrews, they are restricted by the high-water table, which fills all but the shallowest burrows and holes. The far-ranging Fox and Otter cross the bogs, and even on rarer occasions the Badger. Few birds are there to lighten the monotony. The only species which may be seen throughout the year are Raven, Buzzard and Carrion-Crow, together with Snipe and possibly Red Grouse. The first three of these are powerful fliers which regularly travel long distances in search of food, the Carrion-Crow being the least inclined to brave the rigours of winter on these uplands. Snipe may live throughout the year in the bogs, breeding in the hollows; and the Red Grouse is the only bird which is

Plate 11 (*above*). Intermediate Sundew, *Drosera intermedia*, and Marsh
St. John's Wort, *Hypericum elodes*   (*E. H. Ware*)

(*below*). Pale Butterwort, *Pinguicula lusitanica*, Lesser Skull-cap,
Scutellaria minor, and Bog Pimpernel, *Anagallis tenella*.
(*E. H. Ware*)

known definitely to spend the whole year in the central moors. To these may be added a small group of species which occur as summer visitors. Skylark and Meadow-pipit come in smaller numbers than they do to the drier heather moors. Wheatears range in from the margins, and Curlew may nest in the drier spots. Dipper and Common Sandpiper breed along the banks of the streams, and the Merlin has also been recorded as having bred in this region. Rook, Starling, Kestrel and harriers may forage here from afar, and Swallows and Swifts pass over. But other than these, few birds occur except as casual and rare wanderers.

The southern bog, from which rise the Aune (or Avon), Plym, Erme and Swincombe, is more restricted in area and lies at a uniformly lower altitude, at about 1,500 feet. It also differs in quality from the northern blanket bog, and leads to the suspicion that the peat is shallower and possibly younger. Here occur none of the great hags of the Cranmere area, and few signs of erosion or recession are to be seen. Restricted areas of very wet ground occur, and it is here that one of the few dangerous mires of Dartmoor, Fox Tor Mires, is situated. Even the smaller Red Lake Mire quakes uneasily as one walks across it. The name, Red Lake, is derived from the prevailing red colour of the leaves and stems of the Cotton Grass growing so thickly here. The colour is very variable, but in some seasons and in certain lights the whole region glows almost brick-red.

The middle of this bog, close to Red Lake, is disfigured by the remains of a long abandoned clay working. The spoil-heap, never very large, is crumbling away and has been clothed with Heather and grasses. But the old engine-house still stands in a ruined condition, and has served on occasion as a nesting site for a pair of Ravens, providing a niche which would otherwise be offered only by the few tors on these rather smoothly contoured hills. When the pit was working its products were conveyed by a well-engineered light railway to Western Beacon near Ivybridge. Now the tracks have been removed and evident signs were found of its use as a road by military vehicles during the period while the region has been used for battle practice. Fortunately perhaps, the walking is so tiring and wet, particularly on the old turf cuttings about the clay workings, that only those who appreciate the wildness of the place will be attracted thither. Otherwise, this might become as worn and eroded as some of the downs at Yelverton and Roborough which are the regular Sunday afternoon resorts of motorists and cyclists from Plymouth.

It is interesting to find what appears to be incipient carr in the heart of the mire at Red Lake. A few stunted Willow trees have struggled to a height of two or three feet above the surrounding bed of rushes. There are at most three or four other small Willows on the banks of some of the nearby streamlets, but apart from these I know of no others in the neighbourhood. Unfortunately no record has come to my notice of the earlier state of this mire, and I have only my own uncertain memory on which to rely. If this is correct, however, there were considerably more trees when I visited this same spot in about 1933. It may be that the poor soil and acid water, combined with the extreme exposure on a south-westerly aspect, tend to eliminate such larger shrubs as may attempt to become established. On the other hand, an alternative explanation for the disappearance of some of these trees, if indeed this has happened, is suggested by the presence in 1948 of ruined targets straddled by shell holes within a few yards of the mire.

In general, the vegetation of this southern blanket bog is very like that of its northern counterpart. But, owing largely to the greater amounts of surface water, there is less *Calluna*, and rushes are much more frequent, often growing in huge beds and covering the centres of the mires. Particularly in the old turf cuttings, considerable growths of *Sphagnum* occur where water stands on the surface, and up through this grow both *Eriophorum vaginatum* and *E. angustifolium*, together with a considerable variety of small sedges, including such species as *Carex panicea*, *Rhynchospora alba*, etc. These species occur on the northern bog, but rarely there in such numbers as may be found in situations such as these. As might be expected the fauna also is very similar to that of the other blanket area, and the rather surprising occurrence of an Adder, disturbed while basking on the bank of a wet stream close to Red Lake Mire, is probably attributable to the close proximity of the china clay workings with the dry spoil-heap and other artificially raised habitats in which such reptiles might be expected to occur in an otherwise very unsuitable habitat.

THE VALLEY BOGS

Encircling the great *Eriophorum* moors in the centre of Dartmoor is a broad zone of heather moors which extends outwards to the margin of the high land, where it slips away through the metamorphic aureole to the lowlands of Devon and Cornwall. In the courses of the rivers which drain these moors are to be found bogs in a variety of sizes and conditions. The largest are usually found at points where the gradient slackens, and some of the biggest occur at about the 1,200-foot contour, marking an old shore line (vide p. 37). Here the river pauses before descending, sometimes headlong as in Lydford Gorge, into its deeply cut secondary valley. As a consequence of the slowing of the current peat silt tends to accumulate and this is added to by the bog vegetation which grows upon it. In the lapse of centuries the bed of the stream wavers from one part of the flat to another, as its channel becomes silted here and newly eroded elsewhere. The whole floor becomes a large valley bog, its soil a light spongy peat bound into a resistant mass by the roots of the living plants on its surface. Often, however, it is so unstable, and so undermined by water seeping below that it sways and trembles as the walker crosses it. And, as we have seen previously, owing to the slowing of the current here, the river in the past has dropped most of the heavier particles it has carried, and so such places have been the favourite sites for the old tin streamers. As a consequence the lower reaches at least of many such bogs have been thoroughly excavated and the underlying gravel thrown out on top of the peat, and indeed much of the peat removed and used as mats on which to stream the river bottom in order to separate the ore. The strongly hummocked nature of the terrain at the foot of such bogs bears a superficial resemblance to a small glacier moraine, but the picture is entirely false. It may, however, serve even more effectively to retard the flow of the stream through the flat valley and so to extend the bog over a wider extent of ground than it would otherwise have covered.

Sometimes the conditions in these bogs produce a lush, uniform vegetation dominated by rushes (Pl. IX, p. 70), and indeed the wet centre of the flat is usually marked by tall rush clumps. A more diverse and interesting flora is to be found where the margins rest on solid ground and only the centre, if any part, is floating. Then an uneven surface comprises peat hummocks with softer, miry ground and open water runnels between them. Here and there tussocks of

Sphagnum rise above the general level and may then be crowned with Heather or Cross-leaved Heath, or possibly Gorse. The Round-leaved Sundew, *Drosera rotundifolia*, is very common here, growing most frequently deep in the Sphagnum, where it emerges above water level. *Drosera intermedia*, with its longer, strap-shaped leaves, on the other hand, is sparse and much more localised in occurrence. But where conditions suit it, usually with water seeping in a broad shallow front over mud, there it makes almost a closed association, and the scarlet of its leaf hairs glows as a brilliant patch on the bog (Pl. IIa, p. 94). *Hypericum elodes*, its elusive flowers so rarely to be seen fully open, may frequently occur with the *Drosera*, as may be seen from the Plate indicated. The list of plants found on one of these bogs includes, in addition to those already mentioned:

Anagallis tenella	*Pedicularis palustris*
Cirsium palustre	*Pinguicula lusitanica*
Galium palustre	*Potamogeton* spp.
Hydrocotyle vulgaris	*Ranunculus flammula*
Lychnis flos-cuculi	*Scutellaria minor*
Menyanthes trifoliata	*Viola palustris*
Narthecium ossifragum	*Wahlenbergia hederacea*

together with grasses such as *Molinia coerulea*, various *Carices* and the Cotton Grasses. It was in a bog such as this, under Blackaton Tor in the Webburn valley, that the little Bog Orchid, *Hammarbya* (*Malaxis*) *paludosa*, was found again in 1938, after a lapse of some seventy years since it had last been recorded on Dartmoor. It is indeed an inconspicuous plant, and even intensive search may not reveal it. Harris (1938) complains bitterly, " Plant hunting on Dartmoor is not quite the recreative pastime it usually is when pursued in the lowlands. Many of the plants most worth finding may be missed by a few feet. The rare orchid *Malaxis paludosa*, for instance, is said to grow on Dartmoor, yet in spite of tiring search it has never found a place in my vasculum, and I agree unreservedly with Bentham and Hooker that although it is found sparingly over the greater part of Britain it is always difficult to find." Incidentally, he goes on to remark on this species, together with *Empetrum nigrum* and, with some reserve, *Vaccinium vitis-idaea*, as arctic or northern relicts among the flora of Dartmoor.

The cryptogamic flora is rich and a very characteristic feature of

Plate 12. Kestrel, *Falco tinnunculus*, and young at nest on an old quarry ledge

these, as of other bogs. Its members are, however, for the most part inconspicuous except for the *Sphagnum* species and *Polytrichum* sp. among the mosses. But careful inspection of almost any square inch of the ground reveals a great variety of mosses and liverworts, some clinging close to the mud, others twining among the stems of the bog plants. In addition, wherever water stands on the surface, filamentous green algae form a slime in which the flowering plants are enwreathed as they push up to the surface. To these must be added innumerable micro-scopic, unicellular algae. Harris (1938), who paid particular attention to the Desmids of Dartmoor, found this group exceptionally well represented in the bogs, and he states (*loc. cit.*) that, " The freshwater algae of Dartmoor may be safely estimated at some thousand species and varieties."

The fauna of these valley bogs is generally richer and more diverse than that of the blanket bogs. This is due in part to the lower altitude at which they are situated, but more to their smaller size, as a result of which it is readily possible for species from neighbouring habitats to traverse the bogs, either accidentally or in the normal course of their lives. Further, by the time the rivers reach this level they are supporting a much richer insect fauna and the winged adults which emerge from the water tend to congregate about the banks of the stream and so to be frequent in the bogs. The most prominent among them, owing in large measure to their powerful flight and brilliant colours, are the Dragonflies, and many species occur belonging to genera such as *Libellula, Cordulegaster, Aeshna, Sympetrum* and *Agrion*. The beautiful, weakly flying Demoiselles, *Calopteryx* spp., are, however, rare at this altitude, although they may occasionally be seen over the wet hay meadows about Postbridge. Few invertebrates other than arthropods are present. *Arion ater* and a few other species of Slug occur, but very few Snails. Frogs may be numerous, particularly during periods of migration to and from their breeding waters, and they in their turn provide food for visiting Otter, Fox and Heron.

The bogs which most take the eye are what are known locally as feather-beds. They are small and are situated usually along the sides of the valleys at any point where the drainage of water down the hillside is impeded, for instance, by the hollowing out of the under-lying rock to create a pocket in which water may accumulate. In such places a rich growth of Sphagnum rapidly fills the basin which looks, as if it is covered by a brilliant green turf. The unwary may try to walk on this, but finds no support in the feathery loose strands of the moss. However, the worst is usually a wetting to the knee, for these are rarely deep, and one receives full warning with the first step on to the green surface. Usually these are virtually pure sphagneta except round the margins, for little can compete with the mosses under these conditions.

Possibly the commonest type of bog on Dartmoor is that produced where water seeps out of a hillside and trickles down until eventually it reaches the stream below. It is hardly possible to walk a furlong down the course of any Dartmoor stream without encountering such a bog. There may be a central depression, or even a watercourse, which carries the main flow of water, but much of it seeps imperceptibly through the loose peaty soil over a front of anything from twenty feet to fifty yards or more. As a result a broad sweep of soggy ground covering several thousand square yards of the valley side is produced and it supports a rich and diverse flora. Raised hummocks carry patches of Heather and moor grasses, *Nardus stricta*, and *Agrostis setacea*, with the thin stems of Tormentil, *Potentilla erecta*. Between these mounds the lower, wetter ground carries purple Moor Grass, *Molinia caerulea*, many small sedges and rushes, Bog Asphodel, *Narthecium ossifragum*, Bog Violet, *Viola palustris*, and Marsh Pennywort, *Hydrocotyle vulgaris*. Little tumps of *Sphagnum* stud the area wherever the flow of water is momentarily stilled, and on these, as also in the general plant carpet of the waterlogged soil, Round-leaved Sundew, *Drosera rotundifolia*, occurs abundantly. Ivy-leaved Campanula, *Wahlenbergia hederacea*, and Bog Pimpernel, *Anagallis tenella*, thread through the stems of the taller plants, the blue flowers of the one chiming with the delicately veined pink of the other. The plant community is, in fact, very similar to that of the valley bog described above, and all the species listed there may be found here, with the exceptions of the little Bog Orchid, which requires looser, wetter conditions than normally supervene here, and Bogbean, with rather similar demands. The sharper drainage, particularly at the surface, on the steeper slope tends to restrict the true bog flora and to produce a greater admixture of patches of Heather and moor grass, Gorse and the like.

Sometimes, particularly towards the edge of the moor and on the heavier soils derived from the Culm measures, a much coarser vegetation is produced on ground which impedes the run-off of water to such an extent that a deep wet mud is produced. Under such conditions the hillside may be thickly studded with clumps of rushes and

Deschampsia caespitosa in almost a pure stand, grading down at the foot to a willow swamp. And in some more remote valleys it is still possible to find fine, well-grown clumps of the Royal Fern, *Osmunda regalis*. Unfortunately this plant has suffered very heavily from the depredations of collectors, and it is now only to be seen in a few bogs which are little known or difficult to reach, or in a few favoured localities on the banks of rivers. In the latter situations, however, it never reaches the majestic proportions of the ferns in the bogs.

CHAPTER 8

WOODLANDS

THE HIGHLANDS of Dartmoor to-day are practically bare of trees except where these have been planted, as in some of the valleys and in the modern plantations of the Forestry Commission. It has been suggested that in the past there was much more continuous woodland over the uplands, and that the existing small copses still to be seen in one or two areas are relics of this, the intervening cover having disappeared. Some commentators have added the speculation that the agents of this disafforestation were the tin workers, who are said to have used all the readily available timber as fuel in their smelting furnaces. But although there is evidence that natural woodland was once much more extensive than it is now, the ecological evidence does not support the view that the upland coppices are relics of such a continuous forest. Indeed, as we shall see, these woods are almost pure stands of Oak, while such remains as have been found of other woodland are mostly of Birch and Hazel.

In the absence of any analysis of the peat deposits, it is impossible to reconstruct the history of the vegetation, as it has been traced elsewhere, as for instance, in the Pennines or in the New Forest, by Rastrick (1931) and Godwin (1934). But there are many records like that of Rowe (1848), who instances large quantities of timber being dug out of the peat, or Harris (1921), who found Hazel nuts and fragments of Birch in the peat near Postbridge and also in Taw Marsh. In recent years also, during deep draining operations in the peat of the Forestry Commission lands at Bellever and on Soussons Down, the stumps of trees have been revealed *in situ* at depths of several feet below ground level. It is plain then that much of Dartmoor, which to-day is bog or moorland, was at one time carrying trees. Probably tin smelting was responsible for the disappearance of some of the woods. Similar de-afforestation in connection with smelting operations has

E. H. Ware

Eric Hosking

Plate XIII Stonechat, *Saxiola torquatca*. *Left*, Cock and *Right* Hen

Whistman's Wood

Plate XIV a. **Wistman's Wood**: an engraving from **Carrington's** *Dartmoor: a Descriptive Poem* (1826)

b. Cotton Grass, *Eriophorum* spp., on the blanket bog

E. H. Ware

been well documented for the woods of Yorkshire and Sussex, to quote only two instances. But Harris has suggested that in some areas at least it may have been a natural process, due to the steady accumulation of peat in the deep valleys. At the higher altitudes of which we are writing such deep valleys would favour the establishment and growth of trees in their shelter. If subsequently peat began to accumulate over their roots the trees would ultimately be destroyed, and their stumps left mummified in the peat as we find them to-day. This cannot account for the stumps found on Soussons Down, an open hillside. But it must be realised that this area must have been peculiarly vulnerable to the tin workers, for it is immediately adjacent to the valley in which lies the Vitifer Mine. And the whole region has been perhaps more deeply and extensively scarred by mine workings than any other on Dartmoor.

The three upland woods of Dartmoor which may be regarded as indigenous are:

Black Tor Beare (or Copse), on the right bank of the west Okement, facing west under Black Tor;

Wistman's Wood, on the left bank of the West Dart, facing south-west;

Pile's Wood (or Copse), on the left bank of the Erme, between Sharp Tor and Staldon, facing west.

Wistman's Wood is by far the best known of the three woods, and it has been on many an occasion the subject of examination, speculation and poetic inspiration. We need not concern ourselves with the romantic fancies which connected the grove with Druid ceremonies, for there is no evidence whatever that such rites were celebrated here, or in either of the other two copses. The reader who is searching for such speculations may be referred to Rowe's *Perambulation of Dartmoor*, 1848. That the woods are very old is evidenced by historical references to two of them. Risdon's *Survey of Devon*, 1620, refers to Wistman's Wood as " some acres of wood and trees," while an undated *Review of Woods*, of approximately the same date, lists an item of £40 for eight acres of underwood " in a certain place there called Black Tors Beare." Even earlier, in 1587, we find a man presented at the " Manor and Forest Court of Lydford North " and fined threepence for cutting " certain oaks at Blacktors Beare."

The most recent studies are those of G. T. Harris (1921) and Miller Christy and Worth (1923), both of Wistman's Wood, although the second work makes some comparison of this with the other two copses. Wistman's Wood is an almost pure stand of Oaks. There is a slight intermingling of Mountain Ash (*Sorbus aucuparia*), and Worth records one Holly (*Ilex aquifolium*). The Oaks are predominantly the pedunculate species, *Quercus robur*, as is shown both by the acorns, which are produced sparingly and in sporadic fashion, and by the leaf characters. The Sessile Oak, *Q. petraea*, which is stated by some botanists to be the dominant Oak of these wet, shallow, siliceous soils, is conspicuously scarce, and few have been recorded in Wistman's Wood, while a few occur, along with hybrids between this and the pedunculate species, in Black Tor Beare.

The feature of these Oaks which has captured the interest and imagination of everyone who has been to see them is their extremely gnarled and dwarfed growth, and the manner in which they may branch at the level of the boulders among which they spring (see Pl. XV, XVI, pp. 110, 111). An illustration culled from edition of Carrington's *Dartmoor*, published in London in 1826 conveys a very dramatic picture of the relations between trees and rocks, such as is difficult to reveal in a photograph (Pl. XIVb, p. 103). Harris records that some trees possess an upright stem which reaches a height of about four and a half feet before it begins to branch, but that most trees branch as soon as they top the boulders, the branches sprawling over the surface of the rock and often down the far side to the ground. The resulting extraordinary tangle of boughs twining in all directions over the " clitter " of rocks, and the accumulation of a mat of humus which covers both rocks and branches and often bridges deep holes, makes progress through the wood very difficult, often painful, and unless care is exercised even dangerous. Although its estimated extent is only four acres, it is safe to say that very few persons have traversed Wistman's Wood completely, and it would be impossible to make a complete ecological survey of it.

The coppicing and stunting of the trees is more marked here than in the other two woods, as may be indicated from the measurements made by Worth from selected areas in each. His data are as follows:

	Wistman's Wood	Pile's Wood	Black Tor Beare
Number of trees measured ..	26	45	65
Average girth, inches	49	25	27
Average height, feet and inches	14, 7	26, 1	25, 6
Least and greatest girths, inches	23, 99	12, 64	12, 46
Least and greatest heights, feet	9, 20	16, 38	19, 32

It is by no means easy to determine the ages of the trees. We have already seen that the age of the wood is at least 330 years. But the presence of seedlings and saplings indicates that natural replenishment is proceeding, and, as there is little evidence of any marked increase in the area of the copse, it follows that there must almost certainly be a gradual replacement of the older trees during the course of centuries. Indeeed, Worth has pointed to evidence of widespread decay among the older trees, although they show the most remarkable powers of recuperation. Tansley (1939) has suggested that these woods, together with certain others in other parts of the country, are growing just at the limit of altitude to which they can attain, and that they may, therefore, be peculiarly subject to attack by fungi, gall-flies and the like, which may seriously impair their vigour. A number of cross-sections of the boles of trees have been obtained and studied. In some, well over 500 rings have been counted. But some confusion still exists as to the proper interpretation of the readings, and it is probably safer to assume between 300 and 500 years as the age of the older trees. If a comparison is drawn between the dimensions of these ancient trees and the girth and height of Oaks of similar age growing on lowland clay soils it becomes apparent with what pigmies we are here concerned. Lowland Oaks of one hundred or more feet in height and twenty-five foot girth are not uncommon, while the Newland Oak in Gloucestershire, to quote one example, has a girth of $47\frac{1}{2}$ feet at a height of five feet from the ground. The greatest figures recorded by Worth for Wistman's Wood are twenty feet in height and just over eight foot girth; puny indeed by comparison.

Harris in particular, followed by Christy and Worth, has attempted to analyse the conditions which have determined the occurrence and form of these woods. All three comprise narrow strips of scrub Oak facing roughly south-west, and situated at a height of between 1,200 and 1,400 feet above sea level. All grow from clitters of enormous boulders strewn on a hillside. And in each case the gradient is steep and may verge on the precipitous. The positional relation between-trees and boulders is clear, but it admits of at least two explanations. Those who believe that the copses are relics of a more extensive forest which formerly clothed long stretches of the banks of streams suggest (vide, *Dartmoor Memoir*, H. M. Geol. Survey 1912) that the tinners denuded the country of trees in their need to find fuel for the blowing houses. And they point to the evidence of active tin-working in the valley of the Dart, close to Wistman's Wood. But, they argue, owing to the rocky and difficult nature of the ground, the copses were not profitable to work, and so they escaped, as small islands of trees in an otherwise de-afforested landscape.

The argument we have just outlined would be more convincing if it were known that felling kills the Oaks. Worth, without adducing any supporting evidence, states his belief that Pile's Copse was at one time felled, and there is historical evidence of felling in Black Tor Beare. Two instances have already been cited, the one recording in 1587 the imposition of a fine of threepence for " cutting certain oaks at Blacktors Beare "; the other some thirty years later recording a price of £40 for eight acres of underwood in the same place. It follows then, that felling has occurred on occasion, and neither remoteness nor difficulty of terrain has acted as a deterrent in the face of extreme scarcity of wood fuel. As St. Leger Gordon (in lit.) has pointed out, " The practical difficulties would scarcely have deterred the sort of men who built the stone walls and brought down their peat on donkeys." Gordon, indeed, believes that the gnarled and stunted forms of the Oaks in all three woods are due to the influence of lopping. He postulates, " In a place like Wistman's Wood anyone scrounging for fuel would naturally have cut the portable branches rather than the boles, and the effect would be precisely what we now see. . . . It was the Wistman's Wood-like appearance of so many mutilated old hedgerow trees which first suggested a common cause." We may also note in passing that such lopping or felling as occurred in the sixteenth and seventeenth centuries has not resulted in the destruction of Black Tor Beare, which regenerated vigorously.

It is possible that Gordon's view may be in part correct, and that some misshaping of the trees has been due to sporadic lopping. But no evidence exists of this having occurred in recent times, and the effects of severe wind-pruning are most apparent in all the woods. The term wind-pruning is, of course, metaphorical, referring to the manner in which the high south-westerly winds which prevail in winter check the growth of twigs on the windward side and so shape the form assumed by the trees. It may indeed be wind which is primarily responsible not only for the shape, but also for the occurrence and distribution of the trees. Miller Christy has suggested that the significance of the association between trees and clitter is the protection afforded to the young seedling trees against grazing animals. Certainly

the tumbled boulders make it very difficult for sheep, cattle or ponies
to enter the heart of any of the copses, although they may penetrate
the fringes. Harris inclined in the first instance towards this view, but
changed his mind after close examination of Black Tor Copse, where he
found small sections of the upper part growing on ground almost free
of boulders, and indeed producing straight-stemmed trees some twenty-
five feet high which were used by cattle for shade, Moreover. in suitable
spots on the open moor above the copse, where cattle graze freely,
seedling Oaks occur not uncommonly. Grazing is not, therefore, a
limiting factor in this particular instance.

Harris accordingly looked elsewhere for an explanation, and found
it in the physical conditions. Each wood, as we have seen, faces south-
west and lies at a comparatively high altitude, in a region where the
prevailing winds are strong and south-westerly. There is, moreover,
striking evidence of the manner in which the wind shapes the exposed
branches. It seems reasonable, therefore, to adduce as a fundamental
cause of the existence of the woods the shelter initially provided against
such winds by the boulders amongst which the seedling trees have
sprung. They are thus able to develop a firm roothold with which to
resist the force of the winter gales before they overtop the sheltering
rocks and have to face the weather. Once established, the wood
provides its own leeside under which young seedlings can now establish
themselves, as they are doing at Black Tor Copse.

Whatever the causes underlying their origin, these woods are
intriguing and beautiful places, and to see them, as I was fortunate
to do in the early summer of 1949 in brilliant sunshine after recent
rains, creates a vivid and lasting impression on the mind. Then the
young leaves are still unfolding, and from a short distance the copse
resembles less a wood than a plantation of Azaleas. The brilliant reds,
bronzes and yellows, and the apple-green of the various trees stand
each as its own mass of colour, while the whole blends into a rich mosaic
to which the moorland beyond and the nearby river form a softer
frame. I think it is only under conditions such as these that one
appreciates the intense variation in the colour assumed by the young
leaves of different trees. For the span of each tree is so small that the
eye can take in fifty or more trees at a glance, and each tree presents
a sharp colour contrast with its neighbours.

After the trees themselves, the most striking feature of the woods
is the extraordinary abundance of epiphytes on their boles and branches

In this respect, however, Wistman's Wood stands by itself. In both Black Tor Beare and Pile's Copse the boles of the trees rise much higher from ground level before they branch and the epiphytic cover is no more than may be expected in woodland in the warm damp climate of the south-west of England. Boles and branches, like the underlying rocks, are clothed with a dense cover of mosses and lichens, and here and there a Polypody fern, *Polypodium vulgare*, is lodged in a fork. Undergrowth is sparse, except for the continuous carpet of mosses over every surface, an occasional clump of fern or of the Wood-rush, *Luzula sylvatica*, or a thin trailer or two of Honeysuckle, *Lonicera periclymenum*. The impression it conveys, on a still day with the sunlight filtering thinly down through the canopy above, is that of a stage set for a pantomime, and one half expects to see a group of birds bringing leaves to cover the lost Babes, or the wicked uncle stealing off between the boles.

Why Wistman's Wood should be so infinitely richer in its undergrowth and in its tangle of epiphytes has never been analysed. It may possibly be related to the much closer and shorter growth of the trees, but, in the absence of a closer examination than has hitherto been made, it is a waste of time to speculate. Here, however, humus has accumulated to a depth of several inches on all but the most steeply inclined surfaces of rocks and trees. In this ample roothold grows a flora which ranges from Rowan trees to mosses and lichens, and includes species drawn from the surrounding moorland together with others peculiar to the wood itself. The striking contrast between this flora and that of the moor, both in its composition and in the growth forms assumed by species common to both, affords good evidence of the powerful influence of the new microclimate created once the wood has become established. The Wood-rush, which occurs rather sparsely in Pile's and Black Tor Copses, is present as huge clumps on the floor of the wood and on the boles and branches of the trees. Whortleberry, *Vaccinium myrtillus*, is almost equally common in both situations, as are also the Hard and Polypody Ferns, *Blechnum spicant* and *Polypodium vulgare*, and mosses such as *Eurhynchium myurum*, *Dicranium scoparium*, *Hylocomium loreum*, *Ulota crispa* and *Antitrichia curtipendula*. The last species is noted by Dixon (1924) as particularly luxuriant and fertile in Wistman's Wood. To these must be added a rich and diverse flora of lichens and liverworts. The list of phanerogams provided by Harris and Worth includes, besides the above species:

Sedum acre	*Ulex europaeus*
Oxalis acetosella	*Hedera helix*
Potentilla erecta	*Geranium robertianum*
Anthoxanthum odoratum	*Salix aurita*
Holcus lanatus	*Lonicera periclymenum*
Digitalis purpurea	*Teucrium scorodonia*
Corydalis claviculata	*Stellaria holostea*

Ferns additional to those mentioned include *Dryopteris filix-mas* and the two Filmy Ferns, *Hymenophyllum tunbridgense* and *H. peltatum*.

Christy also records two lists of lichens, which include:

Cetraria glauca	*Usnea florida*
Lecanora intumescens	*U. florida* var. *hirta*
Karmelia fuliginosa var. *laeteirrens*	*Cladonia fimbriata*
Evernia prunastre	*C. furcata*
Parmelia saxatilis	*C. squamosa*
P. physodes	*C. cervicornis*
P. perlata	*C. sylvatica*
P. omphalodes	*C. rangiformis*
P. caperata	*C. coccifera*
Sphaerophorus globosus	*Opegraphia herpetica*
Ramalina siliquosa	*Graphis elegans*

Few naturalists other than botanists seem to have visited these woods, and little information is to be found about the fauna of any of them. Mr. H. G. Hurrell has reconnoitred the birds of Pile's Copse on two recent occasions, and has provided two lists, which give a picture of the early spring and winter conditions before the arrival of the summer residents. These include:

16 January 1946	*10 April 1947*
Blue Tit	Blue Tit (1)
Great Tit	Great Tit (1)
Coal Tit	Dunnock (3)
Blackbird	Dipper (1)
Tree-Creeper	Chaffinch (many)
Nuthatch	Buzzard's nest (new)
Woodpigeon	Raven's nest
Woodcock	Kestrel (pair near)

He adds that Crows and Magpies have been seen there, Robin, Song-thrush and Wren probably occur, while Greater Spotted Woodpecker and Whinchat have been seen nearby, and Grey Wagtails nested during 1947. To this list may be added a few of the summer birds which were present when I visited all three copses in June 1949. They are, Yellow-hammer and Wood-warbler in all three, and Tree-pipit and White-throat in Black Tor Copse. The Wheatears common on the moor were observed to penetrate the fringes of the wood, even perching on the boughs, and, at Black Tor Copse, Grey Wagtails were flitting up and down between the wood and the river banks the whole of the time we were there. Probably other insectivorous birds occur, although they have not been observed, for in some parts of Black Tor Copse the Oaks and also the Rowans had already been almost defoliated by the attacks of a small Tortricid caterpillar.

Mr. G. M. Spooner, who observed the birds of most of the tree plantations of Dartmoor during 1936 and 1937, was unfortunately unable to visit any of the indigenous copses. His records from the various plantations, however, indicate that, although many species tend to become scarcer at higher altitudes, and towards the centre of the moor, a considerable population extends right up to the limit of tree growth. His notes probably give us as clear a picture as exists of the woodland birds which are to be expected.

Blackbird, well distributed up to the tree limit—also away from trees.

Song-Thrush, up to near the tree limit, but apparently in decreasing numbers at higher levels.

Mistle-Thrush, less frequent than might be expected: only four records.

Robin, general, to the very upper tree limit.

Dunnock, general to the upper tree limit; three at over 1,500 feet.

Wren, general to upper tree limit, also away from trees.

Chiffchaff, up to 1,225 feet, but scarce owing to lack of suitable undergrowth in most plantations.

Willow-Warbler, in all suitable sites up to the tree limit.

Wood-Warbler, in all suitable sites up to the tree limit: at 1,500 feet near Princetown.

Plate XV.   WISTMAN'S WOOD: (*above*) panoramic view, (*below*) interior, showing the gnarled and stunted trees, the lush flora of epiphytic mosses and ferns, and a ground cover of Wood-rush, *Luzula sylvatica*

(*Photographs by E. H. Ware*)

Plate XVI. Epiphytic vegetation on one of the Wistman's Wood oaks (*left*) contrasted with the much more open character of Black Tor Beare (*right*)

(*Photographs by E. H. Ware*)

Whitethroat, only one record at 1,125 feet; scarcer than at the edges of the moor.

Garden Warbler, one record at 1,050 feet; few suitable dense shrubberies.

Tree-creeper, only one record at 1,000 feet; apparently it declines towards the higher altitudes.

Nuthatch, none recorded; must be very scarce as a nesting species.

Coal Tit, the commonest tit, but this is related to the prevalence of conifers.

Great Tit, one record at 1,250 feet; seem scarcer than at lower altitudes : probably not enough deciduous trees for them.

Blue Tit, only one record; seem scarcer than at lower altitudes, probably not enough deciduous trees for them.

Marsh-Tit, conspicuously absent, possibly due to lack of oak woods.

Tree-Pipit, fairly general at edges of plantations to upper tree limit, 1,530 feet.

Wood-Lark, none, possibly overlooked, but believed to congregate round the edges of the moor.

Chaffinch, general to the extreme tree limit, 1,550 feet .

Bullfinch, one record only, 1,100 feet.

Yellowhammer, not infrequent near edges of plantations, up to 1,100 feet ; not really a woodland bird.

No other finches were observed. Linnets appear scarce, Redpolls are not colonising the plantations, and even the House-sparrow appears not to thrive.

Starling, no tree nests found; moderate winter roost near Princetown, at 1,450 feet.

Raven, one tree nest at 1,250 feet.

Crow, nests generally, showing no apparent altitudinal limitation.

Rook, three rookeries, the highest at 1,450 feet; apparently limited more by absence of enclosed pastures than by altitude.

Jackdaw, no tree-nests found.

Magpie, two records only, but must be abundant in open cultivated parts.

Jay, none seen; probably scarce on high ground, possibly due to limitation of oak and hazel.

Green Woodpecker, sparingly up to 1,500 feet.

Great Spotted Woodpecker, one nest at 1,250 feet; apparently very scarce or absent in the centre of the moor.

Cuckoo, frequent incidental records.

Buzzard, nests in most plantations; highest 1,400 feet.

Kestrel, only one record, but probably more frequent than indicated.

Heron, one small heronry at 1,250 feet (1937), another at 1,300 feet, at Archerton Wood (deserted before 1937).

Woodpigeon, general, nesting to the tree limit, but may decline above 1,000 feet.

Turtle-Dove, one flushed at 1,100 feet, probably only a wanderer.

Pheasant, one record; apparently scarce.

Blackcock, occasional.

It must not be forgotten that Spooner's records were made at a comparatively large number of copses and plantations, the conditions in which are very diverse, and in no case resemble those in the woods we have been considering. It would not, however, be unreasonable to expect to find quite a large proportion of the birds of Spooner's list occurring in the indigenous copses. Indeed, Hurrell's observations in Pile's Copse include a Nuthatch, a species which Spooner was unable to find. But the low canopy and the small circumference of most of the timber almost certainly restricts the occurrence of species like the Raven, Crow and Rook, Buzzard, Kestrel, Woodpeckers and Wood-pigeon.

Outside the copses there are few trees on the open moor, except where they have been planted. Stunted Hawthorns occur occasionally on the hillsides; Rowans, sometimes very well grown, overhang many of the pools along the streams; Willow scrub may clothe old tin-workings, as in the Vitifer area, or cover the banks of streams, or low-lying land. It may even form incipient carr in Red Lake Mire. Although Birch was at one time common on Dartmoor, as indicated by the discovery of its remains under deep peat in many places, to-day it is by no means a common species. Thin oak-birch scrub covers some lower lying and marginal lands, such as Yarner and Trendlebeare and parts of Chudleigh Knighton Heath. But these are for the most part small areas, and the general impression one receives is that Birch does not do well on Dartmoor under modern conditions.

✝ Plantations are numerous except on the high blanket bogs. They vary in size and character between wide limits. At the one end are some of the Forestry Commission plantings of conifers, as at Bellever, Fernworthy and Soussons Down, covering large acreages, and a few large private woods like those of Tor Royal. At the other end of the series are many small copses, some not more than a half-acre in area, and mostly consisting of conifers with a marginal planting of Beech. The amount and character of the undergrowth in all these vary with age and density of the trees, and of course with the species used. During the first few years after enclosure the young trees are small, and the natural vegetation, no longer checked by grazing or by swaling, grows to astonishing proportions by comparison with the unenclosed moor without. Later, particularly where, as is usual nowadays, conifers have been planted, the growing trees form a dense cover beneath which few plants can survive. Very soon a vigorous planting becomes a pure stand, such as may be seen at Clifford Bridge in the River Teign, and the only extraneous species occur along the rides or at the margins. But such success does not attend all the forester's efforts on Dartmoor, and most of the large plantings soon become very uneven in growth, and here a considerable admixture of the indigenous moor plants may be present among and between the planted trees.

The older, small copses and woods were planted in less orderly fashion than are the modern stands, and, being smaller, the marginal strips of hardwoods, particularly beech, constitute a larger proportion of the whole. As a consequence they remain more open and the floor receives much more light. There is, therefore, much more ground cover here, although it is rarely that one finds the diversity reported by Harris (1921) in a wood near Sourton Tor. This, which is presumably Tor Wood, is a mixture of Sessile and Pedunculate Oaks with many hybrids between them and also a light admixture of Ash. There is a shrubby undergrowth of Hawthorn, *Crataegus monogyna*, Blackthorn, *Prunus spinosa*, Brambles, *Rubus* spp., Hazel, *Corylus avellana* and Gorse, *Ulex europaeus*, and the ground flora is characterised by Bluebells, *Scilla non-scripta*, Dog's Mercury, *Mercurialis perennis*, Wood Sage, *Teucrium scorodonia*, Hard Fern, *Blechnum spicant*, (Whortleberry's) *Vaccinium myrtillus*, Honeysuckle, *Lonicera periclymenum*, Marjoram, *Origanum vulgare* and Wood Sanicle, *Sanicula europaea*. This is far more reminiscent of a lowland wood than of most of the copses on the moor. Possibly, as Harris remarks, the very steep slope of the ground and the presence of thorny shrubs has protected the ground flora against excessive grazing by stock. Bluebells are, however, very common, not only in woods, but also carpeting quite large stretches of moorland outside.

The Forestry Commission has been, and still is, subjected to severe criticism on account of its policy of growing huge areas of conifers in serried ranks of uniform species. To this complaint has been added that of the rambler, who finds it laborious, if not impossible, to walk across the deeply furrowed surface of a modern plantation. And, of course, once the young trees are well grown the plantation becomes virtually impassable, except along the rides, until it reaches the stage of being thinned. It is not intended here to offer a defence of the Forestry Commission, but it is as well to consider for a moment a few of the implications of the arguments of its opponents on Dartmoor. It has been claimed that Dartmoor has since time beyond memory been the province of the hill grazier. By fostering this interest, to the exclusion of such "upstarts" as the forester, the character of Moor may be preserved, and it will in consequence retain both its productivity and its charm for the walker. The argument might be acceptable were it possible thereby to maintain the *status quo*, and retain the great stretches of heather moor, the bilberry-covered downs and the huge sponges of the blanket bogs which water more than half the county. But the natural balance is a dynamic state which can only be halted in any of its phases by the most careful control measures. This has not happened on Dartmoor, where overgrazing and indiscriminate heather burning have steadily tipped the balance in favour of Bracken, until this plant is covering ever wider areas of once open moor. A rational policy of fostering hill grazing must take this into account, and the obvious solution is that of improving the pasturage by encouraging hill grasses of the types developed with such success during recent years at the Hill Grassland Research Station in Wales. Thus the logical trend will be towards stands of plants which, although smaller and less obtrusive, are no less uniform and monotonous than the products of the forester. Moreover, they will neither provide wind shelter for stock, nor yield relief to the eye by the discontinuity of colour and form which characterise the forestry plantations.

However reluctant we may be to accept it, the new austerity forces us to use all our land with rigid economy, and we must wring, if not the last, the penultimate ounce of living from the marginal and hill lands of Britain. The further argument may be adduced that the forestry plantations offer a far surer shield than do hill grazings against that spoliation which Dartmoor, in common with so many other wild and beautiful places, increasingly suffers in the name of the defence of Britain. Facing, therefore, the certainty of change in the face of Dartmoor, I, for my part, prefer that towards afforestation. There are good reasons for urging modification of the policy of extreme regimentation which arises from planting pure stands of one species. Mixed plantings are not only more pleasing to the eye, but also are less liable to suffer from epidemic by fungus or insect attacks. But, in any case, it seems likely that uniform stands of this kind may rarely be achieved here, in the face of irregularities in the surface, differences in exposure, soil moisture and texture, and the like. A bird's eye view of the plantations at Bellever, for instance, reveals the most extreme differences in the growth achieved by the trees in different parts of the enclosures. And, in the absence of clear-felling, there seems no reason why each plantation should not present considerable diversity and charm as it comes to maturity; for it must be realised that we have not yet seen a mature planting on Dartmoor. There must plainly be a limit set to the proportion of the region which may be so covered with trees, and probably this limit has nearly been reached with the planting of Soussons Down and the sides of the Walla Brook valley. In the latter, moreover, the trees should make a more positive contribution to the amenity of the scene, by clothing the debris from the tin workings which are at present such a scar on the valley.

We have still to discover what will be the effect on the fauna of these wide areas of cover in an otherwise open landscape. Spooner's reconnaissance of the existing plantations in 1936 and 1937, to which we have already referred, yielded thirty-two species of birds, of which most extended right to the upper limit of tree growth. To this must be added the observations of Mr. W. Robinson during the years 1941 to 1945, while his school was evacuated to Postbridge. An area of approximately five miles, radius around Postbridge provided a total of eighty-six species of birds, falling into these categories:

Resident	49
Summer resident	18
Winter visitor	5
Rare and occasional visitor ..	14

Some of these birds, for instance, Mallard, Teal, Pochard, Tufted Duck, Cormorant, Dabchick, Moorhen, Coot and Gulls, are attracted to the reservoir at Fernworthy, which lies within the circle. Even so, the numbers of some of these species are probably swelled as a result of the cover provided by the plantations which surround the water. Others, including Swallow, House-martin and Swift, are attracted by the few houses of the village, and yet others are ubiquitous on the open moors, Raven, Carrion-crow, Linnet, Skylark, Meadow-pipit, Black-bird, Wheatear, Whinchat, Cuckoo, Kestrel, Buzzard, Plover, Snipe, etc. But the majority are favoured by the trees, in which the neigh-bourhood is much richer than most of Dartmoor. There is a certain amount of admixture of hard-woods, in the shape of Beech, Sycamore and Oak, but the bulk of the trees are the conifers in the plantations at Bellever and Fernworthy. If Robinson's list is contemplated in the light of D'Urban and Mathew's picture of Dartmoor in 1895 as a habitat for birds, it presents a striking example of the changes wrought by these plantations. After remarking that " the early ornithologists of the county, with the exception of Colonel Montagu, who could never be betrayed into such a mistake, were wont to regard the moor as the nesting-place of Goshawks, Eagles, Grey Plovers, and of most of the Waders to be found on our shores, and Great Bustards were supposed to have their home within its unexplored fastnesses," they proceed, " But Carrington, the poet of the moor, had a truer perception of the almost entire absence of life in its central wastes, when he wrote:

'. . . *Nothing that has life*
Is visible;—no solitary flock
At will wide ranging through the silent Moor,
Breaks the deep-felt monotony; and all
Is motionless, save where the giant shades,
Flung by the passing cloud, glide slowly o'er
The gray and gloomy wild.'

The ornithologist who is well acquainted with the moor will perceive at once that it presents no suitable abode for many of the birds which were supposed to frequent it."

There is also direct evidence for the increase of some breeding birds and the encouragement of others during the young stages of the plantings. No one who has seen the vigour with which the native vegetation grows when it is no longer checked by grazing can be surprised at this. The amount of extra cover provided, and of extra food, are very great. Some species appear to be especially favoured by these conditions, and it may well be that the Black Game, which at one time had almost vanished from Dartmoor, may return as a vigorous population. Mr. Hurrell (*in lit.*) says of them, "Although they turn up from time to time over quite a wide area of the moor I should find it difficult to say where to find them outside the Forestry Commission land at any given time." It is not a bird of the open moor, like the Red Grouse, but more frequently inhabits the fringes of woodland and plantations, and the great increase of this habitat has provided it with conditions which may well tip the balance in its favour.

The observations of Lack (1933, 1939) and Lack and Venables (1939), made for the most part in Forestry Commission conifer plantings in Breckland, have indicated very clearly the sort of changes which may be expected in bird populations when open country is planted, and in particular the succession of species which follows the changes in the habitat as the breck- or heath-land is planted, and the trees grow up. The greater altitude of Dartmoor and its wetter climate will modify the picture, but probably an even more important factor will be the irregularity of many of the plantings, on which remark has already been passed. It appears that the Norfolk trees grow with such vigour and uniformity as virtually to exclude the original birds of the open heath. But on Dartmoor it is unlikely that this will happen and there will probably remain considerable open spaces within most of the plantations. We may in consequence expect a greater diversity of bird life as a result of the admixture of moorland and woodland species.

We have very little precise information about the mammals of the Dartmoor woodlands. That characteristic little woodlander, the Red Squirrel, *Sciurus vulgaris*, occurs sparingly wherever sufficient cover and food are to be found. Fortunately, so far, the Grey Squirrel, *S. carolinensis*, has been unable to penetrate the region. Four specimens which were released at Exeter in 1915 have bred a strong colony which has risen to the status of a pest in the area close to the original introduction, and has spread rapidly outward, for the most part along the wooded, populated valleys. It has moved thus down the coast to the east of Dartmoor into the Torquay area, and it has also reached as far as Spreyton, to the north-east of Okehampton.[1] But the Dartmoor

---

[1] They were however reported in small numbers at Yarner Wood, in the spring of 1953, and steady infiltration of the valley woodlands has proceeded since then.

woods and plantations are so far immune, and it is to be hoped that they will remain so. For, not only does this animal do tremendous damage in plantation and orchard, but it also exerts a malign, though ill-defined, influence on its red congener. Miss Shorten (1946) has shown, from her survey of the distribution and status of the two species in England and Wales, that wherever the Grey Squirrel has been established over a period of fifteen years or more, there the Red Squirrel, if not originally absent, has usually disappeared. Fortunately, the bare open country and the hard climate of Dartmoor will not encourage the Grey Squirrel, and indeed suitable habitats for either species are infrequent at present. But as the conifer plantations reach cone-bearing age we may hope that the Red Squirrel may find conditions more to its liking and that it will then increase. Ritchie (1920) has ascribed the virtual extinction of this species in Scotland in the eighteenth century to de-afforestation by ironfounders; and its rapid spread, and rise in many areas to the status of pest, after its re-introduction early in the nineteenth century he regards as due to the fact that by then many of the Scottish river valleys were clothed in close-set woodland again.

Few other truly woodland mammals exist in sufficient numbers to be significant. Although, here as elsewhere, the Fox excavates its earth more frequently under the cover of woodland than in more open country, it would not be true to describe it as a woodlander. Indeed, the Dartmoor Foxes often wear a less rufous coat than their lowland relatives, and this is usually attributed to the fact that they spend most of their lives on the steep, open heather-covered moors, lying out among the sombre tints of the Heather and Bracken and drinking at the bog pools. Although Badgers are seldom seen, they are probably as common as Foxes, or even in some localities commoner. Like Foxes, they locate their setts in the deep seclusion of the wooded hillsides, although there are a few records of setts among the boulders of a clitter out in the open moor. Like the Fox, too, they range very widely, seeking a varied diet through a diversity of habitats. As Neal has confirmed (1946), very little comes amiss to them, from wasp-grubs and honey to young Rabbits or a Hedgehog. They are, however, so seldom abroad by day that they are rarely seen except by those who are out and about between nightfall and early daybreak.

Red Deer have never been the prominent feature on Dartmoor that they are on Exmoor. Occasionally small parties, or more usually

Eric Hosking

Plate XVII. Wood Warbler, *Phylloscopus sibilatrix*, at nest

Plate XVIII a.   Montagu's Harrier, *Circus pygargus*, hen and young

      b.   Grey Wagtail, *Motacilla cinerea;* a characteristic view by the waterside

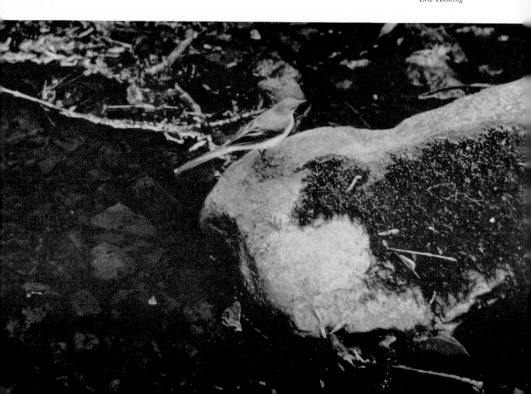

solitary animals, wander across the farmlands that separate the two great moorlands. But they never stay long and have never established themselves. Other indigenous species of Deer are absent, probably because of the very restricted areas of thickly wooded country available to them. But near Moretonhampstead Japanese Deer have recently been introduced, and seem to be becoming firmly established.

No naturalist can but regret the absence of that most beautiful and interesting mammal, the Pine-marten. Never having provided the central figure in the peculiarly English occupation of hunting, this fine animal has suffered the fate meted out to all largish carnivores by advancing civilisation. It has been mercilessly shot and trapped, until to-day it is confined in Britain to a few highland areas in Scotland and, more doubtfully, Wales and the Lake District. Possibly, however, the tide may have turned for this, and some other equally harassed beasts. Game preserving, in the name of which so much extermination is practised, is an expensive occupation which, with the decline of the large landowner, is likely to become less common than in former, more spacious days. Moreover, the move towards a policy of conserving our flora and fauna has now received recognition in the establishment of a Nature Conservancy. There seems no reason why, with the adoption of a more rational attitude towards wild life, the Pine-marten should not gradually increase its range again. It is an animal which wanders long distances where suitable habitats encourage it, and these are likely to be provided by the extensive planting of conifers over the western highlands of England and Wales.

There are very few records of Martens in Devon. Brooking Rowe in 1862, said he knew of no recent records, but quoted J. C. Bellamy for the statement that it lived in woods at Lydford and Buckland-in-the-Moor. There used to be a specimen in the museum of the Plymouth Institution, but its origin was not recorded and opinion differed as to whence it came, although the two localities suggested, Buckland-in-the-Moor and Trowlesworthy, are both on Dartmoor. There is also an unsubstantiated report of a Pine-marten in Pile's Copse in the early nineteen-thirties. But there is little doubt that there were no indigenous Martens living in the area at that date. On the other hand, escapes have occurred at various fur farms on Dartmoor, and not all these animals have been recovered. They would certainly be able to support themselves quite well, and it is possible that the Pile's Copse record was of one of these feral animals, one of which disappeared from a farm at Chagford in 1921 or 1922. Apparently, from escape records, both male and female of the species have never been at large together, and so a chance of re-establishing the animal as a breeding population has not occurred.

THE VALLEY WOODS AND COPPICES

Where the rivers leave the open moors and cut down through the 1,000-foot platform, they excavate deep, steep-sided valleys, for the most part through Culm shales. On the shallow, wet soil of these slopes a scrub-oak woodland grows, which in many places is regularly coppiced, the bark being taken for tanning and the poles used for charcoal. Where it has been left uncut, as, for instance, in the valley of the Dart at Holne Chase, or below Lustleigh Cleave in the valley of the River Bovey, a rather thin stand of Oak, *Quercus robur* and *Q. petraea*, develops with a variable admixture of Ash, Rowan, Holly, Birch, in the lower parts, and Alder along the stream banks. The underscrub is usually sparse, with Holly, Hazel, Blackthorn, Hawthorn, some Willows, and Bramble. Honeysuckle threads over the bushes and climbs well up into the canopy, particularly round the margins of open glades. The ground flora is comprised of Whortleberry, Wood-sage, Bluebells, Primroses, Ling, and less frequently Golden Rod, *Solidago virgaurea*, Cow-wheat, *Melampyrum pratense*, Wood sanicle and Bell Heather. In Drewston Wood, near Fingle Bridge in the valley of the Teign, occurs one of the few colonies of the Flax-leaved St. John's Wort, *Hypericum linariifolium*. Where the woods are not felled the deep accumulations of humus, the fallen logs and branches, and the humid atmosphere combine to provide ideal conditions for fungi, which grow in variety and profusion. So also do ferns. Indeed, there are few situations on Dartmoor in which ferns of one species or another do not flourish. Even the Filmy Ferns, which demand a very high humidity, occur in some of these woods, although they are never very common. The Royal Fern, *Osmunda regalis*, has been almost exterminated by collectors, except in a few remote or protected spots. This beautiful plant may, however, still be found in a few bogs near the fringes of the moor, or sometimes growing at the waterside. As in the upland copses, although to a less marked extent, the lower boughs and the trunks of most of the trees are clothed with epiphytes, among which mosses, liverworts and lichens are prominent, together with the Polypody Fern,

[1] During recent years Mink, *Lutreola vison*, have sometimes escaped from farms and reports suggest that they are establishing themselves in a feral existence in some valleys.

Polypodium vulgare. In some woods a very striking effect is produced by the much more vigorous growth of the epiphytic lichens in particular on the south-westerly sides of the tree trunks and boughs, in response to the greater humidity which supervenes here, the north-easterly aspects being in miniature rain-shadows as the prevailing winds blow through the wood.

Conditions under coppicing are different. The woods are cut at regular intervals of a few years, and so no tall timber is allowed to develop. As a result the canopy is much lower and thinner, and lets in a great deal more light. Most of the timber is cut and burned before it attains an age at which it may die and fall, and so there are few rotting logs or limbs, although occasional bundles of brushwood may be left to decay if they have not been used in firing the charcoal kilns. There is less leaf litter to make humus, and the more open nature of the stand produces a drier local climate. Under these conditions the ground flora develops into a much closer, denser cover of either Heather or Whortleberry. The environment in which the plants grow is different in many ways from that of plants on the open moor, on the one hand, or those in the deep shade of unfelled woods, on the other hand. They are sheltered and provided with a humid climate, are subjected to neither grazing nor burning, and the light they receive, although it lessens as the saplings spring up from the coppiced stools, is never so low as to produce marked etiolation. As a consequence, a dense, shrubby cover grows to about knee-height. Where this is of Whortle-berry it bears a good crop of large berries which ripen much earlier than those at the higher altitudes of the open moor, and so extend a local industry by several weeks in the year. Probably this particular crop depends in large measure upon the coppicing. The plants grow and fruit with great vigour under these conditions, whereas they are much sparser, very spindly in growth and far less prolific of fruit under the deep shade where no felling has occurred, and the individual berries are smaller and less sweet and juicy.

Whether coppiced or no, these valley woods support a rich and diverse fauna. The greater prevalence of leaf litter and mould and of rotting branches and trunks in the unfelled woods results in a greater variation in the ecological niches here, and consequently a more interesting fauna occurs. In both situations the animal which most persistently obtrudes itself on the senses is the Wood Ant, *Formica rufa*. This, one of the largest and most active of British ants, is ubiquitous in many of the valleys although less frequent and quite local on the western and southern sides of the Moor. Its nests are frequent, usually by pathsides or in clearings, consisting of great piles of leaf fragments among and over which the ants swarm. The entrance usually faces the incident light, from whatever quarter this comes, and into and out of it moves a constant stream of foraging lines, which may extend far out into the wood around each nest. Accordingly, everywhere in the woods one comes across these insects, and the whole region is constantly combed by them, from the leaf litter on the floor to the topmost leaves of the canopy. They are remarkably strong and very catholic in their tastes, and appear to be under the necessity of constantly building up their nests with fresh materials. Consequently, the foraging lines are dotted with ants struggling manfully with caterpillars and other insects, and fragments of leaf and stick, each several sizes larger than the valiant porter. If they are irritated they may squirt a little fountain of formic acid into the air, and they bite with great strength and vigour. So numerous are they and so voracious that it is almost with surprise that one discovers other animals living in the woods. But it is not necessary to search very assiduously to discover them. Cryptic species occur in the litter and under logs and stones: Springtails, Mites, Polydesmid and Julid Millipedes, Centipedes, Spiders, Woodlice, Earthworms, Beetles, fly larvae and the like. Snails are scarce on the acid soils, but all the species of Slug in the British list have been recorded for Dartmoor, and most of them are in the woods. Spiders and Harvest men are at home both here and in the world above. Most of the Spiders belong to families such as the Linyphiidae and Lycosidae, rarely spinning webs but searching for their prey and capturing it by their agility. A few small web-spinning species occur in the undergrowth, particularly along the margins of the glades where, not only is the undergrowth thicker, but also there is a much more frequent traffic of flying insects which may be captured in their snares.

Insects occur in great variety on the leaves and twigs of trees, shrubs and undergrowth. Some of these, such as the Snake- and Alder-flies, Stoneflies, Caddises and Mayflies, merely use the plants as resting places, being more directly associated with the river in the valley bottom than with woods on its flanks. But a host of truly woodland species is here, too. Panorpid flies, Hover-flies, Tachinid flies, particularly in the traffic lanes haunted by other Diptera on which they prey, Geometrid and Noctuid and other moths and their larvae, woodland and glade haunting butterflies like the Brown, Purple and Green Hairstreaks, the Silver-washed, High Brown, Pearl-bordered and Greasy Fritillaries and Speckled Wood. Careful search or, more quickly, beating, reveals innumerable Weevils and other beetles, Lacewing flies, plant-bugs, Psocoptera and delicate green Long-horn Grasshoppers like *Leptophyes punctatissima* and *Meconema thalassina*. There is a vast population of Gall-flies associated with the Oaks here, as also in the upland copses. The Hymenoptera include, besides the ants and some of the Gall-flies, Wasps and Hornets, although the latter are always local, Humble Bees which wander into the glades from the open country around, and a large, but never obtrusive population of parasitic species which are usually to be discovered only by the specialist in the groups. Although the Wood-cricket, *Nemobius sylvestris*, has been recorded in Devon, Burr (1936) believes that this requires investigation. It is not recorded in Bignell's list in the Victoria County History, 1906, and certainly, if it does occur, it is very rarely found.[1] An insect which has not hitherto been established in these woods is the White Admiral Butterfly, *Limenitis camilla*, but it is by no means improbable that by the time this book appears it may have become quite common. It has been spreading at quite a spectacular rate into Devon from the east for some years, and is now well established at Lapford, for instance, only a dozen miles from the eastern borders of Dartmoor. It is unlikely, therefore, that such a favourable habitat as is presented by these valleys will remain long uncolonised. Indeed Stidston (1952) now reports it sporadically since 1942 in the Newton Abbot-Bovey Heathfield district, immediately south of Dartmoor.

The vertebrate fauna includes most of the species already noted in the plantations, together with others attracted by the higher canopy, the different nature of the ground cover, and the lower altitude, and also others which are more to be associated with the river and its banks. Otters, for instance, although seldom seen by the casual wanderer, haunt the rivers throughout Devon and the south-west, wandering for long distances along their courses and across country between one valley and the next. The extra cover provided by the woods, and the holts beneath tree stumps and boulders along the river banks, coupled with an ample supply of fish, makes these valleys attractive stopping

---

[1] T. J. Richards (1952) has recently however reported flourishing colonies of the Wood-cricket in the woodlands of E. Devon, and more recently Mr. G. G. Vickers has found a colony in the valley of the Teign above Steps Bridge.

places for Otters. Similarly, birds such as Dippers and Grey and some-times Yellow Wagtails frequent these reaches more on account of the shillets and boulders of the stream bed than for the trees on the banks. But, particularly in the unfelled woods, other, truly woodland, birds are present. Buzzards often nest in the taller trees in remote corners, and their high mewing is a familiar sound above one during spring and early summer. Carrion-crows and occasionally Kestrels and Sparrowhawks may also sometimes nest here. Jays, which seem not to penetrate far into the Dartmoor area, are not uncommon in these marginal valleys, but rarely are they sufficiently numerous to be obtrusive, as they may be in woods in other parts of the country. Nuthatch, Tree-creeper, Woodpeckers, Tawny Owl, Woodpigeon and various Tits may all be encountered. The Long Tailed Tit, which has been very hard hit by severe winters, so that its numbers dropped to negligible size, is happily recovering well, and parties of this enchanting little bird may be met with flitting busily through the trees.

Reptiles are more frequent in the drier, coppiced woods, where Adder, Slow-worm and Common Lizard occur in some numbers. Both Adder and Lizard are, however, less abundant here than on the open moor. The undergrowth is rarely thick enough for the Grass Snake, but it is occasionally to be met with. Those who suffer from complexes about snakes need, however, worry little over the possibility of en-counters with them. Occasionally, when moving quietly about the woods, or among rocks on the moor, one may see an Adder basking in a patch of sunlight. But more frequently the most one sees is the tail as the animal is slipping into cover, having observed one approach before being seen. If the animal has not been disturbed it will remain quiescent, or if it does become aware of the presence of an intruder its immediate reaction is to depart quietly into whatever cover is available. The infrequent incidents in which someone is bitter by an Adder almost invariably result from lack of observation on the part of both reptile and individual. As a result the animal has no warning before a hand or foot descends on it, or so close to it, as to startle it so suddenly that it has no time for retreat. In any case, Adder bites are very rarely fatal, although they require immediate attention if they are not to prove painful and distressing. One man of my acquaintance invariably carries a small tube of potassium permanganate crystals with him, in case of such an emergency, although to my knowledge he has never had occasion to use it.

Enough has now been told of the woodlands of Dartmoor to convey an impression of their diversity and of the interest they may arouse in the naturalist or the casual visitor. On the one hand, the indigenous copses and the plantations of the open moor, exhibiting ecological conditions which range from the bizarre at Wistman's Wood, where the dwarf, twisted trees growing from their bed of boulders are fantastically overgrown with a lush epiphytic blanket, to the formal closed lines of the maturing conifer plantations, in which the density and closeness of the cover precludes the growth of any green vegetation other than the trees. On the other hand, the oak woods of the gorges, where the rivers plunge down from the plateau. These, sometimes managed as coppices, or sometimes neglected, and so producing a somewhat sparse woodland with a fairly high, thin canopy, under which a mixed and spindly undergrowth occurs. In all the dominant features are the thin, shallow soil and the damp climate, and these combine to produce a distinctly scrub woodland, with few really well-grown trees, and a rich growth of phanerogams both on the trees and on the damp floor of the wood.

CHAPTER 9

RIVERS, RESERVOIRS AND
POOLS

THERE ARE AMPLE supplies of water on Dartmoor, but no natural lakes, or even ponds of any size. This interesting fact has already been mentioned, and it arises from the circumstances by which the south-western peninsula of England escaped glaciation during the Ice Ages. As a result its valleys have neither been scoured deeply by grinding ice, nor plugged at their ends by moraines dropped as the glaciers melted. The abundant water drains away freely down gradients which have been carved over long centuries by its own constant falling. The only hindrances presented in its courses are due, either to the accumulation of peat where the gradient slackens over old flood plains, or to man-made obstacles such as dams and weirs which have been erected at various points for the storage or redirection of water for specific human purposes. Until recently there were three reservoirs storing domestic water in the region, at Burrator, Holne Moor and Kennick. The last, Kennick, is not strictly speaking on the moor, but on a granite outlier in the " in-country " immediately south-east of Moretonhampstead. To these has been added since 1940, Fernworthy, while plans are now well advanced for a new undertaking in the valley of the Avon below Huntingdon Warren. [1]

After the reservoirs the only pieces of standing water of any size are incidental to the extraction of minerals. Much of the Lee Moor region is pitted with deep ponds where old china clay workings have been left to fill with water. A few old quarry workings have similarly become submerged, for instance, at Ashburton and just above Meldon Viaduct. Occasionally, as near Headland Warren House, an old tin adit fills from springs. Clasiwell, or Crazy Well Pool, on Walkhampton Common, is another such artificial water. Although the name Pool is not uncommonly applied to various places on Dartmoor, it rarely

[1] This reservoir has now been completed and is open.

Plate XIX. Coppicing and barking for tanning, Teign Valley. The slender growth of the regularly coppiced oaks is very clear

means an open sheet of water. The famous Cranmere Pool, for instance, like Raybarrow Pool and others, is no more than the central depression of a mire. It may contain a little water in a wet season, but more often is a depressing wallow of peat mud.

Little serious observation has been made on the fauna and flora of the reservoirs and ponds. Occasionally some of the smaller species come to notice as a result of their having managed to pass through the filters and thereby reach the outraged domestic consumers of water, and we have in this way records of various Rotifers, or Wheel Animal-cules, Mites, Copepods such as species of *Cyclops* and *Canthocamptus*, Water-fleas, *Daphnia* spp., Nematodes, or Round Worms, like *Alaimus* sp. and the Annelid worm *Nais josinae*. But systematic investigation of the waters will reveal a much more diverse animal population, and this small list cannot be taken to indicate the character of the fauna. Waterfowl, in the absence of natural sheets of water, are attracted to the reservoirs in considerable numbers. Mr. Robinson's records for the Postbridge district, within which Fernworthy lies, have already been noted. They include, besides various ducks, Cormorant, Dabchick, Moorhen, Coot and several gulls. Herons visit them from heronries situated for the most part in the river valleys outside the region. But for some years after Fernworthy was first filled, a solitary pair of Herons remained faithful to a nest which, formerly in the branches of a tree, was then situated only a few feet above the water and well out from the margin of the lake.

The innumerable rivers and streams of Dartmoor present a great variety of ecological conditions. At their sources they are usually mere runnels in crevices in the peat. But, as they gather tributaries, their force increases and they begin to scour beds in the underlying rock, and to descend through long pools which communicate with one another over shallow sills down which the water cascades. On the high moor the gradient remains relatively steep, the pools are corre-spondingly short, and the water moves swiftly throughout their length at all times; and during times of spate the whole course of the stream becomes a turbulent brown torrent. The run-off from the peat is very rapid, and consequently an upland stream may rise by six or nine inches within a few minutes after a rainstorm, and fall again almost as rapidly. As a result, the bottom of these rivers is kept scoured of any-thing smaller than large pebbles, and even these are usually pretty firmly wedged together if they remain in place for long.

The hard bottom excludes most rooted plants, and the flora consists for the most part of Diatoms, which cover the bottom and the sides of the boulders with a thin olive-brown film. A few mosses are able to obtain a roothold, mostly on the downstream sides of large boulders, which may often be thickly covered with the almost black strands of *Fontinalis*. The swiftness of the current also restricts the fauna severely. There are few crevices or loose stones under which animals may creep, and the rushing waters carry away those species which have no specialised means of resisting their force. But careful search of the pools, paying particular attention to the undersides of any boulders which can be turned, will yield a list of possibly a dozen invertebrates. The catch at two such stations in the River Plym may be cited as an example of what may be expected:

Mayflies, Ephemeroptera	*Ecdyonurus* sp.
	Baetis sp.
Stoneflies, Plecoptera	*Taeniopteryx* sp.
	Amphinemura sp.
Dragonflies, Odonata	*Cordulegaster annulatus*
Caddis flies, Trichoptera	*Rhyacophila* sp.
	Hydropsyche sp.
Beetles, Coleoptera	*Haliplus* sp.
Two-winged flies, Diptera	*Simulium* sp.
	Chironomidae
Mites, Hydracarina	Several species
Flatworms, Turbellaria	*Polycelis cornuta*

Probably the most important members of the fauna here are the Stoneflies and Caddises, which are much the commonest species to occur, and these are well equipped to survive in the environment. The Stoneflies are small and slender nymphs, for it is of course the immature stages which occur in the water, and they are beautifully streamlined and so able to utilise the smallest shelter. The Caddises belong either to species the larvae of which build fixed " houses " of small stones, or they live as larvae beneath stones in a tenuous silken shelter. Those species with bulky, free tubes are absent, as indeed we may expect them to be.

A little lower downstream, but still on the open moors, the gradient may slacken and the water slip less turbulently down. Coarse sand and gravel can no longer be swept down, except during a spate, and they are deposited on the bottom, and even a little fine mud may accumulate in backwaters. In this loose substrate some phanerogamic plants root. Water Crowfoot, *Ranunculus aquatilisagg*, and Water Milfoil, *Myriophyllum spicatum*, grow here, their long underwater stems and finely branched leaves trailing downstream and providing cover for the abundant fingerling Trout. The delicate trellis-work of their leaves gives shelter and foothold also for the larvae and pupae of the Black Gnat, *Simulium*, together with the weakly swimming nymphs of Ephemerids such as *Baetis* and of Agrionid and other Dragonflies. Water Slaters, *Asellus aquaticus*, and Freshwater Shrimps, *Gammarus pulex*, rout about among the stones, and small bivalve molluscs like *Sphaerium corneum* and species of *Pisidium* burrow through the mud and finer sand, or sometimes creep over the finely divided leaves of the aquatic plants. Flatworms are represented by species of *Planaria* and *Polycelis*, and Leeches such as *Erpobdella atomaria* and *Helobdella stagnalis* may occur in small numbers, feeding on the other invertebrates in the population.

It is not until the rivers are leaving the moor and have fallen to the level of the wooded valleys that the fauna reaches its greatest diversity. Here the current is slower, although still fast by comparison with a lowland stream. The pools are longer and may be enhanced by the construction of weirs designed to permit the diversion of water into a leat, such as that at Steps Bridge on the River Teign. Under such circumstances a much greater diversity of habitats occurs than we have seen hitherto. The water above the weir may be several feet deep across the whole width of the river bed, and, the current having been checked, it deposits all but the finest materials in a thick layer of sand and gravel spread over the bottom. In this may be found a variety of burrowing creatures, of which perhaps the most interesting is the Freshwater Pearl Mussel, *Unio margaritifer*, which is characteristic of these peaty waters. The pearls which are occasionally to be found within its mantle are, however, usually small and irregular. Few large, rooted plants grow in this deep water, but the bottom is usually olive-brown with a slimy film of Diatoms. The same members of the population which we have observed upstream occur here, reinforced by many more. The whitish grey flatworm, *Dendrocelium lacteum*, may occur sparingly under boulders; Leeches are more abundant, and now include *Piscicola geometra*, *Glossosiphonia complanata* and *G. heteroclita* and more rarely *Protoclepsis tesselata*; Snails are not prominent in the acid waters, with the exception of the little Freshwater Limpet, *Ancylastrum fluviatilis*, which is very common on stones and boulders here, although for some reason it occurs rather rarely in the higher reaches. The insects include a great diversity of Ephemerids and Stoneflies, Caddises, Chironomids, Dragonflies and the like, and in the sand and mud the larvae of the Alder Fly, *Sialis lutraria*. Of fishes, mention may be made of the Loach, *Nemacheilus barbatula*, Miller's Thumb, *Cottus gobio*, Trout, *Salmo trutta*, Grayling, *Thymallus thymallus* and Salmon, *Salmo salar*.

Below the weir, sometimes appearing almost to buttress its stones, is a delta of boulders, shillets and gravelly sand, which may support a rich amphibious flora. Willow and Alder scrub may advance right to the crest of the weir, while below, often islanded in a tracery of small channels, are tangles of Hemp Agrimony, *Eupatorium cannabinum*, Codlins and Cream, *Epilobium hirsutum*, Purple Loosestrife, *Lythrum salicaria*, Skullcap, *Scutellaria galericulata*, and Water Dropwort, *Oenanthe crocata*. Mingled with these are various non-indigenous plants which may either have been washed downstream on freshets, or have more slowly migrated upstream from some source lower down. The extent to which this delta may be covered with water varies rapidly. A spate may cause a rise of several feet in the river by the time it approaches these reaches, and a quiet trickle of clear water threading between the flat shillets may change within a few hours to a murky, thundering torrent rushing along with such force as to scour those same shillets, and much of the vegetation growing on them, downstream with it. Sometimes whole islands are whittled away and the herbs and saplings carried off to add to the flotsam on the flood. On the other hand, sometimes boughs and whole trees, borne down from the woods higher up, may be cast over the weir and become stranded below it, there to serve as a new focal point around which detritus may accumulate, and new plants will sprout in it in the following spring.

Freshets are not the only influences which may affect the depth of water below the weir. The leat may still be functional, as many are, and according as its sluice gate is open or closed, so a greater or lesser amount of water is diverted from the river, and the depth at the sill of the weir may be altered. Consequently, the extent to which the shillets below may be drowned varies, and so also may the depth of water in the main channel of the river. This latter may be important at some seasons of the year when the Salmon are running, for it may affect the chances of the fish being able to pass up the weir. Most weirs of any height on the Dartmoor streams are provided with a fish pass for the express purpose of facilitating the passage of the Salmon on its way up to the redds, or spawning beds. Although not always well constructed or maintained in good order, the fish pass is so designed that most of the water which spills over the weir passes through a comparatively narrow passage down the face, this passage being divided by a series of baffles into a chain of basins each emptying into the one below, and the lowest into a channel which should be so arranged as to form the natural point to which the migrating Salmon come in their passage upstream. As a result, the fish are offered a series of short leaps from basin to basin, instead of having to struggle up the bare face of the obstruction.

The water which passes the weir flows, some of it down the pass into the main stream, some of it straight over the sill and through the narrow passages of the delta below. It is well oxygenated after its tumbles, cool from the depths of the weir pool, and laden with food which has drifted down, some from the rocky reaches higher up, some from the fecund depths and shallows of the pool. It trickles over and among the shillets of a gently inclined slope, down to the next, natural pool below. It is not then surprising to find a rich fauna on and under these stones, and in the bed of the river. The bottom of the stream may resemble a miniature forest of little stiff brown tubes, each carrying an array of radiating branches at its tip. These are the tubes in which live the larvae of a little midge, *Tanytarsus*. On turning over the shillets the same teeming life is revealed as occurs above the weir. But now, owing to the less stable substratum and the more swiftly running, and more erratic water, the relative proportions of species in the fauna are different. Stone-flies, like the large, handsome *Perla carlukiana*, and smaller species of *Leuctra* and *Chloroperla*, and Ephemerid nymphs with a high oxygen demand, like *Chloeon* and *Ecdyonurus* and the like, are prominent. Dragonflies rarely occur here, preferring the deeper, stiller waters, and *Glossosiphonia* and *Helobdella* become the commonest Leeches, the population of which now tends to be sparse.

On the stiller water of these reaches, where the current slackens, or turns in a backwater, close to the banks, Water Skaters skim the surface film. *Velia currens*, the orange bars of its natural pattern often enhanced by clinging scarlet Mites, and *Hydrometra stagnorum* are usually to be seen. And over the water flit innumerable imagines which have emerged from the various aquatic larval forms, and these are preyed

D   K upon by Dragonflies, Asilids and Empids, by Wagtails, Flycatchers, Swallows and Martins; or, as they drop on the water to lay their eggs, or when finally spent, the fish rise from below and take them, carving rings on the water's polished surface. Here, too, the Dipper flits busily from pool to pool, or walks purposefully under water to hunt out the grubs and nymphs under the stones. Plate XX, p. 127, shows a bird with its beak crammed with the food which it has collected in this manner for its nestlings. While it is always to be seen in these reaches, it is by no means confined to them. In fact, it is hardly possible to walk along the course of any of the rivers, whether high on the moors or in the slower, lowland levels, without seeing this charming little bird.

No discussion of the rivers of Dartmoor can be complete without some consideration of the fishing. The clear peaty waters are comparatively free from pollution until they have left the region. The worst fouling occurs in the River Plym, from Cadover Bridge downstream, where the floculent clay from kaolin settling pits permanently whitens the water and clings to stones and weeds on the bottom. The amount present varies, rising to a high peak at times when a pit has been neglected. Thanks to the vigilance of boards of conservators and fisheries officers, this kind of pollution is rarely allowed to persist for long. Indeed, the rivers are watched from source to mouth, in the effort to maintain their cleanliness, and owing to Devon's immunity from large industries, this task is comparatively easy. Many of the urban sewage plants in the county are, however, still in need of modernisation, with the result that the lower reaches of the rivers tend to suffer a chronic, but usually mild, organic pollution, which may suddenly rise to disastrous proportions in times of drought when the water level is low and the temperature high. The organic sewage is not in itself necessarily very harmful, but it, and the bacteria which flourish in it, make such heavy demands on the dissolved oxygen in the water as virtually to de-oxygenate it, with fatal results to those animals which cannot move sufficiently rapidly to escape into unpolluted waters. When drought conditions supervene, however, the concentration of sewage is increased much above normal, owing to the low state of the rivers, and its rate of oxygen consumption is increased owing to the higher temperatures. As a consequence the harmful effects are both intensified and also spread over longer distances in the course of the streams. The fish themselves may no longer be able to escape and are killed, while animals which might otherwise have provided food for other fishes migrating into the region after the trouble had passed, are also decimated. Industrial wastes, which may be directly poisonous, are fortunately rare in Devon, and the only other serious threat to the rivers comes from the reduction of the flow of many streams as a result of extraction of water at source by domestic water undertakings. Although the amount of compensation water which must be forgone by the undertakings has been very carefully calculated and regulated, nevertheless, the flow of many rivers is but a fraction of what it might be, and in some cases is dangerously low. Moreover, in some cases emergency powers have been taken to reduce the water still further, and there is a danger that what has been done as a temporary measure to meet a sudden and transient demand, may come to be regarded as establishing a precedent for more permanent depredations.

Good fishing for Trout and Grayling is still to be found in Dartmoor streams, some of it being maintained by periodic restocking on the part of conservators or riparian owners. But it is fair to say that the major efforts of those concerned with the fishing are directed towards maintaining the Salmon. As is well known, the Salmon is a migratory fish which spends part of its life in the river and part in the sea. It, therefore, presents the conservator with a more complicated problem than do Trout, which remain within the limits of comparatively short reaches of the stream. Briefly, to summarise the life of the Salmon. The eggs are laid by the hen fish in shallow hollows scooped by the undulations of her tail in the gravelly bottom of a stream, which is often scarcely deep enough to cover her shoulders as she works. The male, or cock fish, swims close beside the hen in an excited state, and exudes his milt over the eggs as they are dropped. Often he may shoulder the female aside in his excitement. Having laid a batch of eggs, the fish moves a short distance upstream and repeats the process, the gravel scooped from the new depression being carried back by the water and covering the eggs already laid. In this manner, an active run of Salmon will seed with their eggs wide stretches of the beds of streams towards the headwaters of the river system which they frequent. The young fish ultimately hatch from the protecting gravel, still with a huge pot-belly in which much unused yolk of the egg is stored. But this is rapidly used up, and after spending some time lurking among the crevices of the stones on the bottom, the young fish become slender, and having now to find their own food, they search actively for the tiny Waterfleas and the like, which abound in the shallows where the fish congregate. They grow rapidly on this diet, and assume a brown, red-spotted coat, as Salmon parr. By the end of their first year they may have grown to a length of several inches. Some now exchange the parr coat and assume the silvery colour of the smolt, at the same time changing their habits and becoming migratory, going downstream with the current and away to sea. The majority, however, defer this change, remaining as parr for a second, or even sometimes a third year before going to sea.

In the sea the young Salmon find much more abundant food than the river provides, and as they grow so they are able to tackle larger and larger prey. They grow very rapidly and become large and power-fully swimming fish, the extent of whose wanderings can still only be guessed at from occasional captures of marked fish at up to 200 miles distant from the estuary by which they entered the sea. After an interval which may be only a few months, or may be as long as several years, some force, presumably associated with the reproductive organs maturing within them, draws them back from sea to the estuary of the same river in which they were first hatched. They enter the river and swim upstream, overcoming all obstacles, until they arrive on the redds, or spawning beds, and in their turn spill their eggs and milt in the gravel to start the whole cycle off once again. Sometimes fish die after spawning, but others may retain their vigour and go down to sea again, to return again and yet again in later years to breed.

Every year, therefore, a crowd of fish assembles in the estuary, and they begin to move into the river and upstream as soon as temperature and volume of water coming down are favourable. Some are grilse in their first year after going to sea as smolts, some are maiden Salmon in the second or a later year after this first migration, while yet others may be older fish which have already made the breeding run on one or more previous occasions. The success or otherwise of their visit depends on their being able to reach the redds and complete their mating there, and in the effort to achieve this they display the most extraordinary patience and persistence. In a time of drought and low water they may be forced to lie below some obstacle, either in the estuary or within the length of the river, and they may be held there for days or weeks at a time. Their spell of rich feeding in the sea has fattened them, and they come in, lusty and brilliant, full of vitality and with plenty of reserve fat stored in their tissues. And well they may

E. H. Ware

Plate 13. Common Buzzard, *Buteo buteo*, on nest in a Scot's Pine

need this vigour, for the consensus of opinion is that, however long they may stay in the river, they do not feed there. The occasional flick at a fly, on which the rodsman's chance of sport depends, is no more than idle toying and has no relation to the serious business of feeding.

An extraordinary feature of this run is that different races of Salmon have inbred in them not only the instinct to return to the river in which they were hatched, but also the urge to return at different, quite specific seasons of the year. Some breeds only enter the river in autumn, run straight up to spawn during November and December, and then slip away again. Others, however, enter the river in the spring and lie about in the pools throughout the summer months before spawning in late autumn. Since the fish in any river are derived from specific parent stocks, it follows that they all behave in like manner, and a river may be described as a spring river or an autumn river according to the date at which the fish return. Frequently, however, the character of a stream may be altered by artificial stocking, with the result that it comes to carry both spring and autumn fish, the one group pertaining to the original stock, the other to that which has been introduced usually by seeding eyed ova into the redds. Of the Dartmoor rivers, the Dart is a spring and early summer stream, the Plym late autumn, while the Teign and the Taw and Torridge carry both spring and autumn-running fish.

The conditions in the River Plym illustrate very strikingly the manner in which far remote factors may operate to affect an animal population. The run here is very late indeed, fish only entering the river in December and January, this being the only time in the year during which it is normally possible for them to move upstream. Owing, on the one hand, to heavy extraction from the headwaters, and on the other to the presence of a weir near the mouth, there is a long stretch of the lower reaches which is too shallow to permit fish to enter it except during the winter rains. As the season for salmon-fishing has closed well before December and does not reopen for another month after the fish have left, the Plym presents the extraordinary spectacle of a salmon river which cannot be fished. Fortunately, such a combination of circumstances is rare, although, as has been indicated, too much water is extracted at source from the streams for the comfort of conservators. The weirs although not infrequent, are rarely very high, and the major obstacles they present are due to reduction of the water level below them. A Salmon in good fettle can make a leap of eleven feet in height, provided the water is not too cold, and the few weirs which approach this height are, as we have seen, provided with passes.

In the face of artificial obstacles to the completion of the Salmon's life-cycle most of the natural threats seem puny. The worst is probably disease. A bacterial affection, furunculosis, suddenly appeared in south-western rivers in 1911, and killed large numbers of Trout, Grayling and Salmon, seriously weakening the run of fish. It now appears to be more or less endemic, but far less virulent than formerly, and although occasional outbreaks flare up, it rarely now takes a heavy toll of stocks. Cormorant, Heron and Otter undoubtedly eat a quantity of fish, although only a proportion of this is Salmon or Trout. The Kingfisher also may be a nuisance in isolated cases by taking the young parr, though this may make little material difference to the population. But, apart from a few isolated exceptions, their depredations are light by comparison with the work of legitimate rodsmen and netsmen, and of poachers, and it is a pity that they are so persecuted.

Leaving now the streams, we may turn for a moment to survey some of their artificial derivatives, the leats. A leat is a carefully engineered side channel which is taken off from the course of a stream, at any convenient point, by artificially raising the level of the water by means of a weir and cutting the side channel to lead off water from the pool so formed above the dam. To-day, leats on Dartmoor do little more than provide a modified ecological habitat. Formerly, however, they served the major purposes of carrying domestic water to some communities, as, for instance, the Devonport Leat and the Prison Leat; or of supplying power to the ore-crushing plant of some mines, such as the Wheal Emma Leat; or, finally, and these almost alone to-day may still be used, of supplying power to the watermills of the lowland country which surrounds Dartmoor, such as the leat already mentioned at Steps Bridge. Most of these cornmills are, however, either going over to power, or have been superseded by the huge mechanical mills of the larger centres of population.

On the open moor most of the leats had to carry water over distances of several miles of rolling country. It follows that they had to be carefully engineered along the contours, so ensuring a gradual but constant fall from their source to their destination. It is not, therefore, surprising that after many years of neglect, following the loss of their function and, therefore, their disuse, the courses of some of these leats have become interrupted, and long stretches may now be dry. The erosion due to weather, to seepage of water from above and below, and to treading sheep, cattle and ponies, has broken the banks in many places and here the water takes the easier course, down the hillside. Elsewhere, silt may have accumulated to such an extent as to choke the watercourse, which now terminates in a marsh. As the mud accumulates so it is colonised by Water Crowfoot, *Ranunculus aquatilisagg*, Starwort, *Callitriche* spp., Water Blinks, *Montia fontana*, and the Pondweed *Potamogeton polygonifolius*. Many other semi-aquatic species root in the mud which accumulates and press steadily outwards from its margins towards the centre of the channel. They are followed by rushes and grasses and other plants which require a damp but firm bed, and so the stream becomes steadily narrowed and its current impeded until, never fast-flowing, it is eventually halted. Beyond the break the channel may continue as a dry ditch, except after winter rains, which may produce a few inches of transient water in a few spots. The condition of the boggy ground which results at the point of stoppage does not differ sufficiently from the natural bogs to warrant our dwelling upon it.

Some leats, however, remain open, and there the water runs steadily and at a moderate pace, and is less subject to periodic flooding than are the streams. For the spate water is carried off for the most part by these same streams and only a proportion is diverted by the weirs. And so, being open and shallow and sunny, they provide excellent nurseries for young trout. Food is abundant, insect larvae, small crustaceans and worms being present in quantity on the gravelly bottom and in the occasional patches of weeds. It is rare, therefore, to cross one of these leats without disturbing a number of young fish.

The pool near Headland Warren House provides a good example of what may happen when an old tin shaft fills with water. This pool is situated just below the road which runs under Hookney Tor towards Widecombe. The whole of this part of the moor has been pitted and scarred by tin workings associated with the Birch Tor and Golden Dagger mines. Some of the effects of these works may be seen in Plates VI and XXIa, pp. 55, 178, from which it may be observed that the Moor escaped comparatively lightly from the blighting influence of its "industrial age." Plate XXI in particular presents a panoramic view of the countryside as seen to the north-west from Grimspound. Deep scars are only too plain on the hillside in the middle distance, immediately to the left of Headland Warren House. The latter may be identified by the dark patch presented by what I have always regarded as one of the most incongruous features to be found on Dartmoor, a pair of Monkey Puzzles, *Araucaria*, in the front garden of the house. The ground between the farm and the road, which may be seen crossing from left to right, has been deeply pitted by old workings, the depth of which is artificially enhanced by the great tumps of spoil thrown out between the pits, and now consolidated and overgrown with heather and bracken. One of these gullies, which probably represents an old shaft, has filled with water which drains into it from a spring emerging from the hillside at its head. This water runs quietly into the pool through a narrow course choked with Starwort, Water Blinks and Forget-me-not, *Myosotis scorpioides*. Having newly emerged from underground, this water is very cool, the temperature at 3 p.m. in the middle of June of 1938, for instance, being only 49 degrees Fahrenheit. Enormous numbers of the little black flatworm, *Polycelis cornuta*, with occasional white individuals among them, are always to be obtained here simply by pulling a handful of the submerged stems of the plants which choke the channel. The pool itself is just over fifty yards long, and consists at its top end of a deep narrow cleft, which shallows and broadens towards the mouth of the gully. In the deep part the surface of the water, except for a narrow central section, kept clear by the current, is covered with the floating leaves of *Potamogeton polygonifolius*, the long stems of which rise several feet through the water from roots in the sides of the cleft. Both stems and leaves are usually encumbered by a pale yellowish green algal scum. The lower end shallows over what is probably partly the natural floor of the mouth of the gully and partly an artificial moraine of granite rubble thrown out during the mining operations. Here the surface is islanded by clumps of rushes and grasses, Starwort and Forget-me-not, and in the centre a small clump of Willows grows, on which, incidentally, I once found a solitary larva of the Lobster Moth, *Stauropus fagi*. The surplus water seeps away over the sill, running down through a small bog on the hillside.

The interest of such a pool resides partly in the fact that it is an isolated body of virtually still water in a countryside where such pools are infrequent, and partly in the fact that the water, having percolated down through the granite, is distinctly less acid than the peaty surface waters of the bogs and streams. The water is mildly acid, showing pH values of 6·0 at the deeper end of the pool, and 6·6 in the shallower parts. A full investigation of the ecological conditions was commenced in 1938, but unfortunately it had to be abandoned, partly because of the advent of war in 1939, with consequent difficulties in finding both time and transport to visit this rather isolated spot, but also because it was discovered by domestic ducks from the farm nearby, and the waters became seriously fouled. Preliminary observations on the fauna showed, however, that it contained species which are not to be found in most of the waters of the moor. Besides Mayfly and Dragonfly nymphs, mostly of species which do occur in the streams, there were several small Haliplid beetles and the Great Water Beetle, *Dytiscus marginalis*, several species of Water Boatmen, Corixidae, and the Back-Swimmer, *Notonecta glauca*. The interesting little Brown China Mark Moth, *Nymphula nymphaeata*, was common, its larvae feeding on the leaves of the *Potamogeton*. It is possible that this moth may be commonly associated with the pondweed which is almost universal in the Dartmoor bogs, but I have not seen it in such quantities as in this pool. On the occasion of one visit the water was thickly sprinkled with minute black specks, giving an appearance almost as if a London " particular " had trailed its sooty skirts across the pool. On taking these back to the laboratory and examining them they were found to be the beautiful little Infusorian, *Stentor caerulea*. Newts, almost certainly the Smooth species, *Triturus vulgaris*, frequent the pond, for their larvae are common among the stems of the pondweed. The adults have not, however, been seen on the occasion of any visit. Frogs, *Rana temporaria*, also visit it to breed in the shallower water at the lower end. They are not always successful, however, for their masses of spawn, deposited in little hollows among the weeds where the water may not be more than an inch or so deep, swell until the uppermost eggs are above the water. Like most of the Frogs in the south-west, they are often stimulated by an early spell of mild weather, and begin egg-laying in early or mid-March. As a result, at this altitude, these exposed egg masses are very susceptible to late frosts, and most of them may be killed. There are, however, usually plenty of tadpoles in the water during spring and summer, thus indicating that the animals are normally successful. The general conditions in the pool are therefore sufficiently unusual in the neighbourhood to merit further investigation, and it is to be hoped than an opportunity may occur to re-open its examination.

The tale of the waters of Dartmoor may be concluded with a brief account of a group of transient, or only semi-permanent, pools in the neighbourhood of Yelverton. There are many shallow depressions in various places over the whole extent of the moors in which water may accumulate for a few days, or weeks, after rain. Some are in the form of basins in the actual rock of some of the tors, others are mere depressions in the ground, and are covered with grass and rushes which can withstand being partially submerged for brief occasions. At most they may support a few Rotifers and the like. On the westward margins of the common at Yelverton, beyond what is now the airfield of Harrowbeer, are a few small ponds, the bottoms of which have become pitted and trodden by ponies and cattle coming to water there. Little vegetation grows here, except for clumps of rushes which may be established on the ridges between the pock-holes, and the substratum of each pond consists of a light, shallow mud overlying a stony bottom derived form the shale of the neighbourhood. The extent of each pond varies widely with the season. In wet weather it may cover a few hundred square feet, and be as much as nine inches or a foot deep in the centre. In a dry season the shallow margins rapidly shrink until only the deeper centre remains wet, and even this may dry out in some years. Comparatively few animals are able to thrive under such conditions, but these include a number of species which are able to remain latent and dry for long periods, and to hatch normally when once again they are restored to water. Of such are many Rotifers and small Entomostracous Crustaceans. Often the water in some of the ponds may be tinged pink with vast numbers of the large Waterflea, *Daphnia magna*, for instance. But the most interesting species to occur here, is the beautiful little Fairy Shrimp, *Chirocephalus diaphanus*. This is a little shrimp-like creature, not more than half to three-quarters of an inch long, and translucent brown or greenish in colour, except for the male in the breeding season, when he assumes a brilliant suffusion of rose and green over the head and anterior part of the body. These animals, which may often be present in large numbers, swim about on their backs by means of rows of leaf-like appendages on the underside of the thorax, and by their presence make a notable addition to the fauna of the waters of Dartmoor.

CHAPTER 10

PREHISTORIC CIVILISATIONS

INNUMERABLE REMAINS of prehistoric occupations of the region are scattered over Dartmoor. Hut circles, stone rows and circles, standing stones, cairns and enclosures are abundant particularly over the western, southern and eastern margins of the Moor, a pattern which suggests infiltration from the southern coastal areas by people attracted to the bold hill-lands rising above the forested lowlands and valleys and seeking there the conditions they needed for their pastoral lives. Bronze to Early Iron Age remains predominate and it seems probable that it was during these eras that the region was most intensively occupied. There is evidence however of inhabitation from at least Mesolithic times onward, that is to say, from approximately 6000 B.C., although none of the cave dwellings or long barrows characteristic of these times have been found. At the other end of the picture we can find hardly any sign of occupation on any scale during Roman times.

The natural characteristics of the Moor have made it very difficult to determine the dates of many remains at all accurately. The shallow soils above the granite preclude the preservation of those successions of layers of deposition which have provided conclusive evidence of cultural sequence elsewhere, while the acid conditions have contributed to the rapid destruction of the metal and earthenware artifacts from which the archæologist expects so many clues. Even those which remain to us must be used in evidence with caution, since so many cultural designs and procedures are preserved by tradition long after the epoch in which they were first created and had their heyday. Should this require emphasis one need only refer to our modern use of iron in fashioning tools such as swords, spears, axes, fish hooks and the like which differ only in details of construction from the equipment of Iron Age man a few hundred years B.C.

Stone Age remains of any period are scanty and consist for the most part of chance finds. Of the oldest, the Palaeolothic, there is only a single white flint "hand-axe" of Chellean workmanship found by Mr. R. H. Worth in 1931 at 1,450 feet O.D. on the watershed between the Erme and Avon near Western Whitbarrow. Evidence of Mesolithic occupation is richer although still scanty. Pigmy flints have been found at Yalland near South Brent, Welstor, north-west of Ashburton, Postbridge and Taw Marsh. Yalland has also yielded a typical rough celt of the period and arrows with unilateral tangs. It seems likely, nevertheless, that Dartmoor would have presented many attractions to these people. We have already seen that it was probably never heavily forested, the original copses such as Wistman's Wood and Black Tor Beare being on isolated hillsides which probably carried then little more forest than they do to-day. As all the evidence points to these people having frequented river banks and open forest clearings and having been unwilling, or unable, to penetrate dense woodland, such conditions would have suited them very well.

The Neolithic people too have left little trace behind them. Flint scrapers, leaf-shaped arrowheads and spearheads of the period have been found, sometimes in such abundance as to suggest settlement. Often a typological mixture occurs among these collections; a group taken from one site and level may contain both tanged arrowheads of Mesolithic type and barbed forms of undoubted Bronze Age pattern. Some of the workmanship is particularly delicate, as for instance in a ripple-flaked lanceolate spearhead found at Cullever Steps on the East Okement and now in Exeter Museum. Polished stone axes from Bovey Tracey, Brent Tor, Buckfast, Moretonhampstead, Princetown, Runnage, Tavistock and Wheal Jewell, for the most part on the southern part of the Moor, are made from flint, diabase, epidiorite and fibrolite, while rubbers and pounders of quartzite and sandstone have been found. None of these materials is native to the Moor; some of the flints are black enough to have come from Beer Head near Sidmouth, some came probably from the coast between Sidmouth and Exmouth, while others may derive from the cherty deposits of nearby Haldon. One site at East Combe near Moretonhampstead yielded so many flint flakes as to indicate that nodules had been worked on the spot. But elsewhere only isolated tools have been found. We may therefore conclude with some confidence that these people either engaged in considerable commerce in flint or, less probably, they travelled widely in order to obtain it for

Plate 14. The Teign at Steps Bridge in spring. Wild daffodils, *Narcissus pseudo-narcissus*, in the foreground; a weir runs diagonally across stream with a scrub-covered talus below it

E. H. Ware

themselves. No pottery of undoubted Neolithic type has been found, probably as a result of the slow dissolutive action of the peaty water upon what there was. Nor have there been found either rectangular huts of the pattern described by Willock on Haldon or causewayed camps like Hembury Fort near Honiton.

These remains of earlier cultures become insignificant when contrasted with those of later times. As already remarked, hut circles, barrows, cairns, stone rows, circles and enclosures are numerous and widespread, indicating a relatively dense settlement of the region. The enclosures, or pounds, are most numerous to the south and west, for instance, in the valleys of the Erme and Avon, this distribution supporting the view that here again colonisation was effected from the more southerly regions and its extent was limited by physical considerations; the northern half and the central mass of Dartmoor are higher, wetter and colder and were covered then as now by blanket bog. They therefore offered neither attraction nor subsistence to man or beast, and the infiltration from the south was halted at this point.

The huts of this period are roughly circular in plan, verging on polygonal where particularly large slabs have been used in construction. The door on one side, sometimes supported by bedded uprights, was some two and a half feet wide and was sometimes approached through a five-foot passage which screened it from the prevailing wind. Internal headroom was increased by excavation of the floor to a depth of between one and three feet, and sometimes a low stone bench ran along one side serving presumably as a seat by day and a head-rest at night. Probably the roof, thatched with heather, was supported by rafters with their ends bedded into the top of the wall and converging centrally. Sometimes they were there supported by a centre post, but often this was precluded by the central position of the hearth and then probably a number of supports was placed in lateral positions. The walls, some three or four feet thick, were of drystone construction with flat slabs lining the inner face and a core of "growan," or granite rubble, filling the interstices.

Settlements were in the form of enclosed pounds or of the open village or farmstead type. The pounds, mostly on the southern and western slopes between 1,000 and 1,300 feet up are particularly interesting, the best known being Grimspound, the Legis Tor enclosures, Erme Pounds and Riders Rings. All present certain features in common; the containing wall usually of drystone work but occasionally of earth, and the presence of hut circles within and often of subsidiary enclosures springing from the walls. These subsidiary enclosures are normally larger than the huts, too large in fact to have been roofed, and it is presumed that they were enclosures within which stock could be confined for protection from marauding wolves and bears and to keep them from straying among the dwellings. Grimspound (Pl. XXIb, p. 178) is perhaps the best known of these enclosed settlements; situated on the saddle between Hameldon and Hookney Tors on land sloping westward towards the Webburn River, it is at an elevation of 1,400 to 1,500 feet. The site is overlooked on three sides and is therefore indefensible, suggesting a purely pastoral function, this being the more readily served since a small stream, Grim's Lake, rises just above it and flows under the wall and down the north-eastern side of the enclosure. The entrance faces south, uphill towards Hameldon, in the direction of a trackway along the ridge, and it may be presumed of the grazing grounds. It is an impressive structure (despite some restoration by nineteenth-century excavators) consisting of a paved passageway ten feet six inches long and six feet wide lined by large granite slabs as it passes through the thickness of the wall. The wall itself is unusually massive, ten to twelve feet thick and built with a core of small stones between two faces of roughly coursed boulders; it probably stood originally about five feet high. There are the remains of twenty-four huts inside mostly of small size (twelve to fifteen feet in diameter) as well as several sub-rectangular enclosures built against the pound wall.

Comparatively little controlled excavation has been made of any settlements on Dartmoor, but during the last decade Lady Fox has conducted two important surveys which have thrown considerable light on the two main types of settlement, the one the enclosed pattern exemplified by the pounds, the particular site being on Dean Moor in the Avon Valley (Fox, 1957). The other is of the village, or huts with fields, type the site being on the slopes below Kestor (Fox, 1954). Lack of space precludes me from discussing these surveys in detail, and I can only refer the interested reader to the original descriptions. Suffice it to say that convincing evidence, from the architecture of the huts and from finds such as whetstones, pottery fragments, a spindle whorl, underground store chambers and the like place the Dean Moor site in the late Bronze Age and indicate a pastoral economy with cattle and possibly sheep (as indicated by the spindle whorl) and some cultivation of grain. At Kestor there is undoubted evidence of iron smelting and working, and again of cattle and possibly sheep, while grain growing is evidenced by the presence of a saddle quern in the huts. This is undoubtedly an Iron Age settlement and it is interesting that pollen analyses of the peat from both sites indicates that they are approximately of the same age and that therefore the "pound" economy of the Bronze Age people overlapped with the more open settlements of the Early Iron Age.

Very few megalithic graves, cromlechs or dolmens, occur on Dartmoor, the best examples being between Coringdon Ball and Brent Fore Hill, as a cairn with the fallen uprights of the chamber, and Spinster's Rock near Drewsteignton which collapsed in 1862 and was reconstructed, the great cap stone being placed upon three uprights, but no record of its original state has been preserved. The common grave upon Dartmoor is a round cairn or barrow without a ditch and covering usually a cremation burial. Two varieties may be distinguished; a large mound forty to eighty feet in diameter, four to ten feet high and often, but not invariably, situated in a dominant position on a hilltop or on the crest of a ridge, and a smaller monument twelve to twenty feet across and about two feet high usually in much the same sheltered zone as was used for the huts and pounds on the hillsides. The remains of the burnt bones of the dead were generally placed at or below ground level in a cist, a rectangular box-like structure of stone slabs, beneath the centre of the mound. In many of the smaller barrows the covering material has been removed leaving the cist exposed, and these are marked as "kist-vaen" on the Ordnance Survey maps. Similarly, large stones bedded at the edge of the mound to form a retaining circle often remain in position when all else has been removed for road-metalling or for wall building; such a ring is frequently erroneously called a "stone circle."

The stone rows which are normally associated with these barrows are numerous and a local peculiarity. They usually consist of two rows of bedded stones extending up to the monument like an avenue, as though making a ceremonial approach. The size of the stones varies, many are small and spaced, and the rows are only moderately straight. Usually immediately adjacent to, but sometimes at a little distance from, the end of the row is a particularly large standing stone, a menhir. Such stones varying between five and eleven feet high may also occur independently of the rows, some being shaped into quadrangular section others quite undressed; Beardown Man is a well-known example of these menhirs. The double stone row or avenue may sometimes be replaced by a single row; the longest known example, the Erme Long Row, is single throughout its length of over two miles. On the other hand, a few triple rows exist, as for instance, one on the east flank of Cawsand Beacon and that illustrated in Pl. XXIIb, p. 179, on Challacombe Down. Confined as they are to Dartmoor where some sixty examples are known, often in aggregations as at Merrivale and Drizzlecombe, they suggest the local development in isolation of a peculiar cult.

The large free-standing stone circles, believed to be of early Bronze Age, are also thought to have had religious significance. Varying in diameter between about 65 and 110 feet, the circles of stones each between three and five feet high enclose a level area within which excavations have revealed scattered ashes and charcoal, but no burials. Modern excavation, however, is still awaited and one can only suggest that they belong to the "Henge" tradition of which Stonehenge and the Avebury circle are so much more impressive examples. The Gidleigh or Scorhill, circle (Pl. XXIIa, p. 179) is a particularly good Dartmoor example, nearly ninety feet in diameter, and the Grey Wethers another rather larger in which two contiguous rings occur, these having, however unfortunately suffered "restoration."

In marked contrast with the abundance of the stone relics, finds of metal and pottery have been very scanty indeed. Such barrows as have been opened have yielded little. The practice of providing for the comfort of the spirits of the dead by burying with the human remains an urn and other grave-goods appears to have been only occasionally carried out. In many interments a few flints and some charcoal alone have been found. Beakers in the fine red ware of the transition period from Neolithic to Early Bronze Age have been recovered from small cairns, cists or barrows at Fernworthy, Watern Down and Langcombe Bottom. One of the most interesting discoveries was in a barrow opened on Hameldon, near Grimspound, in 1872. Here, among fragments of charred bone, which were not placed in an urn, was a bronze dagger with a pommel of dark red amber ornamented with a cruciform decoration of gold studs. It is unfortunate that this dagger, unique upon Dartmoor, was lost when the Plymouth Athenaeum was destroyed during the raids on Plymouth, although, luckily, it had been photographed and a good reproduction of the photograph exists. It was of a type characteristic of the Early Middle

Bronze Age and found along the amber route in Europe, and in England in the Wessex area.

For the most part chance finds have been scattered; a flat bronze axe at Drewsteignton, a spearhead near Blackingstone, two palstaves[1] near Chagford and two others near North Bovey, a ferrule[1] near Postbridge, a rapier near Fices Well, Princetown, a dagger near Shavercombe and another fragment at Fernworthy. The only discovery of anything approaching a hoard on the Moor has been at Bloody Pool, north of South Brent, where in 1854 a group of Late Bronze Age barbed spearheads and ferrules was dug up from beneath the peat. It has been suggested that, rather than being a hoard, this represents the scene of a battle in which Bronze Age men were defeated probably by Iron Age warriors, and their weapons thrown into a pool which has since dried out.

In the huts which have been examined very little has been found; a few flints and fragments of pottery; stones bearing the marks of heating and clustered together in cooking pits; little else. The pottery is particularly difficult to place, largely owing to its extreme fragility, which results from the coarse and poorly binding granite debris used in its composition. China clay, which might be expected to have been in common service in the south-west, has apparently only once been found in use, and then only for patching a vessel which had been broken. Much of the ware can therefore not be securely dated or assigned to any particular culture, although the general impression gained from most of the fragments is of Bronze Age work. Chevron and cordon patterns are common, and rims often decorated with tool- or finger-marks on the edge or the upper surface. Some pieces may be assigned to later periods. Two fragments of a jar from a hut at Foales Arrishes, for instance, bore a well-marked carination[1] on which deep gashes had been cut. These are closely similar to a type of Early Iron Age vessel, as found at Ham Hill in Somerset. At Smallacombe Rocks, near Hay Tor, among other pieces of more definite Bronze Age character, segments of two larger vessels occurred, twelve and fifteen inches in diameter. A similar example was found at Gurnard's Head fort in Cornwall in an Iron Age context. The Smallacombe pieces had broad flat rims and were decorated by means of a twisted cord, the one in chevrons and long lines, the other in crude festoons. It must be concluded that we see here a mingling of the cord and chevron techniques

D.   [1] See Glossary.   L

of the Bronze Age with the loops and festooning of the Early Iron Age. A fragment from Huccaby is also of a typical Iron Age rim profile, but its decoration is obliterated and no conclusion may be drawn from it.

Other remains of undoubted Early Iron Age are scanty on the moor itself. The only find of iron has been twelve currency bars of the metal between two slabs of rock outside the hill-fort in Holne Chase. More recently two Greek silver coins of Alexander the Great and of Aesillas, questor in Macedon in 92 B.C. have been found at a distance of about half a mile apart near Holne village. In conjunction with the hoard of Greek coins described by Shortt in Exeter in the early nineteenth century, and others scattered in the same district, they afford evidence of trade with the Mediterranean at this or later periods by the inhabitants of the southern coasts of Devon.

The terraced fields on the flanks of the Challacombe valley below Grimspound, illustrated in Pl. VIIIb, p. 63, are of doubtful date. They consist of a series of narrow fields, the lower boundary of each being banked above the soil below by earth and stones. The fact that some circular huts are situated on the terraces has been used in support of the idea that the two were contemporaneous, without, however, providing means of dating either. Other opinion is, however, that the fields are of later date than the huts, and although the possibility remains that both are of Bronze Age and the terraces may have been the cornfields of the Grimspound community, nevertheless the consensus of opinion is against this, and a Saxon or medieval date seems the more probable.

Pilkington-Rogers pointed out in 1932 that there is only one Early Iron Age fort on Dartmoor, at White Tor to the east of Peter Tavy, while the periphery is ringed about with camps, situated almost invariably close to fords across the rivers. These are at Okehampton, Prestonbury, Cranbrook, Place, Hembury, South Brent, Borindon, Dewerstone, Tavistock, Brent Tor and Burley Wood. Of these, Cranbrook, overlooking the ford of the Teign at Fingle Bridge, has produced pottery of Iron Age B date. The total pattern suggests the long survival of a remnant of Bronze Age people in the wild remoteness of the Moor, encircled by the fortifications of the later comers on the foothills. The Iron Age hut groups within this ring, previously described, would seem to indicate a slow migration into the highland mass from the south and east and over a long period of time. The whole probably represents the sum total of the penetration of the moor and its Bronze Age population during the five hundred years dominance of the rest of England by Iron Age man. It seems most likely that the worsening climatic conditions of the first millennium B.C. were the main cause which terminated the occupation of the region before the Roman conquest.

In conclusion, it must be confessed that this belief and discontinuous history of primitive man on Dartmoor indicates only too clearly that what remains he has left, and they are many and sometimes unique, still hold much of their secret. Hansford Worth in particular has left us an invaluable survey of what remains are known and his posthumous collected works (R. H. Worth, 1953) will live for a very long time as a standard of reference, to be supplemented by the annual reports of the Devonshire Association's Committee on Ancient Monuments and the publications of the Devon Archæological Exploration Society. Even so there may well be ancient constructions still to be found and recognised; standing stones fall as centuries of weathering and erosion undermine them, and once they are down a covering of gorse or bracken soon overwhelms them until even the largest of monuments may be buried in obscurity. Worse may befall when stones are removed altogether to be used in the construction or repair of a modern wall or even broken up for road ballast. Anyone who has walked over a boulder-strewn Dartmoor hillside will understand how easily the tumbled and desecrated artifact may be overlooked among the natural litter of rocks. Moreover, if modern developers have their way, new threats may arise in the course of the afforestation of more open moorland and the deep ploughing of the peat which accompanies this. Protection is afforded to known ancient monuments, although the provisions of the Act are not always as religiously observed as is desirable. But one cannot protect the unknown nor can one expect the eye of a forester necessarily to detect what has escaped the vigilance of trained archæologists. This must not be interpreted as advocacy of a policy of standstill in relation to all progress on Dartmoor—although there are other and cogent arguments against this particular new development in afforestation. It is, however, clearly desirable that good time and facilities should be offered to archæologists to survey carefully any region on which new planting is envisaged so that a minimum of interference is allowed with any remains which may be there. This is done in the case of all major water undertakings, although granted the effects of these operations are perhaps more drastic and final. Indeed, Lady Fox's excavation of the Dean Moor settlement in the Avon Valley to which reference has already been made, was undertaken precisely because this area was to be inundated by the new reservoir which has since been constructed in the valley.

Setting aside, however, the possibility that some ruined sites still remain to be discovered, it will be all too apparent from what has been said of the known prehistoric remains that we still have much to learn from them. Only a very few have been systematically examined, although a number of them have suffered from uncontrolled, and unrecorded, despoilation and from the misguided activities of "restorers." While much has been learned from what has been done, nevertheless a full survey of Dartmoor's Bronze and Iron Age relics will add inestimably to our understanding of the cultures they represent in a region which, during the Bronze Age at least, must have been a highly active and dominating centre of the population of Britain.

CHAPTER II

DARTMOOR'S HISTORICAL
BACKGROUND

by D. St. Leger-Gordon

W HEN COMPILING the history of a country or district, two difficulties
arise. The first is the precise definition of " history," a term so
loosely interpreted nowadays that it covers material which, strictly,
can only be regarded as fiction. Even assuming history to be the
accurate record of events, there remains the second difficulty of
determining the line between reliable data and tradition. History,
again, concerns, not so much the country itself, as the actions of its
human inhabitants. Thus, the story of a land whose original occupants
have perished may remain static for a long period, and this was
certainly the case with Dartmoor after the passing of the ages usually
known as prehistoric. From this era until the Norman Conquest, there
was nothing to distinguish the region from other unenclosed parts of
Devonshire. Even the long story of the tin—Dartmoor's oldest product
—has no beginning, and in the earliest days certainly concerned
Cornwall. Nothing is recorded of mining operations during the Saxon
period, until the close of which everything may be dismissed in one
word—surmise.

For the same reason that her store of folklore and mythology is
limited, Dartmoor has no place in the category of great national events.
A remote corner of a turbulent land, she stood aloof while dynasties
were overthrown, and rival factions or even invading armies contended
for the mastery of British soil. She sheltered no Alfred, no Griffith, no
Hereward. No historic battle was fought upon her wastes. No opposing
armies manœuvred for the possession of her heights, which, indeed,
commanded nothing of military importance. Her fastnesses harboured
no warlike tribes or robber bands to raid her marches. Dartmoor was

152

too far from the sea to provide facilities for old-fashioned smuggling, too desolate to shelter fugitives, who would merely have starved. The one object of an escaped convict is to get away from the Moor. Semi-historical fiction placed neither a Doone nor a Robin Hood in the Devonshire wilds, and King Arthur with his knights seems to have favoured the western side of the Tamar for his legendary exploits. In war at least, Dartmoor has let and been let alone, and the few British camps upon her fringes suggest " last ditches " of resistance constructed by lowland people, rather than " first lines " for the defence of a mountainous region. Indeed, apart from modern artillery practice and manœuvres dating from 1873, there is nothing to indicate that any part of Dartmoor, as we know it to-day, was ever occupied for military purposes, its possession offering no advantages, strategic or material. It was shunned rather than sought by all alike, and until as late as 1771 the main roads skirted, but did not pierce, this great wilderness of the west.

All considered, therefore, it is not surprising that no mention of Dartmoor as a region appears in Domesday Book, which was mainly a utilitarian survey of the country's agricultural resources. Apart from Manors conferred upon noblemen, all Devon was technically " Forest " until 1204, the area still incorrectly termed " Dartmoor Forest " retaining that status until 1239. It was then ceded by Henry III to his brother, Richard, Earl of Cornwall, when, being no longer actually Crown property, it became in official language a " Chase." This, with its surrounding commons, differed in little material respect from other waste ground, and was ignored as possessing no taxable value. With the possible exception of the so-called " Ancient Tenements," above Dartmeet, first mentioned in 1344, there could have been little cultivation or enclosure, and the omission of these holdings from the comprehensive Domesday assessment casts some doubt upon their supposed antiquity. A good deal of surreptitious squatting doubtless took place among people dispossessed by the Conquest—the displaced persons of the period. Anyhow, whatever the origin of the Tenements, it seems only reasonable to infer that necessity rather than choice induced the first occupiers to enclose and settle upon land so barren.

It is, however, inadvisable to dogmatise where proof is lacking and evidence conflicts. Setting aside controversial questions, there can be little doubt that the deforestation of Devonshire as a whole created the Dartmoor of subsequent days. It marked off the area reserved for the

Crown, and, up to a certain point, imposed a limit upon encroachment. Enclosure or squatting there has been almost until the present time, but only upon a minor scale, an insidious bite here and there, in no way approaching extensive appropriation. Once the Moor, as distinct from woodland, must have covered all high ground almost to the southern sea, Haldon and Woodbury probably marking the limits of the heather country on the eastern side, and Roborough Down on the west. Cultivation has now claimed most of it, but everyone familiar with the area knows how thin is the veneer of soil. When a field lies derelict, gorse, bracken and even heather reappear within a surprisingly short time, for the virgin wild still lurks very near the surface.

Actually, the retention of the Moor as royal property saved it from little more than appropriation in the form of enclosure. Exploited, or utilised—if the word is preferred—it has always been, the formidable nature of the land itself providing the measure of control which up to a certain point has preserved its character. Had it proved suitable for cultivation, larger areas would have been enclosed in the early days. Mining experiments upon a much more ambitious scale were undoubtedly prevented by purely practical difficulties, including expense. Climate, altitude, and other unfavourable conditions have discouraged unlimited afforestation. In spite of these natural restrictions, however, commercial enterprises have been numerous, and the only static periods in Dartmoor's industrial history were those during which there was nothing of marketable value to exploit. Since neither the Romans nor the Saxons concerned themselves much with the tin, this industry lapsed during their occupation, for which reason the early Norman surveyors regarded the country as undeveloped, and, therefore, of no immediate importance.

2

This long inaction seems to indicate that the potentialities of tin as a Dartmoor product had been abandoned, either owing to decreased demand, or to the inability of the earlier inhabitants to extract any more with the primitive means at their disposal. It remained for the later Normans to inaugurate mining, if so it could be termed, as an improvement upon the old method of crude " streaming " which it gradually replaced, although there is no record of the circumstances or date. Information is limited, if not entirely lacking, upon so many points, particularly with regard to Dartmoor's place in early industrial activities.

One reads, for example, that Richard I appointed a new *custos* of the Stannaries of Devon and Cornwall, then combined, and a charter drawn up during his reign is considered to be the first direct official reference to an institution so famous or infamous according to its uses or abuses. It was not until the reign of Henry III that " our forest of Dertymoor " was specifically mentioned in a royal document which authorised miners to take peat, defined as " coal," to heat their furnaces. That the Stannaries of Devon in Richard I's time were mainly confined to Dartmoor is sufficiently certain, however, and also that the industry was well established prior to his charter. The mining history of Dartmoor, as distinct from that of Cornwall, really began when the energetic Edward I severed the connection, created the four Stannary centres, Tavistock, Chagford, Ashburton and Plympton, and sanctioned their separate code of laws, administered by their peculiar joint parliament.

Presumably the earliest tin-streamers collected the metal for their own independent profit, either selling it—probably upon some system of barter—direct to foreign traders, or to collecting agents, just as whortleberry-pickers of the present day sell their fruit to dealers. After their revival under the Norman regime, mining operations were Crown-controlled, and the specially instituted Stannary Parliament acted for the Crown like a modern puppet government, with the appointed Warden as Viceroy. In some respects, this medieval mining must have resembled a twentieth-century state-owned industry governed by a ministerial bureaucracy with totalitarian powers. In general, however, the Stannary Parliament was a unique institution, to be cited as a warning rather than as an example.

Although subject to the Crown, in so far that any Act passed required royal sanction, much of the Stannary legislation was eminently one-sided, demonstrating the extent to which a powerful trade-union-like body, controlling an important industry and upheld by government for reasons of expediency, can tyrannise over a community. For a long while tinners possessed the arbitrary powers taken by modern governments in wartime, entitling them to enter and excavate upon private holdings, even if it meant digging up a man's garden, just as some historic demesne to-day is taken over for surface coal-mining. " Class " legislation was even passed, forbidding any man owning property worth more than £10 per annum to dig for tin, except upon his own freehold, although there appears to be no evidence of this exclusive law being given serious effect. Undoubtedly, however, tinners were highly privileged workers, protected against resistance in any high-handed policy they cared to adopt, and very much a law unto themselves. Inevitably, their practices at last became intolerable, and the Stannary Parliament was eventually deprived of its despotic powers over ordinary citizens and their personal rights.

With all their abuses, however, the Stannary laws at least ensured efficiency within the industry. Appeals against restrictive practices were unnecessary in those days. Merchants had no cause to complain about metal of inferior quality. Negligent treatment or faking of the product was severely penalised, and every man worked for what he earned. All mineral was subjected to the test known as " coining " (from the French *coin*, corner), that is, chipping a fragment off each block, to test its purity. It was then weighed and stamped with the Duchy arms, the ritual taking place in any one of the four Stannary towns, which functioned as customs offices, all metal having to pass through these before becoming marketable. As a further check, the owner of every blowing-house was required to mark each tin block from his furnace with a special brand equivalent to the modern trade mark, unmarked metal being forfeit to the Crown.

The toll levied upon all tin passing through the coinage centres was royal revenue. The Crown also claimed right of pre-emption, or the option of buying any of the metal—presumably at its own price. To avoid these dues a good deal of tin was sold through unauthorised channels and smuggled out of the country. The coinage system was not abolished until 1848, at which period Duchy revenues accruing from mineral sources amounted to anything between £11,000 and £12,000 per annum, the Cornish proceeds being presumably included.

Through its long story, west-country mining exemplified almost every condition under which work can be carried on. There was State ownership in so far that the land mined was mostly royal or Duchy property—synonymous in the main—and the Crown supervised output with a priority right. There was the profit incentive to work, the miner being allowed to sell his produce after the dues had been paid, while free enterprise had its chance, since the owner of any Manor could obtain a licence to exploit his own land for minerals. Compulsory labour was authorised at times of national need, and the introduction of continental miners had precedent during the Tudor period. Early in the nineteenth century the speculator entered the field, to try the effect of deeper mining with more up-to-date appliances, and even, in some cases, to revive the old " streaming " upon a bigger scale. This, however, proved a case of Dartmoor controlling its own resources. The practical difficulties were too great for profitable excavation, and the last serious attempts at deep mining came to an end within living memory.

Viewed as a whole in retrospect, the story of Dartmoor mining resembles that of other industries. From first to last, it was subject to periods of prosperity and depression, due to the requirements of the times, and, more particularly during earlier days, to the policy of the reigning monarch. Dartmoor's special record was mainly concerned with the tin found in its granite formations. Copper-mining barely scratched the fringes, and beginning only in the middle of the eighteenth century, lacked the unique and picturesque atmosphere inseparable from the tinners.

There is a tendency to represent tinners as a race apart, constituting something akin to a warlike and dangerous tribe, truculent and even dangerous if approached. Collectively, they were certainly aggressive, and in the exercise of privileges injudiciously allowed, they must have been more than a nuisance to everybody but themselves. Individually, a tinner was doubtless a simple, harmless Devonian, differing somewhat in dress, less in speech, and very little in character from the turf-cutter whom our parents might have met on the hills. Human nature was much the same when Plantagenet or Tudor sat upon the Throne, and neither character nor outlook changes very much in quiet corners of the world, where time moves slowly. When deeper mining superseded streaming, the primitive streamers turned miners in the more literal sense, and when tin yielded place to copper as the principal mineral product, the tin-miners doubtless became the copper-miners who persisted until half a century ago. The oldest native inhabitant of this moorland village of Sticklepath worked in both tin and copper mines, and probably others live who did the same, particularly on the southern side of the Moor, where mining continued later than elsewhere.

Apart from imported and directed labour, which could never have amounted to very much, and the floating element which mining always attracts, tin-workers were just ordinary country people, then, as now, combining any profitable alternative employment with the primitive agriculture upon which they otherwise depended.

3

Even at an early date, the Moor itself can scarcely have maintained its inhabitants, few as they were, without other means of support. Indeed, since the abandonment of the hut settlements, the wilder parts were more sparsely inhabited than to-day, and the occupiers of the Ancient Tenements and other isolated squattings probably worked as miners, attending to their meagre holdings at odd times. The encroachment of cultivation into the Moor was piecemeal, as in the stock example of the Tenements. Here, upon the death of an occupier, the heirs were entitled to enclose an additional eight acres, if, in Crossing's words, " the father and grandfather of the tenant had held the farm successively."

The same sort of thing went on all round Dartmoor, with or without any recognised precedent, and the worthlessness of many such encroachments is obvious from their subsequent reversion to the wild. The remains of walls indicating long-abandoned intakes often fringe the Common boundaries, and there are few enclosures or settlements actually surrounded by unbroken moorland. A Dartmoor farm or hamlet usually stands at the extremity of cultivation, which may penetrate the Moor, but has an unbroken continuity with the " in-country."

So Dartmoor " farmers," as they are often erroneously called since little of Dartmoor is farmed in the literal sense, are really " in-country " farmers who do not live on the actual Moor, but enjoy the benefit of its pasturage. The twenty-five villages in which the old Venville rights of common and turbary were vested stand near but not on the wastes of rock and heather, for the genuine heather people passed with the prehistoric population.

Certainly, Dartmoor was not always the great public ranch which, in theory if not in practice, it has now become. The elastic and always controversial " Venville rights," like so many old institutions, have no traceable origin. They evolved as the country grew more populous, eventually obtaining recognition in the various charters and documents so often quoted. There is no doubt that originally the potentialities of the Moor were estimated upon a mineral rather than an agricultural basis, even its pastoral value being overlooked. There were fewer cattle and cattle-owners, no teeming national population to feed. Most of the concessions granted upon Duchy land under the so-called Venville system, concerned such questions as the taking of peat and stone and the pasturing of cattle. Minerals, together with " verte and venison," remained Crown property. The Forest was reserved as such mainly for the maintenance of deer, with the essential cover—hence the " verte and venison " proviso—the precise interpretation of which phrase has always been a source of controversy.

The pioneers of farming or ranching were the Cistercian monks, established at Buckfast in the reign of Henry II, and the rearing of sheep or cattle in large numbers was over a long period confined to the monastic establishments. Even so, the extent to which the monks grazed their immense flocks upon ground now classified as Moor is doubtful, as implied by the name given to the area still known as Buckfastleigh, meaning land owned by Buckfast Abbey. Their holdings were considerable, and ample pasturage of better quality than bog and clitter was at their disposal. Until within comparatively recent times, the high moor was not considered good sheep country, and was stocked mainly with ponies, and a limited number of bullocks during the summer months. The old laws of *levancy* and *couchancy* compelled the withdrawal of all beasts between sunrise and sunset, and the right to pasture cattle was subject to the owner's ability to provide for them in winter. Until the first official Perambulation in 1240, there was no distinction between " Common " and " Forest," and no barrier has ever existed to control the movements of animals from one to the other. Thus friction between users of the ground and Crown or Duchy officials has been inevitable all down the centuries, and persists to the present day, mainly for lack of a definite ruling upon simple points—sporting rights, for instance—which should have been clarified long ago.

Whether the actual line taken by the Perambulators—with an obvious eye to the difficulties of the ground—was ever intended to mark a definite boundary across the open moorland, or, as seems more probable, to indicate Dartmoor generally as a " reserve," is a question which nobody can now answer. In any case, the imaginary " boundary" serves little purpose to-day. The lordship of the soil, whether Forest or Common, is vested in the Duchy. The Commoners pasture their cattle, cut their turf or peat, and do virtually what they please on either side of the " line," and matters must have taken much the same course had no division ever been made.

Under almost any system, the gradual development of Dartmoor from a deer forest into the great grazing area that it is to-day was inevitable, such being the most advantageous and, indeed, the only agricultural use to which the country can be put. Even as a deer forest it was not a success. It lay too far from the centre of affairs to provide relaxation for reigning monarchs, who preferred to take their sport in Windsor or the New Forest. Even as many modern foxhunters are shy of the clitters, mires and mists, so royal or ducal stag-hunters found conditions too severe. The deer were maintained *in case*, rather than *because* they were needed for the royal pleasure, and were never very numerous, as few animals can live upon these hills in really hard weather. During harsh winters they raided cultivated land as they would to-day, and as the country became more populous pleas for the extermination of the deer became more frequent. They were practically wiped out by the Duke of Bedford's hounds in the eighteenth century, the last genuine Dartmoor deer being killed about 1780.

For many years afterwards the ponies remained in almost undisputed possession of the hills. Whether originally indigenous or introduced is another question which will never now be answered. Among the earliest records of upland animals in a domesticated state, they are mentioned as " horses," which suggests larger animals. Even allowing for the existence of an original wild stock in any form, a considerable amount of crossing with imported blood must have taken place to produce the Dartmoor pony as recognised to-day. Running free over the moors they required little care, and the coal mines provided a regular market for as many as were reared. The introduction of electricity into many pits gradually reduced the demand and consequently the price, which between the two world wars sank so low that a mare and foal could be bought for 30s. and a young foal for 1s. Export for slaughter offered almost the only market, and although the value of ponies, like everything else, has risen astronomically under modern artificial conditions—at a recent auction a foal realised as much as £27—the complete recovery of their old status seems more than doubtful.

Even before the pony trade almost touched zero, however, the higher financial potentialities of cattle had been realised. When the laws of levancy and couchancy were relaxed, allowing beasts to remain on the Forest during the night, summer grazing for considerable herds became customary, the animals being removed to lowland pastures in autumn. This continued until, with the demands of a steadily increasing population, restrictions as to the number of cattle reared and provision for their winter maintenance gradually slackened, and though never officially abolished, ceased to be enforced. The animals came from near and far. All inhabitants of Devonshire, excepting the parishes of Barnstaple and Totnes, had grazing rights on the Commons, while the Forest was divided into four sections, each under the charge of an appointed Warden empowered to " take in " stock at a nominal rate. Meanwhile, local farmers increased their herds far beyond the capacity of their own holdings. Alien breeds such as the long-horned highland cattle, black Aberdeens and the hornless Galloways—which were most successful in the main—were introduced, until the present situation eventually developed, of a mountainous region perennially stocked and State-subsidised.

It was not until early in the present century, however, that the Moor became, as it is now, primarily a great sheep range. A certain number of sheep had always been kept on suitable ground, but only during summer and within reach of supervision. These consisted mainly of the native breeds, and when the woollen industry was at its height, wool was considered more important than mutton. The big flocks of to-day were unknown a hundred years ago, and their equivalent had not been seen even upon the intakes since the dissolution of the monasteries. The change came with the introduction of the Scottish sheep, which first appeared upon northern Dartmoor—that is to say upon the highest and wildest ground—about 1910. They proved to be animals singularly adapted to the country and climate, and in course of time became almost general. Sheep-rearing—largely of the Scottish breed, but also the Devon long-wool, the Dartmoor, and the " improved Dartmoor "—became the principal moorland industry, if so it could be called, and will doubtless continue under much the same conditions whatever the future holds in store. Upon this general subject, however, more will be said in a subsequent chapter.

4

As already remarked, the inaccessibility of Dartmoor has always hindered its exploitation. Before about 1780, the Ancient Tenements for the same reason represented the only attempts at cultivation within the Moor itself. Again, in medieval times, no roads crossed the waste, no bridges other than the stone " clappers " and cyclopean structures, now preserved as relics, spanned the streams. Communication, even between monastic establishments—the principal centres of commerce —was maintained by rough tracks which can have differed little from the turf tracks of to-day, always difficult, sometimes impassable.

This continued until the end of the eighteenth century, when the present road from Moretonhampstead to Tavistock linked east with west and facilitated new attempts at development A Bill authorising the construction of this road was introduced into Parliament in 1771. It encountered strong opposition—not upon aesthetic grounds, which then were scarcely considered—but as a probable cause of diverting traffic, and consequently trade, from towns on the old highway. It materialised mainly upon account of the vigorous support it received in the House of Lords from the Duke of Bedford, and became established as a macadamised and serviceable thoroughfare in 1792.

Various historians have expressed surprise that the new road did not follow the route already more or less marked by existing tracks. The reasons, however, seem obvious enough. A course suitable for pedestrians or pack-horses is not necessarily the best for wheeled traffic, and the old paths merely followed the most direct way from monastery to monastery. The new road system was intended, not only to cross the Moor, but to provide access to the new settlements, either already in being or under contemplation, on the southern and western sides. The building of Tor Royal was completed by Sir Thomas Tyrwhitt in 1798, and concurrently with his activities, two contemporary pioneers, Gullet and Bray, had been busy converting the gentler slopes of the West Dart into the oasis now known as Two Bridges. Very little of the present Postbridge came into being until a century later, this little outcrop of civilisation being Dartmoor's first taste of the "ribbon development" which has since followed the new roads into so many of her once-lonely stretches.

With these roads began the era of experiments described by Rowe in the supplement to his *Perambulations*, published in 1856. Much of their story is told by the derelict and abandoned workings which tourists, using the same road nearly a century later, observe with mild interest. Principal pioneer of this utilitarian movement was the famous Sir Thomas Tyrwhitt, Lord Warden of the Stannaries, M.P. for Okehampton and subsequently for Plymouth. He is mentioned in every guide-book because inseparably associated with the history of Dartmoor. Upon him must rest, among other things, the responsibility—creditable or otherwise according to outlook—for Princetown Prison, since its erection was due to his tireless inspiration and his influence in high circles.

The settlement which the prison, with its many requirements, brought into being, was named by him after " his friend, the Prince." The work began under Tyrwhitt's supervision in 1806, to accommodate, first French and later, American prisoners-of-war, and his almost obsessional desire to develop this particular locality certainly prompted its selection. For the time being, this purpose at least was achieved. The prison became a centre of commerce, the country-people finding a ready market for their produce among those of the inmates who had any money to spend. When the wars ended, however, so did trade, and it seemed probable that Sir Thomas's prison, together with the " town " which the prisoners had largely built, would head the list of Dartmoor's abandoned enterprises. Then the idea of a penal institution evolved, and in 1850 took the final concrete shape which disfigures the landscape to-day.

The unpopularity of Princetown and its prison is mainly due to its isolation—Dartmoor's characteristic safeguard but also drawback— and to the rigour of its winter climate. In few southern localities does one encounter such bitter rain or icy cold as when even the turbulent Dart freezes from bank to bank. It is the home and rallying centre of the blind moorland mist which also brings Princetown so much into the news, thanks to the opportunities it offers to escaping convicts. The prison has been retained in its present capacity for reasons of necessity alone, and may yet be abandoned, like the old powder-mills near Postbridge, the tin mines at Vitifer and Hexworthy, or ancient Grimspound itself. When eventually discarded as a prison, it can scarcely be converted into a " social " institution, since the same objections apply—with greater force. The only possible use that circumstances suggest would be a summer holiday camp—a gratifying, if somewhat ironical destiny for the most dreaded centre of penal servitude.

Sir Thomas Tyrwhitt did not live to see the prosperity of Prince-town revived by the establishment of its convict prison. He and his kindred spirits were not idle, however, during the years which inter-vened after the restoration of peace. Foreseeing a slump, they decided that the best way to ensure a commercial future for the district was to make it more accessible to development. So evolved the bright idea of linking remote Princetown with the outer world by rail, and this project was adopted by the Plymouth Chamber of Commerce in 1818. The railway was opened five years later, and enthusiastically hailed by its promoters as the beginning of Dartmoor's millennium. More than a railway was required, however, to transform a wild region into a thriving centre of business. Means of transport being provided, it remained to find passengers and goods for conveyance, and to utilise the new line, or to justify its construction, other ventures were started.

Princetown then consisted of about thirty houses. The entire district was still very thinly populated, and the housing problem was not the least of the many difficulties which confronted the disciples of progress. Dartmoor, true to traditional character, refused to be civilised. Few of the enterprises justified the outlay expended upon them, and ten years after the completion of the railway from which so much had been expected, Sir Thomas Tyrwhitt died, an impoverished and disappointed, if not an entirely disillusioned man.

Sir Thomas was not the first pioneer whose " white bones paved the way for others' feet," and his enthusiasm certainly sowed the seeds of later and more profitable experiments. The period over which his direct or indirect influence extended saw the construction of the road and railways, the birth of Princetown, Postbridge, Two Bridges and Tor Royal, and the opening of the granite quarries under Foggin Tor. All these were definite steps along the progressive way, although achieved at the cost of many setbacks and failures.

5

During Sir Thomas Tyrwhitt's regime a great deal of land had been brought under permanent cultivation, and the possibilities of forestry had not been overlooked. He inaugurated the first planting of conifers along the upper valleys of the Dart, with a fair measure of success. Formerly the hillsides had grown little but the stunted oaks, of which Wistman's Wood and Black Tor Copse still provide notable examples.

The early experiments proved that conifers could be grown even on bleak Dartmoor. And still they grow, both in the big afforested enclosures and in little isolated groups or spinneys, to provide shelter for modern houses, although many are warped or wind-bitten. The height attained by the trees, of course, is always governed by their situation, by the contours and altitude of the ground, and, above all, by aspect. Upon northerly slopes they are never so good, deteriorating as the land ascends. Many which may be seen to-day have stood for half a century or more without reaching a height of thirty feet. On bleak ridges, the boles, bowed by the gales, fork at an early stage, and often an old upland larch looks more like a warped oak in its malformation. Indeed, the question of Dartmoor's ability to produce conifers can be answered in a short walk through old plantings. Within a few minutes one may pass from mighty larches or pines whose crowns wave high above stately mast-like trunks, to contemporaries of pigmy Christmas-tree dimensions, whose development has been limited by their position.

The measure of success achieved, however, was enough to encourage further efforts. Periodical plantings during the past hundred years followed the early ventures, and now extensive afforestation covers areas of original moorland, particularly in the Postbridge district, with Fernworthy as its northern limit. The main acquisitions now extend over a rough triangle formed by lines drawn from Postbridge to Princetown, and from Princetown to Laughter, a total of 5,000 acres being the present estimated aim of the Forestry Commission.

In the meantime, while one government department was bent upon planting, other possibilities had not been ignored. The suitability of northern Dartmoor as a military training ground was obvious, and late in the last century the wild hills suffered yet another indignity in the building of Okehampton Camp, with all its unsightly accessories of flag-staffs, range-indicators, danger-signal boards and splinter-proof shelters. The latter alone, of all the military paraphernalia, soon mellowed into not unpicturesque features of the landscape. At first, both camp and artillery range were used for summer practice only, but in course of time the camp became recognised as a necessary, and from some points of view, not undesirable perennial institution.

Trade always follows the troops, and although moorland villagers complained that artillery practice, by denying access to parts of the Moor, would deter many visitors, actually more lodgings were let to families and friends of army personnel than would ever have been booked by ordinary holiday-makers. When, after the First World War, a rumour arose that the range was likely to be abandoned as not sufficiently extensive for modern guns, it was greeted with dismay rather than relief.

Neither range nor camp were abandoned, however. On the

contrary, the range was extended to meet growing requirements. Originally, about half the area north of the Moretonhampstead to Tavistock road was affected, with long-range guns posted on Blackdown or Halstock reaching to Hangingstone, and machine-gun fire covering much of the ground between Willsworthy and the Tavy. Practice took place on five days of the week during the summer months only, and apart from the shell-pits—mostly in peaty soil where they soon resembled ordinary bog-holes—the defacement was not extensive.

The splinter-proof shelters were connected by roughly-cut tracks which the moormen found useful for their turf-carts or for driving cattle. Later, when motor-lorries began to supersede horse-drawn vehicles for all forms of military transport, these tracks, once little better than water-courses, were converted into serviceable roads. Their surface, being mainly sand dug from the hillsides, readily washed away, but was as readily restored, and their repair proved a source of employment for local labour. New roads also were cut, until an elaborate system traversed the ranges, which for the first time became accessible to private motorists. During week-ends and in autumn after artillery practice had ceased for the season, these moor-ways were as populous as any country side-roads, the great attraction being Cranmere Pool, which could now be approached to within a short distance by car.

These conditions prevailed until, once again, " war's loud summons shook the land," and, almost literally, wild Dartmoor. During the 1914-18 war the ranges were little used. Gunners learned their craft by actual experience, firing at the enemy instead of artificial targets. From 1939 onwards, however, all this was changed. First British, then Dominion and, finally, American forces trained upon Dartmoor. Artillery, machine-gun and aircraft practice monopolised the ranges, winter and summer, with short interludes, for seven days a week. The requisitioned area was extended in all directions. Flag-staffs appeared on Cosdon Beacon, Waterton and remote Fur Tor, to mention only a few of the new erections. The central moor became a hive of military activity, operating as far south as the heather wastes of Holne. Only the fringes remained unaffected.

For the time being, these conditions were regarded as temporary, to meet the national emergency. When hostilities ceased, however, much of the newly requisitioned ground remained under the control of the War Department. The advantages of the Moor as a permanent

Plate 15. The River Walkham in autumn

training ground had been realised, and then arose one of the most bitter controversies associated with Dartmoor's history—bitter, at least, as far as the local population was concerned. Sheep and cattle-owners visualised a drastic curtailment of their " rights "; hotel proprietors and shopkeepers welcomed the prospect of augmented trade, while ramblers and antiquarians feared the loss of amenities and the probable destruction of ancient monuments and features. The dispute took the inevitable course. Numerous arguments—many sound, as many specious—were advanced in an effort to preserve the Moor in its entirety, or at least to confine military exercise within the original area.

The issue was no less inevitable. Resulting from a public inquiry, some modification of claim was made by the authorities, while Dartmoor surrendered yet one more bite to feed the ever-growing utilitarian giant. The outcome of it all was that the area which the War Office retained amounted to 32,800 acres, the public being excluded from 29,000 acres, at least during practice. This, roughly, amounts to about one-quarter of the entire Moor, including much of its wildest and most attractive country.

6

Dartmoor, all down the centuries, has been to all intents and purposes, everybody's ground, offering scope to the early squatter, the miner, the speculator, the political economist, the enterprising and optimistic agriculturist. Being the principal watershed of the south-west, its utilitarian possibilities in this respect were first recognised by Sir Francis Drake, who, by way of his famous leat, brought the earliest public supply into Plymouth. As the populations of southern towns increased, centuries later Drake's example was followed upon more ambitious and modern lines. Burrator, the first big Dartmoor reservoir, was completed in 1898. It impounded the upper waters of the Meavy, and in 1907 was followed by Vennaford, or Wennaford, on Holne Moor, fed by the Vennaford brook, to supply Paignton. Hennock reservoir, built by the Torquay Corporation, can scarcely be regarded as Dartmoor, although a conduit from the Moor provides some of its water. Again, the recently completed reservoir at Fernworthy actually flooded, not moorland, but a freehold farm. Since it contains nothing but moor water, however, provided by the South Teign, and is bounded upon two sides by original moorland, it has been hailed as Dartmoor's latest and most "natural" lake—if any expanse of water artificially confined can be regarded either as a "lake" or "natural." Picturesque, Fernworthy reservoir has certainly become, flanked, as it now is, by afforested hills, and since it has made no real encroachment on Dartmoor's dwindling acres, it offends no aesthetic considerations.

During the mining period and the wool boom, there were few moorland streams which did not provide water-power for industry in some shape or form. Almost every brook worked its mill upon reaching an inhabited level, while refuse from the tin-streaming at times constituted a nuisance. On the Tavy and the Walkham, out-of-date activities have given place to more modern manufacturing plant, and much of the flood which once descended the long gradient of Tavy Cleave with such spectacular effect has been diverted to generate electricity. Within living memory, two of the largest water-wheels in the country overlooked the upper Taw valley at the point where this picturesque north-flowing river leaves the Moor, and in the adjoining village of Sticklepath, Taw water still operates one of the few remaining iron smitheries—almost the sole surviving example of Dartmoor's bygone industry. The river Taw, however, together with its smaller sister stream, the Okement, has for some time attracted attention as offering scope for the most ambitious water scheme ever attempted in connection with Dartmoor's vast potentialities.

In 1937, a Bill—the second of a similar nature—seeking powers to dam the great natural basin of Taw Marsh, failed to obtain Parliamentary sanction. The effort was made by a private company and encountered strong local opposition. A later scheme, sponsored by Devon County Council, has been more successful, and in course of time, various undertakings devised by the North Devon Water Board will convey piped supplies of water to big areas of the country, along routes other than those which Taw and Okement waters have followed since time unknown.

So once again, the grasp of the utilitarian tightens, for the public benefit no doubt, but, as ever, at Dartmoor's cost, since any innovation cannot do otherwise than spoil wild country. And while Government Departments and private speculators compete for facilities to develop or exploit the Moor's resources; while the Forestry Commission requisitions land for planting, the War Office extends its operations, the Board of Agriculture subsidises cattle-breeders to augment flocks and herds already too numerous; while streams are drained to provide water elsewhere, or to generate power, yet another use for this remote but hard-pressed area is under consideration.

The possibility that Dartmoor would end its story as a National Park "for all time" has figured in every proposal for its future advanced within the past half-century. This was vigorously urged during the controversy over the extent of military acquisitions, when it seemed probable that the project would take definite shape in the near future.

At any rate, Dartmoor was one of the areas recommended as National Parks by the National Parks Committee, and became one in 1951; and the only question that really remains is the effect of semi-nationalisation upon country as yet so little altered by progress. The great wild Moor with its stern beauty and grey antiquity is something more than an open space for "air and exercise," and the original idea of preserving the region unchanged as a monument to vanished conditions appeals most strongly to those who know it best. The old is not always better, but it is a wise policy to leave well alone, and if Dartmoor as a National Park had meant Dartmoor saved from further exploitation, its conversion could have been regarded with more satisfaction than is now possible.

As Crown land, Dartmoor's relation to the Law of Property Act has been challenged. At the same time, no zealous Commoner willingly admits the sovereignty of the Duchy, unless some advantage is attached to the recognition. To a stranger, therefore, the position may well seem anomalous, procedure upon the commons at least being subject to no apparent control. Is, one might ask, any collective jurisdiction exercised over a Common by the parish to which it is nominally attached? If so, why are practices allowed of which the greater number of parishioners disapprove? Why, for instance, is the beauty of the Moor destroyed each year by foolish and more often than not actually harmful heather-fires? The answer lies in the popular and elastic interpretation of the term "common rights," or rather, in the case of heather-burning, in the warped conception of a right, for the most part wrongly assumed and generally misused.

In law, vague and unsatisfactory at best, a "Commoner," defined as a householder and therefore ratepayer, may burn gorse and heather for pasturage or any practical purpose, such as turf-cutting. He may not authorise anybody else to do it, nor does the right extend to other members of his family. Under no circumstances are children or youths entitled to ignite a bush. None the less, this distinctly limited " right " has degenerated into the practice of indiscriminate burning for amusement in which village youths and schoolchildren freely indulge, whenever and wherever the fancy takes them. This is not only a source of constant annoyance to responsible people, but it frequently endangers private property, as proved by the numerous calls upon the fire services recorded in the local papers, and occurring principally during weekends, when most wanton mischief is done. The custom, incredible to anyone who does not know Dartmoor, might well seem too pernicious to be tolerated. And pernicious it is considered by most people. Among the householders of this village, four to one favour drastic control, which, none the less, they are powerless to impose, since no law specifically *forbids* the practice. The efforts of village schoolmasters and others to curb the children are offset by a few intransigent parents who, clinging to the fetish of " Common rights," encourage their assertion to palpably absurd lengths.

A few years ago, I was walking on a Common with the chairman of the Parish Council. Some boys appeared, and before we realised what they were doing, had quite openly lit several fires. The representative of parochial law naturally asserted his authority by forbidding further ignitions. For this, however, the children cared nothing, and even disregarding the menace of his brandished walking-stick, merely ran to a safe distance and lit more fires.

Every child and almost every adult enjoys a blaze, and that is the real reason why so much heather, unfit for burning, is set alight. Too often, even the stolid sheep-farmer cannot resist putting a match to " a piece that will run." He can always argue that he is " making pasturage," such being the rock upon which the ships of logic and reform invariably founder. It is the child's excuse, the man's pretext —although he may have no animals to pasture—and in general, the justification of much that is unjustifiable. There remain many issues; the distinction between swaling to provide grass and indiscriminate destruction; the inequity of one man being allowed to burn, for amusement, vegetation that another needs for grazing or shelter. In all such matters a reasonable policy, based upon practical values and common sense, could easily replace the muddled thinking and disorder which misgoverns procedure upon Dartmoor to-day.

7

In an age at least nominally realistic, common rights should no longer be a matter of controversy, maintained by archaic proceedings such as " beating the bounds," almost the last of the old parochial rituals still more or less seriously observed. This custom, of course, is a perambulation of the parish boundaries, which upon the Moor are often as undefined as that which divides Forest from Common, and for practical purposes as unimportant, under existing conditions. It takes place at seven-year intervals, and during the walk, representatives of adjoining parishes, each in turn, adjust landmarks, according to their ideas or supposed interests. Wherever possible, also, regulations imposed by the Duchy of Cornwall are infringed upon principle. For example, guns are discharged and fires are lit. The proceeding is regarded as an assertion of *rights* by the practice of *rites*.

When the party reaches a certain " bond-mark," it is still customary for the oldest man to turn the youngest boy upside down and tap his head three times upon the top of the stone, the idea being to impress the exact position of the boundary upon the rising generation. Whether the inverted posture was originally symbolic of the non-progressive outlook upon such matters then deemed desirable, is a point which tradition has not elucidated. However that may be, zeal to preserve parochial territory at times outweighs logic and sense of proportion.

A resident in this village once planted a few unsightly yards of derelict wayside ground adjoining his entrance with ornamental shrubs, mainly to screen the litter which passers-by habitually deposited there. The shrubs were torn up by inebriated members of the next bounds-beating party, the argument being that they monopolised public land for the improvement of private property. Rent had actually been paid to the parish for use of the ground, which in all did not amount to more than a couple of square rods. To its continued use as an unofficial rubbish-tip no objection has ever been raised.

Obviously, the attitude towards individual appropriation of common land cannot always have been so pronounced, or little of the ground originally acquired by squatting would ever have been " taken in." The tiny enclosures which surround the Moor, decreasing in size as the slopes ascend and the soil becomes more rocky, testify to the constant nibbling which went on until the practice was finally abolished. Anybody who had acquired a few rough fields sought to increase his holding by extending a wall to include another corner, or to make a fresh bite into the hillside, insignificant in itself but insidious. A stranger is often impressed by the worthlessness of these little intakes, sometimes comprising no more than an acre or so of rocks which nowadays would never repay the cost of fencing. The acquisitive instinct was strong, however, and in those times sympathy was always on the side of the squatters.

Any ground that could be appropriated was not regarded as filched from common land, and therefore from the local community, but as something wrested from the Duchy or Crown. In other words, to enclose moorland and if possible to keep it, began to be considered as yet another " right " which anyone might have the opportunity of exercising at some time. It was a practice to be supported rather than discouraged, like the despoiling of stone circles and other ancient monuments to provide materials for walls and gate-posts.

Even as during wartime or similar circumstances there are always offences for which no jury will convict, fearing possible inconvenient repercussions, so commoners of all periods have connived at practices which anyone upon some future occasion might desire to emulate. An old convention which must have operated more frequently in theory than in reality entitled any man to appropriate as much ground as he could enclose within one day, defined as " between sunrise and sunset."

This convention, or mere " belief " as Crossing described it, had no traceable legal foundation unless in the elementary law of which possession constitutes nine-tenths. To eject a man from a holding upon which he is once established has always been and still remains a matter of some difficulty, as proved by the numerous recent instances of " squatting " upon State property. To prevent a *fait accompli* would therefore have been the object of everybody disposed to resist the encroachment, and rapid work to evade prevention correspondingly essential on the part of the squatter. His activities could scarcely escape notice for more than a day or so, and probably the time-limit enforced by necessity eventually became the rule more or less accepted by custom.

Since " enclosure " apparently meant the erection of a genuine fence, as distinct from the mere marking of a claim, and the undertaking imposed a further condition that a habitable dwelling must be built upon the ground within the same period, little value, one might think, could have attached to such a privilege. Effectually to fence an area the size of a tennis court and build a serviceable hut upon it within twenty-four hours would defy the ability of any man single-handed. To achieve the otherwise impossible, however, friends and relatives of an aspiring squatter assembled in force upon an arranged date, and by collective effort contrived to comply with the letter of the requirements.

Stories reminiscent of the *Arabian Nights* are told about holdings created faster than a mushroom could grow, and even allowing for inevitable embellishment, they are not entirely fictitious. Tourists are still shown a cottage near Hexworthy representing the last of these one-day erections. In this case, the right or claim was not officially allowed, a nominal rent being subsequently paid to the Duchy by the squatter. Appropriations of this kind were carried out by force of numbers, partly, as already remarked, in order to conform with requirements, but also to overrule opposition, not so much from other commoners as from the authorities. To fulfil even the letter of the law, if so it can be termed, many hands must have been required, as well as considerable preparation in advance, and unless the squatter's personal following was numerous enough to constitute a veritable clan, little could have been accomplished without fairly general local co-operation, active or passive.

To circumvent authority in high places was always the primary object, and this attitude was demonstrated when, late in the past century, the Duchy took action against some fairly extensive attempts at encroachment upon the South Tawton commons. The parishioners literally rose in arms, not to save the ground from annexation by private persons, but to oppose the Duchy's authority to prevent enclosure. In this case, somewhat similar to that of Hexworthy, the squatters eventually bought the land at a nominal price, and everyone was satisfied. The position of the Duchy as lord of the soil had been further strengthened; the commoners had experienced the gratification of once more opposing the Duchy and so perpetuating the immemorial conflict of claims; while the squatters retained the land they had enclosed, or, as the commoners regarded it, wrested from the Duchy. That it really amounted to so much common land being lost to the parish, and that the real " common " interest would have been better served by supporting the Duchy, were points overlooked in an issue characteristically confused.

This incident marked the end of enclosure for private purposes upon northern Dartmoor, and the attitude of the parishioners in this matter differed curiously from that displayed towards the planting of a few shrubs on a little wayside corner. Some knowledge of rural mentality—or the mentality peculiar to Dartmoor people—is necessary before one can appreciate the subtle distinction between the two situations.

Upon various parts of the Moor, remains of walls and banks which serve no present purpose may be traced. Where these coincide roughly with the recognised boundary between Common and Forest they are usually regarded as evidence of old barriers designed to separate two areas, and subsequently breached. Since neither the parishes nor the Duchy could have benefited from any such divisions, however, they clearly have some other origin, although here again history and legend are inextricably mingled.

Most typical, perhaps, is the *Irishman's Wall*, near Belstone, said to be a relic of an unsuccessful attempt at enclosure, contemporary with the early activities of Sir Thomas Tyrwhitt and his associates elsewhere. The wall, the building of which must have been a notable accomplishment, stretches across the Belstone ridge from the Taw river to the East Okement, reaching the latter stream near its confluence with the Blackaven. It then follows the Blackaven, at least in fragments nearly to the source, connecting with banks which cross two intervening heights to rejoin the Taw valley. Local tradition ascribes its origin to the ambitious efforts of two Irishmen who, together with a gang of their countrymen imported for the purpose, set out to enclose some 2,000 acres of Forest, and had made good headway when obliged by active local opposition to abandon the work.

As usual, the story lacks any sort of reliable confirmation, and has its obvious weak points. The magnitude of the alleged attempt presupposes that such a task would never have been undertaken without the necessary authority. This could easily have been obtained from the Duchy of Cornwall at a time of general exploitation and experiment, when the reclaiming of moorland was regarded favourably in influential quarters. Since Crown land, and not common, was concerned, unauthorised acquisition upon such a scale could not have passed unchallenged, while the solid character of the work, as apparent to-day, in no way resembles or suggests that of adventurous squatters whose position was at best uncertain. The well-built wall, with its long

Plate 16. Trenchford Reservoir (Kennick) in light snow

extensions reaching back towards its starting point, obviously represents the labour of years, and its true history, if known, would probably be far more interesting than the local version, into which an element of fiction has inevitably crept.

However that may have been, the " Irish " tradition, commonly accepted as gospel, is quite accountable upon other than historical grounds. Owing to the predominance of Irish labour in the mines, the term became symbolic of anyone from overseas, and, by association, of wild or lawless behaviour generally. The mining village of South Zeal, notorious for high-handed conduct, was known as " Irishmen's Town," and irregular proceedings were automatically attributed to Irishmen, even as " boys " are blamed for a plundered orchard as a matter of course. The dubious character of any venture was quite enough to suggest " Irish " complicity, and suggestion is the father of many " old tales."

Of all this Ethel Lega-Weekes, writing in the *Transactions of the Devonshire Association* upon an entirely different subject, provides unintentional confirmation. She records that as long ago as 1463 an unsolved murder at Tawton Fords in the same district was ascribed to " one, John of Ireland," whose actual existence as an individual could not be established. It might be interesting to add that in some parts of England the country name for fairies is " Irishmen," and speaking for Devonshire, at any rate, the mere introduction of the word into a story renders that story suspect.

In conclusion, and returning to the more general subject, I should perhaps emphasise my previous statement that Dartmoor people are not usually hostile to outsiders of Irish or any other extraction. The convention that " they may quarrel among themselves but heaven help the stranger " entirely lacks foundation. As a general rule, even parochial jealousy does not extend to their most cherished privileges such as pasturage, sporting rights—where any exist—or to the picking of whortleberries. Cattle and sheep wander freely across parish boundaries, and people cut turf or pick whorts indiscriminately.

Occasional disputes arise, of course. Exception may be taken to wandering gipsies whose acquisitiveness in the matter of wild fruit leaves very little for residents. I once heard an acrimonious discussion between two old village " toughs," both of whom claimed the prior right to cut a certain patch of bracken for cattle bedding, and an interesting case on the question of pasturage was recently taken to court. Damages were claimed against a man whose ponies, entitled to graze upon West Down Common, had "trespassed," in legal phraseology, upon the adjoining Roborough Down. For the defendant, the right to pasture cattle upon either Common was pleaded "per cause de vicinage" (by reason of vicinity), and the arguments ploughed through the old grounds of "ancient privilege" upon which, as often as not, no definite ruling exists. Judgment was given for the plaintiffs (Roborough Commoners), the defendant later appealing successfully against the decision. The case was mainly interesting as an example of the various constructions that can be placed upon Common rights and their interpretation when subjected to the test of actual law. Were legal proceedings the rule rather than the exception, the general position upon Dartmoor to-day might be very different.

CHAPTER 12

DARTMOOR PEOPLE— THEIR CUSTOMS
AND SUPERSTITIONS

by D. St. Leger-Gordon

I ONCE KNEW a farmer who could beat off the attack of an angry bull with indifference, but was nervous on a lonely road in the dark. Similar inconsistencies are common enough in individual or national character, in conventions, or in the fashionable outlook of the period. We live in a scientific age, and memory need not travel back over more than a generation or so to recall the rejection of many old notions in the coldly naturalistic light of research. But beside the nettle usually grows its antidote, the dock, and while myth after myth disappears with increasing knowledge, the popular taste for fantasy and superstition—such as the horoscope or trite ghost story—gathers strength to oppose the scientific trend.

Dartmoor, one might think, should be the home of romantic legend. The wild grotesque hills and coombes, rich in relics of prehistoric life and suggesting untold stories of vanished peoples, might well have evolved a mythology of their own. Nature, again, has provided abundant material in the ghostly, baffling mist, the will-o'-the-wisp, and the curious effects which in certain lights distort perspective and bewilder the novice. There is ample material upon which the primitive imagination might have worked, yet none of these things appeal to the native mind with enough force to bear the fruits that might have been expected.

Concerning the ancient inhabitants, there survives no fable, no eerie tale to stiffen the hair of the turf-cutter or moorman returning after dark past the old hut-circles or some even more suggestive ancient burial place. To the country-people, stone circles and kistvaens have suggested nothing more than a source from which granite gate-posts might be filched whenever possible. Even the historic moorland tracks, trodden for centuries by wayfarers as varied and picturesque as those who used the road to Camelot, have gathered scarcely a ghost story, and certainly no ghost that has troubled the countryman for many a long year. The romantically minded visitor, or the topographical writer in search of local colour, is far more interested in such things than is the native. The folk-lore of the district has been mainly preserved and passed on by means of guide-books and other descriptive writings. It would probably be no exaggeration to say that most of the genuine Moor people live and die without ever hearing the legends in which they are supposed to be so deeply versed.

During the last war one read frequent serious references to Drake's drum, but it is not difficult to imagine the reply of an ordinary Plymouth-born rating if asked whether he knew the sound of its ghostly roll. The modern seaman is familiar with Drake's statue on Plymouth Hoe, or at Tavistock, knows him in song, and in recent years may have read about the drum. There his knowledge and certainly his interest would end, however, and the attitude of the moorland people towards the Benjie myth of Cranmere Pool, or Lady Howard's phantom coach on the Tavistock to Okehampton highway, would be very similar.

Comparable with the " Drake's drum " revival is the modern pixy mentality, that being the only expression applicable to the repopularised idea that the primitive Devonian still believes in the " Little People " of the hills. Certainly the pixy is inseparable from Devonshire folk-lore. But here again, convention is as far removed from reality as is the moorman's belief in any kind of sprite. He has at least heard of the pixy, but only in the way that he has heard of Santa Claus, and through the same channels. Indeed, he probably took Santa Claus much more seriously, and retained his faith in the ancient Christmas benefactor considerably longer. The age of the pixy receded like the rainbow with attempts to establish contact. Research would probably elicit that the grandparents of each successive generation believed in pixies until the patriarchs of the Stone Age repudiated such credulity. As for the present outlook, village children scoff at, and the oldest inhabitants definitely resent, the romantically-minded visitor's questions as reflections upon their intelligence. More than any other country myth, pixies have been kept alive to make " atmosphere." It is the visitor, not the native, who talks about them, the " arty-crafty " shop which sells " pixy bowls " and other knick-knacks, and the newcomer who

Plate XXI a. Looking north-west over Grimspound. A hut circle in the foreground, with the retaining wall of the pound beyond. Headland Warren Farm with its Araucarias in the middle distance, with the hillside to its left scarred by tin workings

     b. Grimspound, the main gateway

Plate XXII a.   Gidleigh stone circle

      b.   Challacombe triple stonerow

names his equally new bungalow " Pixy Dell." The pixy, Drake's drum, Childe the Hunter, each and all belong to a world which the rural mentality has outgrown. It is the natural, the tangible world of which the countryman thinks and talks.

The stories really told around cottage or farmhouse hearths—and I have heard a good many—deal with country life, sport, actual experience and adventure, and certainly not with anything of a legendary character.

2

The same lack of a legendary background is noticeable in the songs of the district. Rather, perhaps, it is reflected in the exceedingly meagre musical store. Apart from *Widecombe Fair*, and the *Tavistock Goosey Fair* ditty—which is more or less a variation of the same theme—there is no outstanding Dartmoor song. Our village patriarch, mentioned before as having once worked in the old tin and copper mines, was a popular vocalist at country-inn evening gatherings. Even in those old mining days his repertoire consisted of Irish—not Devonshire—ballads, and that is typical in the main.

One might live for many years in the Widecombe district without hearing one bar of the song which has made that village famous. Excepting radio presentations, during a thirty-year residence in the locality, I have heard *Widecombe Fair* once only. Upon that solitary occasion, the original version—differing considerably from that in common circulation—was sung to me, unaccompanied, by a son of the man from whom Baring Gould first obtained it.

Widecombe, indeed, eminently typifies the atmosphere that popular song or story imparts to the place associated with it—an association of this kind being more pronounced as a rule than any genuine historical connection. A few years ago a leading London newspaper published a correspondence in which various colleges claimed the distinction of having graduated Sherlock Holmes. A Dorsetshire house is pointed out to tourists as that in which the equally fictitious Tess of the D'Urbevilles passed her wedding night, and similarly, the ghost of a name has invested the remote village of Widecombe with an attraction which the genuine homes of either Drake or Raleigh have failed to provide.

Apart from his double appearance in the chorus, it is difficult to imagine why Uncle Tom Cobleigh—not even the central figure of

D   N the song—should have achieved particular immortality. There is no apparent justification for connecting him with Widecombe over and above the " all " who made up the unlucky party. Even assuming a foundation of fact, or that the original song commemorated some mishap which overtook a tipsy cart-load visiting the fair, the Tom Cobleigh, generally assumed to be the individual included in the verse, never *lived* at Widecombe. Even in the rhyme he was merely *going* to the fair, as hundreds still go to-day, attracted by an association not even justified in the song.

The actual identity of Uncle Tom Cobleigh and his connection with the song are questioned by the descendants of the only man who in real life could have fitted the part. He lived and died many miles from Widecombe, and lies buried in the comparatively unknown churchyard of Spreyton, where few of the tourists who succumb to the magic of his legendary exploits have ever thought of visiting his grave. There is no reason why anyone should, since during his lifetime Tom Cobleigh was a person of little significance. Yet thousands of people flock to Widecombe to stare at imaginary souvenirs of this same undistinguished personage who may or may not have fallen out of a cart after once visiting the place as one of a crowd. Neither Colebrook, the reputed Tom Cobleigh's native hamlet, nor the picturesque old Belstone farmhouse where the original song was first set upon paper by Baring Gould, attracts the visitor. Nor is this surprising, for the wonder of the mirage does not extend to the objects that it reflects.

3

Returning to genuine folk-lore, it is more than doubtful whether any labourer on the Oxenham lands has ever heard of the " white bird " any more than the Yorkshire miner is familiar with Barguest, the phantom dog of the North-country.

Although unversed in local folk-lore, however, unsophisticated Dartmoor people certainly were superstitious until comparatively recent times, and pronounced traces of this tendency still linger among the older folk. It is disappearing fast, of course, and now the middle-aged villager recounts the ideas and beliefs of his parents with amused tolerance.

A few years ago, I was discussing the problem of an overgrown hedge, bounding a Dartmoor common, with the owner—an old lady who was unable to keep it cattle-proof. It carried a lot of heavy wood, and I suggested that some local hedger might be glad to cut and layer it for the fuel. She replied that none of her neighbours, most of whom belonged to her own generation, would burn the wood, as it was mainly elder. By way of contrast, I recently saw two younger men cutting a hedge much of which was also elder. To test their reactions, I remarked that elderwood on the fire was supposed to be unlucky. The answer from one of them—and he is primitive enough—was brief and to the point: " Gar! An old tale that is! " Yet it was well within his own time that both elder and mountain ash were carefully excluded from the faggots and left to rot where they lay, since upon no account could they be taken into the house.

The example of the elder is typical of old country superstition. It had nothing to do with phantoms or legends, but bristled with omens and portents, inhibitions, procedure to counteract ill-luck, charms and conventions. It comprised all the stereotyped signs of good or bad fortune, which, being in no way peculiar to Devonshire, need not be enumerated. For that matter, very few superstitions are purely local; most of them are common to many districts, and, one might also say, to many countries. Their interest lies in their survival, however modified, in the face of a materialistic outlook, and not least, in the stubbornness with which they have persisted until the present day. The unlucky third cigarette—a product of the First World War—is no more logical than the old-fashioned housewife's fear of washing blankets in May.

In the *County Book of Devonshire*, I described the prevalence of this idea among all classes. Since writing that account, other examples have come to light, illustrating the reactions of later generations in an interesting way. A washerwoman, still in her thirties, referred to her mother's rigid observance of the rule, to which she herself still conforms, not because she necessarily believes that she would wash one of her family away with the blanket, but because she prefers to respect the old custom. In other words, although mildly sceptical, she hesitates to take the risk, lacking the complete conviction which would supply the courage.

Another and younger domestic worker, a girl from the Isle of Wight, has quite decided views on the subject. " I call it silly, see," was her verdict. Until coming to live in a Dartmoor village after marriage, she had never heard of May's unlucky propensities, and regards the prohibitions imposed by her Devonian mother-in-law with unconcealed scorn.

Not long ago, the possible existence of that ultra-modern and purely whimsical invention—the Gremlin—was actually discussed over the air by as august a body as the " Brains Trust." That the subject was treated with tongue in cheek must go without saying, but the remarks made would not have conveyed that impression to the ordinary unimaginative listener. We poke fun at the quaint ideas of our forebears, yet, to emphasise one point already made, old people would have derided the very idea of their eminently practical grandchildren giving the horoscope, and much more the Gremlin, a moment's serious consideration.

In village communities rural superstitions have already outlived genuine folk-lore. I know a young farmer who, when setting out for an expedition in his car, expresses genuine satisfaction if he meets a flock of sheep. From that moment he seriously expects a successful day.

The Devonian never " touched wood," nor bothered about the unlucky third cigarette. Cigarettes were not so generally smoked in villages during the period when the superstition evolved, and modern notions of the kind take no root in his philosophy. Upon the other hand, no genuine cottager would have dared to leave a lamp burning from sunset to dawn, the origin of this superstition being obviously traceable to the " corpse candle." The old-fashioned night-light was apparently excepted, as this only functioned in its recognised sphere. There were few front doors over which a horseshoe, corroded with the dust of many decades, did not hang, with points upwards to imprison the luck, even as the young moon on her back was believed to hold the rainfall in her lap. Good fortune might be contained in any talisman, not necessarily conventional, but rather, subject to personal idiosyncrasy.

One old farmer sedulously hoarded a quart pot, brim full of sovereigns, which he would not change, even when the soaring price of gold doubled their value. His miserly instinct, although amounting to an obsession, proved weaker than the fear that with his cherished gold his luck would also leave him. Here again, it might be interesting to compare the modern outlook with the " ancient." " I think he's right," was the verdict of a young farmer—himself something of a hoarder—when discussing the old man's peculiarity. " What good's your money if you invest it at two and a half per cent? And it's safe where he's got it, anyway." No question of luck entered *his* calculations, which were purely practical.

There are, of course, grotesque ideas which have persisted practically unchanged. It was a very young housemaid who protested in all good faith to my wife that the sure way of curing a cold was to " give it to somebody else." " Giving " in this context does not mean conveying a germ by natural processes, but involves a deliberate transaction. According to rural tradition, certain infectious complaints are transferred in a very different way.

Once, when walking through the woods with a sixty-year-old countryman, I casually expressed hope that he would not catch the heavy cold from which I happened to be suffering. He had already commented on it, but made no effort to avoid proximity as I should have done, had the case been reversed. But when I *suggested* that he might catch the cold an entirely new position arose. With a vehemence and haste quite unaccountable to me at the time, he declared that he " didn't want the cold," and having clarified that point, evinced no further interest. He feared no germ, but the danger that I might transfer the cold as a *gift*—quite permissible according to local belief and custom —was very real to him. Against this contingency he took the precaution of *declining* it, no further safeguard being considered necessary. Thus rendered immune, he would have drunk from my flask, had I proffered it, without a qualm.

Upon this same principle, a trick supposed to be very effective for getting rid of warts was practised in the very near past, if not actually to-day. Anyone troubled with warts on the hands collected a corresponding number of small stones, and wrapped each separately in a square of toffee-paper reserved for the purpose. These were packed together in one parcel and dropped beside the road, in the hope that some passer-by, ignorant of the trick and impelled by curiosity or greed, would pick it up. The unwary finder who opened such a package acquired the equivalent number of warts, and by this means the entire " crop " could be passed on. The same maid who " gave away " her colds took this practice also quite seriously. Whenever she found anything lying about—and she possessed the " finding " knack—she carefully kicked off any wrappings before picking it up, suspecting some booby-trap of the type described. The belief in transferring a complaint by such means was so prevalent that the possibility was always considered as a matter of course.

This is all of a piece with the by no means obsolete practice of
" charming " away ailments, also described at some length in the
Devonshire County Book. The ceremony often takes the form of purchase
at a nominal price, the " charmer " buying the disorder for perhaps a
halfpenny from the sufferer. In such a case the complaint is not
transferred to the purchaser, provision against anything of that kind
being doubtless made.

A similar idea was probably responsible for the belief that any ill
consequences from a snake-bite could be averted by the death of the
reptile. To kill the Adder which bit a man or an animal belonging to
him was regarded as a long step towards recovery, if not actually
insuring it. The elementary theory was obviously to acquire the life
of the snake for the purpose of reinforcing the other life threatened by
its poisoned bite. Many people who have not yet reached old age will
remember the convention that a dog whose teeth had once drawn
human blood should be instantly destroyed, not because it was
necessarily rabid at the time, but " in case it should ever go mad." In
that event, anyone whom it had bitten in the past—no matter how long
ago—would develop hydrophobia. That the death of the dog could
in no way affect the operation of a germ once transmitted was a
scientific fact completely overlooked, and illustrates in a remarkable
manner the narrowness of the division between practical precaution
against epidemic and mere sacrifice to superstition.

This lack of distinction between the natural and the mystical
applied to the primitive outlook upon anything beyond its positive
comprehension. Confusion between the witch's magic and the health-
giving concoction of the wise old village herbalist was inevitable. Their
period was contemporary, and their roles often combined to heighten
the confusion. Both in a large measure have been consigned to an
" unenlightened " past, but incredible as it may seem, the charm has
definitely survived the primitive medicine. The " white " witch's
charm is still invoked with a certain amount of faith, while old herbal
remedies are laughed at as mere quackery, or denounced as an imposition upon public intelligence.

In this village lives a man, still in his sixties, whose mother
specialised in home-made remedies for all common ailments. Her
medicines were prepared from hedgerow plants, the gathering of which
was a " whole-time job," her prescriptions being in constant request.
To-day, though few may believe it, people who scoffed at the herbalist,

while still despising such vegetable remedies, go to a local man who has gained a considerable reputation for charming, and the practice is taken as a matter of course. While the old village wife cured war s with pennywort and " spade-leaf " (possibly, but not certainly a sorrel), her successor works by invocations only, and—if the statements of his numerous patients can be accepted—achieves a remarkable measure of success. The same procedure is often adopted with ailing livestock, such as horses suffering from skin trouble, or bullocks " horned " by others. I have known many farmers whose beasts have been cured by these methods only—or at least no other aid was solicited.

Indeed, among the older country-people of the last generation, including many otherwise practical and hard-headed men and women, faith in witchcraft, white or black, was almost unshakable. Ill luck, especially if prolonged, was often seriously attributed to the evil influence of some malevolent neighbour. As recently as 1934 a local doctor told me that he was then experiencing considerable difficulty in dealing with an old countrywoman patient. She was suffering from some obscure malady, and insisted upon ascribing it to the deliberate malice of an acquaintance who had " overlooked " her. Endless patience and tact were required to overcome the obsession.

To give one more example: In a neighbouring village some years ago, a lady resident was asked to visit a girl suffering from a poisoned arm, apparently the after-effects of a burn. It transpired that after the accident the girl had been immediately taken to the local white witch for treatment. The witch had dug up two earth-worms, sewn them into the raw wound, and then " said some words over them." Upon this occasion, it would seem, the magic had not worked, the result being a terrible arm necessitating careful medical treatment.

4

In the native mind one found the same confusion with regard to natural phenomena. When I asked a Devonian with a lifelong and probably unique experience of Dartmoor whether he had ever seen a will-o'-the-wisp, he shook his head and smiled, with the same air of mildly contemptuous toleration that he would have shown had I inquired about pixies. To him one was as fanciful as the other, for although he had tramped the hills by night more than any man living, then or now, it so happened that *ignis fatuus* had never featured for his edification. Actually, this ghostly effect is seldom seen on High Dartmoor, so to John Bennet, for all his unrivalled hill lore and grey wisdom, it was just another " old tale." He disbelieved in the ghostly illumination, it should be emphasised, entirely upon account of its supposed unearthly origin. It was regarded as something " spooky," and therefore unacceptable to his practical philosophy. What his reactions would have been upon personal acquaintance with the phenomenon is another question. He believed implicitly in charms, but charms are quite apart from " old tales " by village standards.

Bird and animal lore also has been coloured by an element of superstition, but this, again, is certainly declining with the decline of the countryman's interest in natural history. The latter, of course, is due to easy modern transport, which has placed urban attractions at the disposal of all young people. A villager of the rising generation scarcely knows the wild animals and flowers, let alone any super-stitions attached to them, and the old ideas occasionally encountered are usually dug up out of the past by inquiry. In these cases, once more, the enthusiasm is on the investigator's side, and it is he, not the countryman, who attaches any importance to them.

A typical example was the correspondence lately current in the press concerning " May cats." Oddly enough, before it started, I happened to notice a couple of kittens, obviously May-born, at a neighbouring farmhouse, and with this chapter in mind, made the obvious comment to the farmer. Both he and a younger man, who happened to be listening, expressed the now customary contempt for the superstition, and when a day or two later the newspaper corre-spondence began—evidently between people in quite another walk of life—the example was as interesting as the coincidence was curious. For one thing, the discussion took quite a novel line, unwittingly illustrating the manner in which quaint notions could evolve, as many doubtless have, upon a very slight foundation.

May-born cats were once considered unlucky or undesirable owing to the convention that " they bring snakes into houses." As I have remarked elsewhere, this may be literally true, up to a certain point, their kitten stage coinciding with the abundance of reptiles which provided inevitable playthings. The term ' snake,' of course, covers anything, and in this case is usually applied to slow-worms, with which kittens often play. In the correspondence, one owner of a May cat described the finding of a full-grown viper in his house, but did not accuse the kitten of actually bringing it in. The inference was that the May kitten, being "unlucky," was indirectly responsible for the snake's entry, even as a light burning at night was an invitation to death.

Probably, the taboo on May cats originated in a simple precaution against a nuisance, the superstitious element in this case arising from the fear of almost any reptile or amphibian which is ingrained in country people. Not long ago I came across an interesting example of this, as displayed by a local village woman of a quite intelligent type. She is a shopkeeper, and not the least nervous of being left alone at night with a considerable amount of money in the till. But upon encountering a toad in her garden she was genuinely terrified. Unable to touch it herself, she rushed for help to the nearest neighbour, who, almost equally scared, shovelled the inoffensive creature into a stream at the bottom of the garden. In this respect at least the toad was fortunate, as it doubtless swam to safety instead of suffering the destruction designed for it.

The anti-toad complex is, of course, a survival of the many old superstitions which formerly surrounded this animal. Nobody minds a frog in the least. Indeed, another village woman, whose garden adjoins mine, once asked me not to cut some grass on the boundary bank as she had tamed a frog which might be lurking in it. When I inquired whether she meant a frog and not a toad, she most emphatically repudiated any association with toads.

This and many similar aversions usually originated from ignorance of natural history, some having outlived others. To-day, the flight of a Magpie across his way no longer perturbs the rustic. "The bird has to cross the road, I reckon, same as I got to pass along it," was the logic of one man who, in his youth, had been taught to regard such an incident as ill-omened. When an amorous dog howls at a farmyard gate, the modern farmer no longer calls in his doctor or sees that his will is in order. He merely heaves the nearest stone at the troubadour, and shuts up his sheep-dog bitch. Fear of the Raven, again, seems to have passed with the old mining days, when men refused to descend a shaft over which the bird's ill-omened shadow had passed. An inspection of the machinery was demanded, to discount the possibility that an accident had been predicted.

Conventional aversion, of course, does not necessarily extend to positive superstition, although sometimes amounting to little less, as in the case of the toad, and in a minor degree, the Hedgehog. Rustics dislike Hedgehogs, still firmly believing that they " suck cows," and once more it is astonishing to hear this antiquated absurdity discussed by people who should be more intelligent. It would be as reasonable to accuse a mouse of swallowing a duck's egg.

It is curious, too, that no wild creature has a " lucky" association. An odd mixture of affection and superstition invests the Robin, which is more feared than liked by village people. Its " weeping " note is taken to be a warning of disaster, which, also, is believed to follow any interference with its nest. To them it is much the same as a stormy petrel to a seaman. Country people, again, regard the Pied Wagtail with suspicion, declaring that no cat will touch it, upon which account they conclude that it must possess uncanny properties. I know one old woman, the village matriarch, who warned my wife never to stuff a pillow with feathers plucked from game-birds. " If you go to sleep on they, my dear, you'll wake wi' a headache." The same octogenarian would certainly never harm a spider, but her granddaughter, another former housemaid of ours, subscribes to no such notions. " They say it's unlucky to kill a spider: I *don't* think," was the young woman's pronouncement, as she vigorously applied her broom to a cobweb and its occupant.

It is strange now to think of the days when one heard old agriculturists talk about weather portents in which natural lore and fantastic theory were picturesquely mingled. " Moon lore " is not, of course, peculiar to Dartmoor, but has, perhaps, persisted longer here than elsewhere. I remember old countrymen, some of them not long dead, who took the phases of the moon into serious account when sowing their seeds, docking the tails of lambs and puppies, or cutting the hair of their children. If growth was desired, as in seed-sowing or haircutting, a waxing moon was chosen, tail-docking being reserved for a waning moon, to discourage subsequent growth.

The girl who exercised such care when handling treasure trove declared that human hair always fell like leaves at " blackberry time " —the fall of the year, when birds go through a second moult. Her grandfather, an old shepherd, from whom most of her lore was derived, kept his cabbages immune from the caterpillar nuisance—or so he insisted and believed—by the simple if barbaric ritual of catching the first white butterfly of the season and impaling it alive upon a thorn bush. He encouraged this practice among his grandchildren, whose activities may have been as efficacious as the charm in saving his plants, since not necessarily confined to the first butterfly only.

The meteorological office has outmoded the countryman's weather wisdom as completely as modern machinery has replaced the old hand implements, new agricultural methods the old husbandry. Progressive, no doubt, yet in this still primitive locality I have yet to meet a more consistently successful farmer or gardener than one man who never heard the radio, and cultivated his crops by old rules and ideas that would be considered nonsensical if written or broadcast. That was some time ago, in the days so often called " bad," but in the same days when, as an old labourer in our little Dartmoor village prefers to express it: " we was all happy together."

5

Generally speaking, rural communities have a great deal in common, and even as the tinners differed in no material respect from other workmen of the period, so characteristics ascribed to Dartmoor people are not necessarily peculiar to the district. Manners and customs, of course, vary like dialect, being mainly the result of outside contacts, and the more isolated the region, the longer its inhabitants remain true to type. Actually, Dartmoor has no dialect distinct from that of rural Devonshire generally, although the moorland people have local words for things peculiar to the hills. They talk, for example, of " veins " and " vags," of " tors " and " clitters," of " in-country " and " out-over " to distinguish the lowland from the Moor, but apart from such minor peculiarities, Dartmoor has no language of its own.

Up to 1939, the genuine rural population of Dartmoor—or, more literally, of the surrounding villages, since the Moor itself has so few inhabitants—had changed very little with the passage of time. More and yet more new houses spread along the lanes approaching every settlement, but these are mostly occupied by the ever-increasing class of people who retire to live in quiet country, without ever becoming true countrymen or countrywomen.

For the most part, the old cottages, and granite or cob farmhouses, some mentioned in Domesday Book, are still inhabited by descendants of the original squatters and settlers, the men who enclosed the Ancient Tenements, or, at a later date, provided labour for the ambitious

agricultural experiments in flax, millet, and fine grasses with which
Sir Thomas Tyrwhitt and his contemporaries cropped the virgin soil.
Recently, a new figure, that of the amateur farmer, has gained a foothold on the old ground. This may be all to the good. New blood
usually proves beneficial, and the Moor is quick to accept or reject
candidates for the manner of life she has to offer. The right man takes
root, and roots which once have gripped the rocks of Dartmoor are not
easily dislodged. Few upland trees blow down, even in the fiercest
gale. They cannot fall, since they have already been tested, their
survival proving their ability to stand. The same principle applies to
people who for generations have wrested a livelihood from Dartmoor's
slopes, and have learned how to avail themselves of her resources.

It is true that many Dartmoor people originate from alien stock,
not primarily rural. Since, from medieval times until the beginning
of the present century, the district was mainly a collection of mining
communities attracting labour from all parts of the British Isles, a
certain proportion of this " foreign element " was inevitably absorbed.
For several centuries, therefore, people living around Dartmoor not
only grew up industrially rather than agriculturally minded, but also
acquired some characteristics and qualities from the men who worked
and eventually settled among them. Accordingly, up to a certain point,
they differ from villagers who, all down the generations, have lived and
worked entirely upon the land, descending from an essentially rural
and for the most part local stock.

Dartmoor people are considered tough, and they certainly lack the
docility or simplicity usually associated with agricultural workers. They
are no longer, indeed, a community of labourers in the generally
accepted sense. They are mostly small-holders, or independent crafts-
men working upon their own account. In the typical moorland village
from which I write, consisting of about fifty dwellings, there are only
six men who might be described as whole-time labourers in regular
employ, as compared with thirty who find other means of livelihood.
In the next village, somewhat larger, there are no regular labourers
at all apart from a couple of gardeners. Many small-holders take casual
or periodical work to supplement their means, and there is always some
pooling of resources for special occasions, such as haymaking or
potato-planting. For the most part, they " live off one another," as
the saying goes. The carpenter, the blacksmith, the chimney-sweep, the
cobbler, the village shopkeeper, and not least, the local pig-killer, is

in frequent demand, each in his own department, and all around the Moor summer visitors provide a general source of income.

Thus, by its very wildness and sterility which attract the holiday maker, Dartmoor brings more prosperity to the surrounding villages than would a corresponding acreage under cultivation. Indeed, far from being regarded with the suspicion or dislike so often—and quite incorrectly—described by writers of country books, strangers are welcomed with open arms, and this in the main applies equally to new residents. Socially, it is a pleasant part of the country, its atmosphere being eminently friendly. Surtees wrote about the hospitality of its inhabitants, who, in this respect, have changed very little since his time. Of course there is always a certain proportion of social misfits—newcomers to whose outlook or actions exception is taken, reasonably or otherwise, and although Dartmoor people do not proceed to the drastic lengths of " wild Irishmen," they have remained very much a law unto themselves since the days of the tinners, and their dislike may take forms both active and convincing.

6

In the more populous districts, employment is usually provided by big industrial undertakings, such as the granite quarries, the china clay or lignite workings, to which, of course, in most cases the settlement owes its existence. Dwellings for the operatives spring up around any centre of work the world over, and a new housing scheme to accommodate employees upon the afforestation area at Postbridge supplies the latest example.

To-day the simple life of their grandparents, or even their parents, no longer satisfies the younger generation of moorland villagers. Incredibly primitive as much remains, the general outlook has kept pace with the times. The solitude of the quiet moorside has lost its appeal, access to amenities being now considered essential. Life in a settlement such as Princetown is officially recognised as a hardship, requiring special inducements, while remote dwellings occupied by small-holders of the old-fashioned type have within living memory been abandoned to disintegrate, or are now inhabited by people of another type seeking a return to nature.

In the matter of work, it is much the same. Walls once solidly built with rough granite boulders which required the combined strength of two men to shift, are now repaired and largely replaced with wire and posts. Only a few of the older women still collect dry ling and gorse stumps for firewood. Coal and logs from the lowland, cut by rotary saws and delivered in lorries, now blaze upon hearths which formerly consumed little but turf and peat. The panniered donkeys which, as old people remember, once brought most of the fuel down from the bogs, have become a picturesque legend, belonging to those arduous, but at the same time, leisurely days when, between hay and corn harvest the " rude forefathers of the hamlet " trudged well-worn tracks across the purple Moor to and from the peat-ties, to collect their winter fuel. Many of the tracks have disappeared, and the turf-carts which supplanted the donkeys, and were in common use not so long ago, are likely to swell the growing list of the outmoded in the near future. A few may still be seen, but as a rule these are driven by veteran moormen who persevere with the work because accustomed to it from childhood. In this district, most of the peat, and any other moorland product, is brought down in lorries, nor is it difficult to visualise a time when all material inaccessible to motor-driven vehicles will remain as nature left it—unless new road systems of a National Park " open " Dartmoor for all time and purposes.

It is impossible to know the country people really well and at the same time cherish any illusions concerning their outlook upon the Moor and its future. It is essentially utilitarian, men who appreciate the wild for its own sake being few. " They got no sense o' beauty," was a local storekeeper's recent criticism of his neighbours, the particular subject being the burning of wayside flowering gorse by children whose parents encouraged the practice rather than otherwise.

Ideologically, the " wild hills " may " belong to the people," but whether the idealist likes to admit it or not, " the people " who live among such scenes care little about them. The old-fashioned village woman seldom sets foot on the moors, except to collect fuel or to pick whortleberries. Her daughters do so even less frequently. Why should they? Thin high-heeled shoes and nylon stockings do not take kindly to boulders and heather-stalks, and " What's there to see after all? " they ask. What, indeed? The time-scarred peaks, the mountain streams, the granite-strewn slopes over which cloud-shadows sweep into a blue distance—a wild wide landscape, a wider sky, but its fascination lies entirely in the eye of the beholder. To those who lack the necessary vision, the Moor remains a desert, a barrier, a background with which they would gladly dispense, as useless and even inimical to their way of life.

Speaking for the country people generally, Dartmoor is outside the women's province. Few of them ride, and since most of the work is connected with sheep- or cattle-herding, for which ponies are used, one seldom sees a farmer's wife or daughter bringing down the stock or helping at a round-up. Riding girls of the hunting type abound, of course, but they belong to a different category. Turf or peat-cutting is the only form of manual work done upon the moor, and that upon a steadily declining scale. Less use is made of the abundant bracken than might be supposed. Indeed, as this plant spreads owing to the constant destruction of the heather by irresponsible burning, its value declines. With quick transport available, it is easier to fetch cheap or waste straw from " in-country " farms than to cut and harvest bracken on rough hillsides. In any case, either harvesting bracken or digging peat has always been considered a man's work, and even the modern land-girl does not appear on the hills.

<h2 style="text-align:center">7</h2>

In general, during ten months of the year, village women shun the Moor. Until the near past, however, there was one annual period during which they took complete possession of the hills—or rather those parts where whortleberries grow. In July and early August, almost every rocky slope and peaty excrescence becomes a wild fruit-garden, and during that time the local population was transferred to the ridges, to collect the purple harvest upon which many housewives depended, not only for jam supplies but for money to provide some of life's actual necessities. Whortleberries have always commanded a ready sale, and village women of the poorer classes set aside their surplus earnings at this profitable work to buy clothing and boots for their families. The children helped, accompanying their mothers to the hills, and in the " good old days " each was set a quota which had to be reached under threat of chastisement for failure. They took to the work eagerly, however, and schools were closed for the period, whortleberry-picking being regarded as seriously as any other form of harvest.

The trek to the hills began in early morning, as soon as the women were free to leave their homes, and while dewdrops still loaded the ling-stalks every upland path leading to coombe or clitter was threaded by files of picturesque figures, wearing purple-splashed aprons and carrying

huge fruit-baskets. Even more picturesque was the return at sundown
—for they worked long hours—when fingers and lips, as well as aprons,
were dyed, and shoulders drooped under the now laden baskets. But
the tired processions none the less moved with a triumphant air against
the reddening sky, like old-fashioned gleaners after a good day on the
stubble.

Whortleberry-picking needs a special technique which seems to be
natural rather than acquired. At any rate, almost without exception,
real proficiency is entirely confined to the country people. Even as a
born farmer is usually a good rabbit shot, so the true villager, as a
matter of course, can pick whorts at a profitable rate. It is not even a
question of practice. People of a different type seldom, if ever, acquire
an equal skill. A thick-fingered labourer can and does pick more
berries in an hour than a deft musician can gather in a day, although
both may be equally accustomed or unaccustomed to the work.
Years ago it was mainly done by women, as men could find more
lucrative employment. For the most part a " scrounger " or, now and
again, a man out of work turned whortleberry picker. In more recent
times, as the price of the fruit soared to fancy heights, all kinds of
people participated. They still do so, but under changed conditions,
much of the old picturesque atmosphere having passed. At the present
time whortleberry-picking has become almost entirely a commercial
proposition. While more berries than ever are picked, fewer and
fewer find their way into the country housewife's store cupboard. The
whole procedure has changed. The basket-laden processions are no
longer seen trooping homewards at dusk. Dealers from the towns
now drive their motor-vans on to the Moor itself to meet and buy
the fruit at its very source. The pickers, no longer confined to local
villagers, arrive from longer distances by motor-bus and even private
car, while only the older of the genuine village women and comparatively few children are seen among them.

The financial value of Dartmoor's whortleberry crop is seldom
realised or taken into account when the question of material considerations, as compared with the purely aesthetic, are discussed. Few people
would believe that the craggy peaks and granite-strewn hillsides,
rugged and apparently sterile, are really more productive than many
cultivated gardens. Fruit gathered from one acre of rocky slope may
realise as much as £20, and since this is produced at no cost whatever,
it amounts to a return which most agriculturists would envy. Judged

Humphrey & Vera Joel

Plate XXIII a. Dartmoor ponies

b. Dartmoor architecture, cottage at Lettaford

E. H. Ware

Plate XXIV. River Dart, near Dartmeet

by bald statistics, whortleberry growth is more remunerative to the
local community than pasturage, from which only one or two men
benefit. Of course, the high value of wild fruit is due to modern
artificial conditions. But everything is relative. Old people tell me
that in their young days they picked quantities of whorts for 2½d. per
quart, as compared with the modern price of 4s. 6d. (early in the
season), and considered themselves well paid.

Devonshire country people never made much use of whortleberries
for vintage purposes, although a potent drink can be brewed from the
purple juice. Home-made wine was considered as indispensable as
jam by thrifty housewives of long ago, but blackberries and sloes were
the wild fruits mainly used, the common parsnip, as well as rhubarb
and red currant, being also popular and capable of producing distinctly
" heady " beverages. Every cottage had its store of blackberry and
sloe wine—the latter called " snag " in the old days—for festive
occasions. The modern housewife, however, is not interested in wild
fruit beverages, the making of which had virtually ceased even before
it became the fashion to step round to " the local." The taste for home-
brew has been lost, and the art of concocting it will pass with the
grandparents of the present generation.

8

The story of the home-made loaf, once the mainstay of the countryman's table, is much the same as that of home-made wines. In many
old farms and cottages the bread-oven, now used for drying sticks or
as a receptacle for oddments, may still be seen, built into the masonry
of the open hearth, but it survives only as an interesting relic. Even
around Dartmoor, there are few homesteads so remote that the baker's
van cannot reach them, and the occupiers of the most inaccessible
dwellings find it simpler to collect their bread from the nearest neighbour's house than to bake for themselves. I have seen a pile of loaves
stacked against a wayside hedge, waiting to be picked up, like cans of
milk, although so primitive an arrangement is unusual even for
Dartmoor. So dependent upon the village " bakehouse " have the
once self-reliant country people become that during the severe winter
of 1946-47, when outlying hamlets were isolated by deep snow, the
distribution of bread became a major problem. It was brought round
on tractor and hand-drawn sleigh—often by moonlight. Some people

D   O trudged miles to fetch it, staggering back with heavy sack-loads, to supply others less vigorous or enterprising than themselves.

In many farms a modern range has now been installed beside the open hearth where the old-fashioned housewife " raked and scraped and boiled and baked " so efficiently. Yet the change is not always appreciated. I know one farmer's daughter—a young woman—who, although provided with an up-to-date oil-cooker, still prefers to cook over the logs in a great flat-topped fish-kettle, used by her mother before her. This hangs from the chimney crook above the hearth, hot embers from which are repeatedly piled upon the flat iron lid. No oven, the girl declares, produces a finer roast or pudding. Her sister, newly married and established in a " convenient house," has gone one better. She has declared active war upon the modern range, and is actually having it removed in order to restore a hearth similar to that on which she learned her craft at home. Like her sister, she maintains that no food tastes the same as that prepared in the more natural, if primitive way. I can testify to the success of both girls as cooks, which speaks well for the old methods.

Many moorland farmhouses, not to mention cottages, still lack comforts and facilities which modern standards consider essential. A piped water-supply remains the exception rather than the rule, a bathroom being installed mainly as a concession to summer visitors. One " guest-house " where I have stayed on the southern Moor—an ancient farm dating from Domesday Book—boasted two bathrooms. One, only approachable by way of the yard, was a converted pigsty, through which the hill winds whistled, glass windows being regarded as superfluous. The latchless door allowed free entrance to anyone, including the original inhabitants. The second bathroom was a concrete annexe, provided with an ill-fitting skylight through which rain poured and flooded the concave floor to a depth which made it scarcely distinguishable from the bath itself.

It is perhaps only natural that provisions for comfort or convenience should mainly be confined to the kitchen, which is the hub of west-country home life. There, meals are cooked and eaten, employers and employees sharing a common table. There the family sits, reads, plays games, and there the modern television set is installed, for it would be useless in any other room, while master and man take part upon equal terms in topical discussion and card-play. I have known kitchens which were even more communal: in another farmhouse where we stayed it was quite usual to meet hens or pigs straying along the passages. Nowadays, however, it is customary to draw the line at pigs or poultry, which are fed in more suitable places, dogs, cats and occasionally a sickly or bottle-fed lamb being the only members of the lower "staff" admitted to the freedom of the kitchen.

Although the farmhouse kitchen remains a unique institution, it never was a comfortable room, being large, cold, stone-floored, and sometimes even cobbled, if the house is really old. For the most part, the door remains perennially open, to facilitate the constant comings and goings of man or beast inseparable from busy farm life. The room is furnished with one or two chairs at most, and those hard and straight. Until quite recently the family sat on backless benches, or on the fixed settles which still span the wall. In genuine old kitchens there remains the huge fireplace, the chimney-corner or inglenook of olden days, inside which short benches hug the hearth. The one comfort is the immense fire, kindled by an entire faggot and kept ablaze with logs of the same length.

It is true that one did occasionally see a stiff, but never comfortable, armchair, in the kitchen, a concession to an ageing agriculturist's "rheumatics." But it was very much of a concession and a compromise, adopted from necessity rather than from choice. One old moorman, when invited into my study, always insisted upon carrying in with him a polished wooden chair from the hall. I also remember a farmer who, conducted by chance through our kitchen, deposited himself with a sigh of relief upon the hard settle which, in our old farmhouse, still occupies its time-honoured place. Obviously, he had hoped to be entertained in the room where he was most at home, and he eventually followed me into the study with the greatest reluctance.

9

Peat and "vags," as turf blocks are called, still smoulder upon oldworld hearths, and the aromatic smell of peat-smoke clings to many moorland villages from which tracks wind across adjacent hills to the peat-bogs. The disuse into which the greater number of these tracks have fallen, however, emphasises the decline of turf-cutting. Formerly, venville parishioners who were unable, through lack of transport or other disability, to procure moorland fuel for themselves, could always obtain it by employing the necessary labour, the turf or peat itself being free to all. Even allowing for cost of cutting and transport, twenty years ago it was still the cheapest fuel available, but in course of time soaring prices reversed the situation. With high labour charges local peat became more expensive than coal, and now only those possessing the necessary facilities can benefit from the still abundant supply.

Turbary, indeed, is one of many jealously guarded venville rights which, under modern conditions, are of little real benefit to a moorland parish as a whole. The advantages of public pasturage are used to a far less general extent than was once the case, and in the main, the cottager's or small-holder's few beasts—sheep, ponies or bullocks— have been replaced by large flocks and herds, the property of one or two people in each parish who have concentrated on the breeding of moorland stock upon a large scale. This is, perhaps, an inevitable development, but scarcely consistent with the general idea of common land or the purposes which it was designed to serve, since it amounts to the extensive appropriation of public rights by a few individuals.

Nowadays upon Dartmoor, the principal stock-owner in any parish is not necessarily a farmer, since the obligation to provide winter keep for beasts pastured on the hills is no longer enforced. Under the conditions which have arisen, the big-scale sheep- or cattle-owner may be a mere investor in livestock, employing no labour, and paying no proportionate share of local expenses since he occupies no holding of high rateable value. Also, the national food shortage has given a further peculiar twist to the situation. Since upland pasturage is virtually free, or subject to little more than nominal Forest due, the cost of rearing beasts which winter on the hills has not been affected by the general rise in prices. None the less, a subsidy per head is now paid by the Government, and some people in the circumstances described derive considerable additional and entirely gratuitous income from this source alone. So arises the anomalous position of individuals monopolising public rights, not only unrestricted, but actually paid for doing so out of public funds.

The old and now disregarded regulations limiting the use of pasturage did more than discourage private monopoly. They also prevented over-stocking and winter famine, instances of which too often occur. The worst recent example was the " blizzard " of early 1947, which eclipsed all previous records by its long duration. In the Old Testament story of ancient Egypt, each plague, when at its height, promoted good resolutions which were not implemented after normal conditions had been restored. Upon the same principle, measures to prevent recurrence of disaster during severe winters on Dartmoor are never taken when the hard times have passed. So the Arctic conditions of 1947, which set in during early January and continued upon the high Moor until mid-March, caught the hill flocks —or their owners—once again unprepared. The first heavy fall found thousands of animals upon the hills, and for the greater number no alternative provision was available. Their position became more desperate as the hard weather persisted, and the R.S.P.C.A. organised a campaign to relieve distress wherever possible. The efforts of the Society, although highly commendable, should not have been necessary, since responsibility for the animals' welfare clearly rested with their owners.

Early March, however, witnessed the real climax, which took the form of a remarkable glazed frost, or " ammil " in Dartmoor language —the most disastrous and at the same time most magnificent natural phenomenon of modern times. For two months white Winter had allowed his artistry full scope, as displayed in fantastic snowdrifts and frozen waterways, but the climax came with light rain, falling with the thermometer well below freezing point. Every bush, tree, sprig of heather, bracken-frond or reed, every rail or post, each inanimate object, was sheathed in ice as though in a glass case. So evolved the memorable 1947 ammil which spread over much of southern England, but on Dartmoor, where snow lay deepset, and frost was most severe, achieved its utmost splendour. The tors, usually stern and grey, now stood like mighty glaciers, towering above a tumbled sea of crystal. Under the cold bright sunshine, each wooded coombe of the foothills was a shining wonderland where great trees stood, as if rough-carved in ice, and nothing seemed alive or real but the chill wind which rattled the branches and now and again brought an over-weighted bough crashing down to snow level with a roar like falling masonry.

The grandeur of the scene was unsurpassable, but in this enchanted world no living thing had a place. It was Winter's last and deadliest blow, administering the *coup de grâce* to countless already perishing creatures. " I've been on the land for fifty years," one local farmer remarked to me, " but I never saw rabbits starved to death before." When even the sturdy wild rabbit could not exist, the plight of the less resourceful sheep and ponies baffled description.

The melting snows of every Dartmoor winter tell a sad story, but seldom a grimmer one than that of 1947. No steps have been taken to prevent a recurrence of the disaster, however, and history will certainly repeat itself, if subsidised flocks continue to depend upon the Moor's precarious winter provision. The plight of the ponies at such times arouses most sympathy, because most noticeable, nor can their maintenance on the hills under harsh conditions be justified, since their removal presents no difficulty, and facilities for winter keep should be a condition of ownership.

10

The position of the hill pony has already been described, and although it has long since ceased to occupy its once predominant place, it still remains an attractive feature of the moorland. Nothing was more spectacular than the annual pony drifts which took place every autumn, and indeed continue to-day, although upon a greatly diminished scale.

In the heyday of the pony trade, when big droves roamed the moors, the drift was a highly organised and important function. It takes the form of a general round-up and rough census of all ponies grazing within the Forest boundaries, each of the four Quarters in turn being subjected to a similar stocktaking. It is conducted on behalf of the Duchy, and preceded by a standstill order, prohibiting anyone from evading the census by the removal of his animals. Years ago, when ponies were numerous, the drift resembled a big cattle-drive on the American prairies, rather than anything seen in England to-day. It involved the impounding of the entire number in one central enclosure, expert herdmanship being required to achieve this end. The droves came in from every direction at the whirling speed which unbroken ponies, once upon the move, maintain for many miles, and the drivers' skill was best displayed in the final task of steering them into the pound. When this had been accomplished, a general inspection by the Duchy portreeve and Warden of the Quarter followed. Branded mares, with foals at foot, were claimed by their owners. Animals which bore no brand were regarded as ownerless, and, like unstamped tin in the old Stannary days, became the property of the Duchy. Forest dues were paid, " reckoning " (a west-country term for settling accounts) being an established order of the day, which concluded with the communal meal of bread and cheese and cider, inseparable from Devonshire functions.

Formerly, all parishioners who claimed common rights were required, as one of the conditions attached to the privilege, to assist at the drifts. With the passing of time, however, attendance has slackened, and observance of the ritual as such is now scarcely even nominal.

As mountain sheep by degrees supplanted the pony, the annual " dip," which takes place on 25 July, gained predominance over the drift as the great moorland ceremony, and affects every man who pastures sheep on the hills. The initial procedure is much the same, entailing the compulsory clearing of the Moor on the previous day. Although much more extensive, preparations for the great " dip " are less spectacular than the pony round-up. Although thousands of sheep are upon the move, there is, of course, no general impounding, since the incoming flocks converge upon many different points. For this very reason, however, the display is in some ways more varied, and viewed from the air on 24 July the Moor presents a panorama of slow-motion pictures, as the grey files troop down from every ridge to the accompaniment of barking dogs and the peculiar yodelling cries of the moormen on their rough ponies.

For this occasion several flock-owners usually pool their resources, since every moorland farm is not provided with a " bath," nor can one man, single-handed, dip his own flock. There are no shepherds on Dartmoor. A farmer, when riding round, might help a busy neighbour by casting an occasional eye over his sheep, but in general, each owner himself tends—or neglects—his flock. Indeed, the lack of care in some instances is a frequent cause of complaint against the prevailing system, and, even allowing for inevitable exaggerations, criticism is far from being groundless. If Dartmoor " ranching " is to continue upon an increasing and permanently subsidised basis, a review of the entire position is necessary.

II

From a strictly legal standpoint, the full extent of rights vested in Dartmoor commoners or venville tenants too often lacks precise definition. The old grants and charters upon which most claims are based have been fully set out in the works of Crossing, Rowe and other writers, so need not be included here. These ancient enactments still constitute the moorman's code, any book which contains them being handed down from father to son, like title deeds to prove the ownership of his land. They are mainly valuable as evidence of immemorial custom, although it by no means follows that the antiquity of a practice justifies its continuance. Indeed, the diametrically opposite policy is usually urged with regard to institutions dating from " the bad old days." In any case, enactments by Norman kings are somewhat remote, and have never been exempt from modification necessitated by altered circumstances.

CHAPTER 13

POSTCRIPT

W ILFRED GIBSON, in dedicating one of his books to his shepherding ancestors, implored them, with, I feel sure, a secret pride, "Forgive me that my flocks and herds are nought but barren, bleating words." I suppose few authors reach the end of a book without wondering why they have written it, whether they have made themselves clear, whether it has really been worth undertaking. So I now. It has been my object in the chapters I have written to set out a picture of the countryside, its geological and physiographical structure, and the patterns of the communities of plants and animals which live there. Complete success was precluded from the outset, because so much remains to be discovered before the full canvas can be covered, but I have done my best with the materials available. Underlying this endeavour has been the thought that this is one of a series of books about regions which have been, or may be, made into National Parks, and which, therefore, may come to hold a very special place in our minds. It has consequently proved inevitable that I have had to enter into controversial fields. For the most part, I have tried to weigh the issues impartially, for it is only by the clear delineation of argument on either side that we may expect to arrive at wise decisions. I may therefore, I hope, be forgiven if I return briefly to these major issues, since the only way to a true National Park of Dartmoor lies through solution of the various problems they raise.

We have seen that the impacts of human activity are likely to effect profound changes in the amenities of the region. Of these impacts the most drastic are:

Overstocking and burning by commoners.
Afforestation with conifers.

Development of water undertakings, and
Military exercises.

Other lesser, or more local, influences include, extraction of china clay,
mining and quarrying for ores and stone, injudicious siting of buildings,
car-parks and the like, coupled with the use of materials incongruous
in the local setting.

As I write I have before me an issue of *Nature* (No. 4204, Vol. 165
of 27 May 1950), in which appears an editorial on " The National
Parks Commision." This article does not relate specifically to Dartmoor, but the argument of this book is summarised succinctly in two
sentences which I am pleased to be allowed to quote. These are,
firstly, " Here (in National Parks) amenity must come first, just as in
other areas the claims of water supply, agriculture, military training,
housing or industry must come first if conflict arises," and secondly,
" Failure in a National Park area to make the preservation of natural
beauty the supreme national interest is not only to repudiate the very
conception and meaning of a National Park, but also to threaten the
whole principle underlying the planned utilisation of our limited
resources. We must to the best of our judgment designate the social
functions which in particular areas are to be paramount, and then see
that those functions are, in fact, supreme."

What of Dartmoor then, if we were to come to our senses and
implement the policy stated in these sentences, and in a proper conception of the value of National Parks in maintaining our national
health? I think the following measures might succeed:

(1) The problems of pasturage, and of bracken and heather control,
are not easily to be solved. There is no doubt, however, that the
haphazard and often over-intensive burning to which most moors are
subjected now does far more harm than good. But the optimum
treatment to suit the climatic conditions can only be determined by
experiment. In fact, such experimental treatment was in the minds
of some members of the Devon War Agricultural Executive Committee
as far back as 1942, but it was never initiated because of lack of labour,
time and money during the middle years of the war. It is time a series
of plots was laid out and subjected to controlled treatment, with a view
to determining the optimum conditions for maintenance of good young
heather and grasses, and for controlling the spread of the bracken.
The results would be valuable not only as a yardstick for determining

the general policy to be adopted, but also as a means of convincing local opinion and so securing the co-operation of the commoners, which is essential to any radical change of practice.

At the same time an effort should be made to estimate the optimum head of stock which the moors can carry, at all seasons of the year. This, then, should not be exceeded, except in so far as future improvements in the pasturage permit. By such measures we might eventually increase the stock-carrying capacity of the Moor, while at the same time sparing users of the Moor the sight of ill-fed ponies such as now all too often offends them.

(2) What has been done by the Forestry Commission and by private planters cannot be undone. We must therefore make the best of the existing conifer plantations, and it must be confessed that, in my opinion, not all the changes made are to the bad. There are horrible mistakes, like the Bellever plantations. But some of the newer areas promise to add to rather than detract from the amenities of Dartmoor. The walker's lament that he can no longer traverse them at will is a just one, and is only partially offset by the new scenic values created in a few settings. The determined critic who cannot tolerate regimented conifers will of course refuse even this compensation. But, for some at least, there is new beauty to be found, particularly in the Fernworthy region. To the naturalist the plantations offer many gains, and promise more. The new habitats created attract a succession of new species as the trees mature, and some of these compensate, and more than compensate for local losses. And if the potential gains are realised, as in time they well may be, I think few biologists will complain, provided that the acreage planted now, in 1950, is not increased. The principal reservation to be made in relation to this is that the felling policy, when this eventually becomes necessary, shall be determined in such a way as to preserve the amenities of the Moor, as they then are.

(3) There is no doubt that the reservoirs of Dartmoor, being the only large bodies of water there, contribute a great deal to its scenic value and to its ecological interest. Probably these contributions outweigh, at the moment, the losses due to submergence of valleys, restrictions to passage, and reduction of stream-flow. But with the creation of the new reservoir in the Avon valley it may be argued that the balance has been struck, if not over-tipped. It is very doubtful whether we can afford to give up more of the valleys, or reduce the flow of any more rivers without seriously detracting from

many other values. That domestic water supplies can be provided without such detriment to rivers and scenery is amply demonstrated by the undertakings which supply Exeter and above all, London, in which water is extracted at points far below the sources of the rivers. It seems legitimate to inquire therefore, whether extraction at lower levels should not be more adequately explored before any new high-level reservoirs are considered in the potential National Park.

(4) On the question of military usage I am well aware that I have abandoned impartiality. I find it impossible to reconcile the liberal conception of a National Park with the stultification of human endeavour involved in war and in preparations for defence. I am convinced that, if the criteria for a National Park which John Dower postulated are correct—and I believe they are—then we cannot allow military exercises to be conducted in them. It is, therefore, a *sine qua non* that, now that Dartmoor is a National Park, the present tendency of the armed forces to concentrate more and more within its boundaries must be reversed and the region declared sacrosanct from all such activity.

LIST OF SOME PLANTS AND
ANIMALS OF DARTMOOR

There are no lists existing that pertain specifically to all the plants and animals of Dartmoor. The following lists have therefore been compiled from the various county lists cited in the bibliography, supplemented by the personal records of myself and many friends. It should be borne in mind that they relate not only to the moors, but also to the whole diversified country of the National Park area, and they are therefore more extensive than would be lists referring to the more specialised moorland and bog habitats.

The Latin name of plants follow, with slight modification, Clapham's *Check-list of British Vascular Plants* (1946). Where names differ from those used in Martin & Fraser (1939) or Clapham, Tutin, & Warburg (1952), the synonyms given in those two works will, in most cases, enable cross-reference to be made without difficulty.

The mosses, hepatics and lichens are not included here, but a comprehensive and classified list of the moorland species is to be found on pp. 73-76.

R	(Col. 1)	Resident	F (Col. 2) Few
SR		Summer Resident	R (Col. 2) Rare
WV		Winter Visitor	G General
T		Transient	W Widespread
A		Abundant	L Local
C		Common	O Occasional

(A.) VASCULAR PLANTS
RANUNCULACEAE

Anemone nemorosa L.	Wood Anemone	C oakwoods, Teign **and** Dart
Ranunculus peltatus Schrank	Water Crowfoot	
R. pseudofluitans Bak. & Fogg.	„ „	Locally plentiful
R. lenormandi Schultz.	„ „	A
R. flammula L.	Lesser Spearwort	A
R. auricomus L.	Goldilocks	L (calc) Ilsington
R. acris L.	Common Buttercup	C
R. repens L.	Creeping Buttercup	C
R. bulbosus L.	Meadow Buttercup	C
R. sardous Crantz	Pale Hairy Buttercup	L
R. arvensis L.	Corn Buttercup	Rare colonist. Teign Val.

R. ficaria L.	Lesser Celandine	A
Caltha palustris L.	Marsh Marigold	C
Helleborus viridis L.	Green Hellebore	R (calc) Ilsington, Ashburton
H. foetidus L.	Stinking Hellebore	VR (calc) Ashburton, prob. escape
Aquilegia vulgaris L.	Columbine	W not C
Aconitum anglicum Stapf.	Monkshood	VR Ilsington, Lydford

BERBERIDACEAE

Berberis vulgaris L.	Barberry	O doubtful native

PAPAVERACEAE

Papaver rhoeas L.	Common Red Poppy	C
P. dubium L.	Long Smooth-headed Poppy	W not C
P. lecoquii Lamotte		Ashburton 1925
P. argemone L.	Long Rough-headed Poppy	R
P. hybridum L.	Round Rough-headed Poppy	VR Bridford 1927
Meconopsis cambrica (L.) Vig.	Yellow Welsh Poppy	O
Chelidonium majus L.	Greater Celandine	FC

FUMARIACEAE

Corydalis claviculata L.	Climbing Corydalis	FC
Fumaria boraei Jord.		C
F. officinalis L.	Fumitory	Not C

CRUCIFERAE

Cheiranthus cheiri L.	Wallflower	W
Nasturtium officinale R. Br.	Watercress	Not C on Dartmoor
Rorippa sylvestris (L.) Bess.	Creeping Yellow Cress	O
Barbarea vulgaris R. Br.	Wintercress	G
Arabis hirsuta (L.) Scop.	Hairy Rockcress	L (calc)
Cardamine pratensis L.	Lady's Smock	C
C. hirsuta L.	Hairy Bittercress	Not Dartmoor
C. impatiens L.		Very L
Eriophila verna (L.) E. Meyer	Whitlow Grass	C
Arabidopsis thaliana (L.) Heynh.	Thale Cress	C
Sisymbrium officinale (L.) Scop.	Hedge Mustard	C
Alliaria officinalis Andrz.	Garlic Mustard	A
Erysimum cheiranthoides L.	Treacle Mustard	R, L
Brassica nigra (L.) Koch	Black Mustard	C
Sinapis arvensis L.	Charlock	C
Diplotaxis tenuifolia (L.) DC.	Wall Rocket	L
Capsella bursa-pastoris (L.) Medic	Shepherd's Purse	A

Coronopus didymus (L.) Sm.	Lesser Wartcress	C
C. Squamatus (Forsk.) Aschers.	Swine's Cress	C
Lepidium campestre (L.) R. Br.	Field Cress	C
L. smithii Hook.		C
L. draba L.		L, Horrabridge
Thlaspi arvense L.	Pennycress	W, Locally A
Teesdalia nudicaulis R. Br.	Shepherd's Cress	C
Raphanus raphanistrum L.	Wild Radish	Not uncommon

RESEDACEAE

Reseda lutea L.	Wild Mignonette	Ilsington, Ivybridge
R. luteola L.	Dyer's Greenweed	Fairly C

VIOLACEAE

Viola odorata L.	Sweet Violet	G
var. *dumetorum* (Jord.) R. & F.	White Violet	More freq. than type
V. hirta L.	Hairy Violet	(calc) Ilsington, Ashburton
V. calcarea (Bab.) Greg.		(calc) Ashburton
V. riviniana Reichb.	Dog Violet	C
V. canina L.	Dog Violet	C
V. lactea Smith	Pale Violet	F
V. palustris L.	Bog Violet	C Peat bogs
V. lutea var. *sulphurea* Drabble		Once Moretonhampstead
V. arvensis agg.	Heartsease	C

POLYGALACEAE

Polygala vulgaris L.	Common Milkwort	A
P. oxyptera Rchb.		A
P. serpyllifolia Hose		A

CARYOPHYLLACEAE

Dianthus armeria L.	Deptford Pink	L
Saponaria officinalis L.	Soapwort	L
Silene cucabalus Wibel	Bladder Campion	C
S. anglica L.	English Catchfly	Locally C
Melandrium noctiflorum (L.) Fr.	Night-flowering Catchfly	W R
M. album Mill.	Evening Campion	Not uncommon
M. dioicum (L.) Coss. & Germ.	Red Campion	A
Lychnis flos-cuculi L.	Ragged Robin	C bogs
Agrostemma githago L.	Corn Cockle	R at present time
Cerastium viscosum L.	Broad-leaved Mouse-eared Chickweed	W
C. vulgatum L.	Common Mouse-eared Chickweed	C
C. arvense L.	Field Mouse-eared Chickweed	Once Moretonhampstead
Moenchia erecta (L.) Gaertn., Mey. & Scherb.	Erect Pearlwort	L

Stellaria media (L.) Vill.	Chickweed	A
S. neglecta Weihe	Stitchwort	C
S. holostea L.	Greater Stitchwort	C
S. graminea L.	Grassy Stitchwort	C
S. alsine Grimm	Bog Stitchwort	C
Arenaria trinervia L.	Three-nerved Sandwort	C
Sagina apetala L.	Annual Pearlwort	C
S. ciliata Fr.	Ciliated Pearlwort	Not C
S. procumbens L.	Procumbent Pearlwort	VC
S. subulata (Sw.) Presl	Heath Pearlwort	C
S. nodosa (L.) Fenzl	Knotted Spurrey	R
Spergula arvensis L.	Corn Spurrey	W
S. sativa Boenn.	Corn Spurrey	L
Spergularia rubra (L.) Presl	Red Sandwort	W not C

PORTULACACEAE

Claytonia alsinoides Sims	Claytonia	L
C. perfoliata Willd.	Perfoliate Claytonia	L
Montia fontana L.	Blinks	C

HYPERICACACEAE

Hypericum androsaemum L.	Tutsan	W not C
H. perforatum L.	Perforate St. John's Wort	C
H. dubium Leers	Imperforate St. John's Wort	L
H. quadrangulum L.	Square Stalked St. John's Wort	C
H. undulatum Willd.		Southern border
H. humifusum L.	Creeping St. John's Wort	C
H. linariifolium Vahl	Narrow-leaved St. John's Wort	L Teign valley
H. pulchrum L.	Upright St. John's Wort	C
H. montanum L.	Mountain St. John's Wort	L (calc.)
H. elodes L.	Marsh St. John's Wort	C

MALVACEAE

Malva moschata L.	Musk Mallow	C
M. neglecta Wallr.	Round-leaved Mallow	Not C

TILIACEAE

Tilia cordata Mill.	Lime	Rather R

LINACEAE

Radiola linoides Roth	Allseed	W
Linum catharticum L.	Purging Flax	C
L. bienne Mill.	Binding Flax	W

GERANIACEAE

Geranium versicolor L.		L Postbridge
G. phaeum L.	Dusky Cranes-bill	L
G. pratense L.	Meadow Cranes-bill	L Two Bridges, Brent Vor
G. pyrenaicum Burm. f.	Mountain Cranes-bill	L
G. molle L.	Dove's-foot Cranes-bill	C
G. pusillum L.	Small-flowered Cranes-bill	Not C
G. rotundifolium L.	Round-leaved Cranes-bill	Not C Ilsington, Fingle Bridge
G. dissectum L.	Jagged-leaved Cranes-bill	C
G. columbinum L.	Long-stalked Cranes-bill	W
G. lucidum L.	Shining Cranes-bill	C
G. robertianum L.	Herb Robert	C
Erodium moschatum (L.) Ait.	Muskniuty Stork's-bill	W
Oxalis acetosella L.	Wood Sorrel	C
Impatiens glandulifera Royle	Indian Balsam	L

AQUIFOLIACEAE

Ilex aquifolium L.	Holly	F

CELASTRACEAE

Euonymus europaeus L.	Spindle Tree	F

RHAMNACEAE

Frangula alnus Mill.	Alder Buckthorn	C

ACERACEAE

Acer pseudo-platanus L.	Sycamore	C
A. campestre L.	Maple	C

HIPPOCASTANACEAE

Aesculus hippo-castanum L.	Horse Chestnut	

LEGUMINOSAE

Genista anglica L.	Petty Whin	L
Ulex europaeus L.	Gorse	C
U. gallii Planch.	Western Furze	Locally A
Sarothamnus scoparius (L.) Koch	Broom	C
Ononis repens L.	Rest Harrow	Not C
Medicago lupulina L.	Black Medick	W
M. hispida Gaetn. var. denticulata Willd.	Toothed Medick	Once, Moretonhampstead Ashburton
M. arabica (L.) Huds.	Spotted Medick	
Melilotus alba Medic.	White Melilot	
M. officinalis (L.) Lam.	Melilot	
Trifolium pratense L.	Red Clover	C

D.

P

T. medium L.	Zigzag Clover	L
T. repens L.	White Clover	A
T. campestre Schreb.	Hop Trefoil	W
T. dubium Sibth.	Lesser Trefoil	A
T. filliforme L.	Small Trefoil	Okehampton only
Lotus corniculatus L.	Bird's-foot Trefoil	A
L. tenuis Willd.	Narrow-leaved Trefoil	Ashburton
L. uliginosus Schkuhr	Marsh Trefoil	C
Ornithopus perpusillus L.	Bird's Foot	C
Vicia hirsuta (L.) S. F. Gray	Hairy Vetch	C
V. cracca L.	Tufted Vetch	C
V. sylvatica L.	Wood Vetch	Okehampton
V. sepium L.	Bush Vetch	C
V. angustifolia L.	Narrow-leaved Vetch	C
Lathyrus pratensis L.	Meadow Vetchling	C
L. sylvestris L.	Everlasting Pea	Okehampton, Tavistock
L. montanus Bernh.	Wood Pea	W

ROSACEAE

Prunus spinosa L.	Blackthorn	C
P. insititia L.	Bullace	Okehampton, Tavistock
P. avium L.	Wild Cherry	W
Filipendula ulmaria (L.) Maxim.	Meadowsweet	C
Rubus idaeus L.	Raspberry	L
Rubus spp.	Blackberry	A
Geum urbanum L.	Wood Avens	C
G. rivale L.	Water Avens	R Last rec. Tavistock 1930
Fragaria vesca L.	Strawberry	C
Potentilla sterilis (L.) Garcke	Barren Strawberry	C
P. erecta (L.) Räusch	Tormentil	C
P. procumbens Sibth.	Creeping Tormentil	W
P. reptans L.	Creeping Cinquefoil	C
P. anserina L.	Silver Weed	C
P. argentea L.	Silver Cinquefoil	L
Alchemilla arvensis (L.) Scop.	Parsley Piert	W
A. vulgaris L. agg.	Lady's Mantle	R
Agrimonia eupatoria L.	Agrimony	C
A. odorata Mill.	Fragrant Agrimony	Not uncommon
Poterium sanguisorba L.	Salad Burnet	L
Sanguisorba officinalis L.	Great Burnet	Not C
Rosa arvensis Huds.	Wild Rose	A
R. stylosa Desv.		W
R. spinosissima L.	Scotch Rose	O
R. canina L.	Dog Rose	W
R. obtusifolia Desv.		W
R. tomentosa Sm.		Not C
R. rubiginosa L.		Not C

R. micrantha Sm.
Sorbus aucuparia L.   Mountain Ash   C
S. devoniensis E. F. Warb.   French Hailes   Meavy
S. torminalis (L.) Crantz   Service Tree   R
Pyrus communis L.   Pear   R. Ashburton, Oke-
                                                       hampton

Malus pumila Mill.   Crab Apple   C
Crataegus monogyna Jacq.   Hawthorn   C

SAXIFRAGACEAE
Saxifraga tridactylites L.   Rue-leaved Saxifrage
Chrysosplenium oppositifolium L. Golden Saxifrage   C

GROSSULARIACEAE
Ribes rubrum L.   Red Currant   O
R. nigrum L.   Black Currant   O

CRASSULACEAE
Umbilicus pendulinus DC.   Pennywort   A
Sedum telephium L.   Orpine   O
S. anglicum Huds.   English Stonecrop   C

DROSERACEAE
Drosera rotundifolia L.   Round-leaved Sundew   C
D. anglica Huds.   Long-leaved Sundew   R
D. longifolia L.   Lesser Long-leaved Sundew Not uncommon

HALORAGACEAE
Myriophyllum spicatum L.   Spiked Water Milfoil C
M. alternifolium DC.   Water Milfoil   Rather uncommon
Callitriche palustris L.   Water Starwort   R
C. stagnalis Scop.   The common Moor sp.
C. intermedia Hoffm.   Uncommon
C. obtusangula Le Gall.   R

LYTHRACEAE
Peplis portula L.   Water Purslane   C
Lythrum salicaria L.   Purple Loosestrife   C in river valleys

ONAGRACEAE
Chamaenerion angustifolium
   (L.) Scop.   Rose-bay   W
Epilobium hirsutum L.   Codlins and Cream   C
E. parviflorum Schreb.   Downy Willowherb   C
E. montanum L.   Smooth-leaved Willowherb C
E. lanceolatum Seb. & Maur. Spear-leaved Willowherb F
E. roseum Schreb.   Pale Willowherb   R

E. tetragonum L.		G
E. obscurum Schreb.		W
E. palustre L.	Marsh Willowherb	Commonest sp. on Dartmoor
Circaea lutetiana L.	Enchanter's Nightshade	F

UMBELLIFERAE

Hydrocotyle vulgaris L.	Marsh Pennywort	A
Sanicula europaea L.	Wood Sanicle	C in woods
Conium maculatum L.	Hemlock	C
Apium graveolens L.	Celery	F. C
A. nodiflorum (L.) Lag.	Common Marshwort	C
A. inundatum (L.) Reichb. f.	Water Honewort	Pools Bovey Heath
Carum verticillatum (L.) Koch	Whorled Caraway	R. Moretonhampstead, Cornwood, old recs.
Petroselinum segetum (L.) Koch	Corn Parsley	Ashburton, Ilsington
Sison amomum L.	Stone Parsley	Ashburton
Aegopodium podagraria L.	Ground Elder	C cultivation
Pimpinella saxifraga L.	Burnet Saxifrage	C
P. major (L.) Huds.	Great Burnet Saxifrage	R. Cornwood, Postbridge
Conopodium majus (Gouan) Lor. & Barr.	Earth Nut	C
Myrrhis odorata (L.) Scop.	Sweet Cicely	Rather R. Manaton, Buckland, Chagford
Chaerophyllum temulum L.	Rough Chervil	A
Scandix pecten-veneris L.	Shepherd's Needle	R. Cornwood
Anthriscus scandicina (Weber) Mansf.		Uncommon
A. sylvestris Hoffm.	Wild Parsley	C
Foeniculum vulgare Mill.	Fennel	Uncommon
Oenanthe pimpinelloides L.	Pimpernel Water Dropwort	C
O. crocata L.	Hemlock Water Dropwort	C
Aethusa cynapium	Fool's Parsley	C cultivation
Angelica sylvestris L.	Angelica	C
Pastinaca sativa L.	Wild Parsnip	Chudleigh Knighton, Cornwood
Heracleum sphondylium L.	Cow Parsnip	A
Daucus carota L.	Wild Carrot	W
Torilis infesta (L.) Spreng.	Spreading Hedge Parsley	R
T. anthriscus (L.) Gmel.	Upright Hedge Parsley	C

ARALIACEAE

Hedera helix L.	Ivy	A

CORNACEAE

Cornus sanguinea L.	Dogwood	Local. Ashburton, Cornwood, Chudleigh

ADOXACEAE

Adoxa moschatellina L.	Moschatel	C in woods

CAPRIFOLIACEAE

Sambucus nigra L.	Elder	C
S. ebulus L.	Danewort	R. Widecombe
Viburnum opulus L.	Guelder Rose	W
V. lantana L.	Wayfaring Tree	O Ashburton Bovey Trac.
Lonicera periclymenum L.	Honeysuckle	A

RUBIACEAE

Rubia peregrina L.	Wild Madder	Ashburton, Ilsington, Dunsford
Galium cruciata (L.) Scop.	Crosswort	Locally A
G. mollugo L.	Hedge Bedstraw	A
G. saxatile L.	Heath Bedstraw	A, esp. moor
G. palustre L.	Marsh Bedstraw	C
G. debile Desv.		Confined to clayworks Bovey Heath
G. uliginosum L.	Bog Bedstraw	Not C
G. aparine L.	Goose-grass	A
G. tricorne Stokes	Three-horned Goose-grass	R. Cornwood, Buckfastleigh
Asperula odorata L.	Sweet Woodruff	G
Sherardia arvensis L.	Field Madder	G

VALERIANACEAE

Valeriana officinalis L.	Valerian	C
Valerianella locusta L.	Corn Salad, Lamb's Lettuce	C
V. rimosa Bast.		F
V. dentata (L.) Poll.		F

DIPSACACEAE

Dipsacus fullonum L.	Teazle	G
Succisa pratensis Moench	Devil's Bit Scabious	A
Knautia arvensis (L.) Coult.	Field Scabious	C

COMPOSITAE

Eupatorium cannabinum L.	Hemp Agrimony	C
Solidago virgaurea L.	Golden Rod	C
Bellis perennis L.	Daisy	C
Erigeron acris L.	Blue Fleabane	L Heathfield
Filago germanica (L.) L.	Cudweed	G
Gnaphalium uliginosum L.	Marsh Cudweed	C
G. sylvaticum L.	Heath Cudweed	F outskirts moor
Inula conyza DC.	Ploughman's Spikenard	C
Pulicaria dysenterica (L.) Bernh.	Fleabane	C

Achillea millefolium L.	Yarrow	A
A. ptarmica L.	Sneezewort	F
Anthemis cotula L.	Stinking Mayweed	G
A. nobilis L.	Chamomile	L
Chrysanthemum segetum L.	Corn Marigold	L
C. leucanthemum L.	Ox-Eye Daisy	C
C. parthenium (L.) Bernh.	Feverfew	L cultivation
Matricaria inodora L.	Scentless Mayweed	G
M. chamomilla L.	Wild Chamomile	Sparse
Tanacetum vulgare L.	Tansy	C
Artemisia absinthium L.	Wormwood	Uncommon
A. vulgaris L.	Mugwort	C
Tussilago farfara L.	Coltsfoot	C
Petasites hybridus (L.) Gaertn., Mey. & Scherb.	Butterbur	Not uncommon
Senecio vulgaris L.	Groundsel	A
S. sylvaticus L.	Mountain Groundsel	G
S. erucifolius L.	Downy Groundsel	L. Ashburton, Teign Valley
S. jacobaea L.	Ragwort	C
S. aquaticus Hill	Marsh Ragwort	C
Carlina vulgaris L.	Carline Thistle	Uncommon, Belstone
Arctium minus (Hill) Bernh.	Common Burdock	C
Carduus nutans L.	Musk Thistle	L
C. crispus L.	Welted Thistle	L. Bovey Tracey
Cirsium vulgare (Savi) Ten.	Spear Thistle	C
C. palustre (L.) Scop.	Marsh Thistle	A
C. dissectum (L.) Hill	Meadow Thistle	Uncommon
C. arvense (L.) Scop.	Creeping Thistle	C
Onopordum acanthium L.	Scottish Thistle	R Chagford
Serratula tinctoria L.	Saw-wort	F
Centaurea nigra L. agg.	Knapweed	C
C. nemoralis Jord.		C
C. scabiosa L.	Great Knapweed	Fairly C
C. cyanus L.	Cornflower	L cultivation
Lapsana communis L.	Nipplewort	C
Crepis taraxacifolia Thuill.		Ashburton
C. capillaris (L.) Wallr.	Common Hawksbeard	C
Hieracium lachenalii Gmel.	Hawkweed	Uncommon, Chagford
H. umbellatum L.	Wood Hawkweed	C
H. boreale Fr.		W
H. pilosella L.	Mouse-eared Hawkweed	Fairly C
Hypochoeris glabra L.	Smooth Cat's-ear	R. Holne, Hennock, Moretonhampstead
H. radicata L.	Long-rooted Cat's-ear	A
Leontodon leysseri (Wallr.) Beck	Hawkbit	C

L. hispidus L.	Rough Hawkbit	C
L. autumnalis L.	Autumn Hawkbit	C
Taraxacum officinale Weber	Dandelion	A
T. laevigatum (Willd.) DC.		F
T. palustre (Lyons) DC.		G
Lactuca muralis (L.) Fresen.	Wall Lettuce	L
Sonchus oleraceus L.	Sow-Thistle	C
S. asper (L.) Hill	Rough Sow-Thistle	F
S. arvensis L.	Corn Sow-Thistle	F
Tragopogon pratensis L.	Goatsbeard	C
T. minor Mill.		Probably C

LOBELIACEAE

Lobelia urens L.		R very L

CAMPANULACEAE

Jasione montana L.	Sheep's Bit Scabious	C
Wahlenbergia hederacea (L.) Rchb.	Ivy-leaved Bellflower	C in bogs
Campanula trachelium L.	Nettle-leaved Bellflower	R. Manaton 1929
C. rotundifolia L.	Harebell	Uncommon. Holne, Chagford
Specularia hybrida (L.) A. DC.	Venus Looking-Glass	O cultivation

VACCINIACEAE

Vaccinium vitis-idaea L.	Cowberry	V R
V. myrtillus L.	Whortleberry	C
Oxycoccus quadripetalus Gilib.	Cranberry	V R

ERICACEAE

Calluna vulgaris (L) Hull	Ling, Heather	C
Erica ciliaris L.	Dorset Heath	R L
E. tetralix L.	Cross-leaved Heath	C
E. cinerea L.	Bell Heather	C

PRIMULACEAE

Primula vulgaris L.	Primrose	C
Lysimachia nemorum L.	Yellow Pimpernel	F
Anagallis arvensis L.	Scarlet Pimpernel	C
A. tenella (L.) Murr.	Bog Pimpernel	C in bogs
Centunculus minimus L.	Chaffweed	Probably C

OLEACEAE

Fraxinus excelsior L.	Ash	C

GENTIANACEAE

Centaurium umbellatum Gilib.	Centaury	C

Gentiana campestris L.	Gentian	Okehampton, Cornwood, Lydford,
G. amarella L.		R Okehampton

MENYANTHACEAE

Menyanthes trifoliata L.	Bogbean	C in bogs

BORAGINACEAE

Symphytum officinale L.	Comfrey	C
S. peregrimum Ledeb.		R. Holne, Lustleigh
Anchusa sempervirens L.	Evergreen Alkanet	F
Lycopsis arvensis L.	Small Bugloss	Locally C
Myosotis caespitosa K. F. Schultz		C
M. scorpioides L.	Water Forget-Me-Not	L
M. secunda A. Murr.		C
M. arvensis (L.) Hill		C
M. versicolor Sm.	Scorpion Grass	C

CONVOLVULACEAE

Calystegia sepium (L.) R. Br.	Greater Bindweed	C
Convolvulus arvensis L.	Lesser Bindweed	C
Cuscuta europaea L.	Great Dodder	R
C. epithymum (L.) Murr.	Dodder	C

SOLANACEAE

Solanum dulcamara L.	Woody Nightshade	C
S. nigrum L.	Black Nightshade	L cultivation

SCROPHULARIACEAE

Verbascum thapsus L.	Mullein	F
V. nigrum L.	Dark Mullein	Rather R
Linaria cymbalaria (L.) Mill.	Ivy-leaved Toadflax	C
L. elatine (L.) Mill.	Sharp-leaved Fluellen	L cultivation
L. repens (L.) Mill.	Pale Toadflax	L (calc)
L. vulgaris Mill.	Yellow Toadflax	C
Antirrhinum majus L.	Snapdragon	F
A. orontium L.	Corn Snapdragon	Rather R
Scrophularia nodosa L.	Figwort	C
S. aquatica L.	Water Figwort	C
Sibthorpia europaea L.	Cornish Moneywort	G edge of moor
Digitalis purpurea L.	Foxglove	A
Veronica hederifolia L.	Ivy-leaved Speedwell	C cultivation
V. agrestis L.	Green Field Speedwell	C cultivation
V. persica Poir.	Buxbaum's Speedwell	C
V. arvensis L.	Wall Speedwell	C
V. serpyllifolia L.	Thyme-leaved Speedwell	C

V. officinalis L.	Common Speedwell	C
V. chamaedrys L.	Germander Speedwell	C
V. montana L.	Mountain Speedwell	F
V. scutellata L.	Marsh Speedwell	F
V. beccabunga L.	Brook-lime	C
Euphrasia officinalis L. agg.	Eyebright	C
Odontites rubra Gilib.	Red Bartsia	G
Parentucellia viscosa (L.) Carvel	Yellow Bartsia	G
Pedicularis palustris L.	Marsh Lousewort	C
P. sylvatica L.	Lousewort	C
Rhinanthus minor agg.	Yellow Rattle	F
Melampyrum pratense L.	Cow Wheat	C

OROBANCHACEAE

Orobanche rapum-genistae Thuill.	Great Broom Rape	Not C
O. apiculata Wallr.	Common Broom Rape	C

LENTIBULARIACEAE

Utricularia neglecta Lehm.	Bladderwort	R Bovey Heath
Pinguicula vulgaris L.	Common Butterwort	Very R. Perhaps extinct
P. lusitanica L.	Pale Butterwort	C bogs

LABIATAE

Mentha rotundifolia (L.) Huds.	Round-leaved Mint	L
M. aquatica L.	Water Mint	C
M. gentilis L.		R Widecombe Moretonhampstead
M. arvensis L.	Corn Mint	C cultivation
M. pulegium L.	Pennyroyal	L Widecombe
Lycopus europaeus L.	Gipsywort	G lowlands
Thymus drucei Ronn.	Thyme	C
T. pulegioides L. agg.	Thyme	Rather R. Bovey to Moretonhampstead
Clinopodium vulgare L.	Wild Basil	C
Calamintha ascendens Jord.	Calamint	C
Glecoma hederacea L.	Ground Ivy	C
Scutellaria galericulata L.	Skull-cap	Not C
S. minor Huds.	Lesser Skull-cap	C bogs
Prunella vulgaris L.	Self Heal	C
Melittis melissophyllum L.	Bastard Balm	G
Marrubium vulgare L.	White Horehound	Not C
Stachys officinalis (L.) Trev.	Wood Betony	C
S. palustris L.	Marsh Woundwort	C
S. sylvatica L.	Hedge Woundwort	C
Galeopsis angustifolia Hoffm.		Not C
G. tetrahit L.	Common Hemp Nettle	G

Lamium amplexicaule L.	Hen-bit	R. Chagford, Ashburton
L. hybridum Vill.		Not C. Manaton
L. purpureum L.	Red Dead Nettle	C
L. album L.	White Dead Nettle	C
Galeobdolon luteum Huds.	Yellow Archangel	G
Ballota nigra L.	Black Horehound	Not C
Teucrium scorodonia L.	Wood Sage	C
Ajuga reptans L.	Bugle	C

PLANTAGINACEAE

Plantago coronopus L.	Buckshorn Plantain	C
P. lanceolata L.	Ribwort Plantain	C
P. major L.	Great Plantain	C

ILLECEBRACEAE

Scleranthus annuus L.	Knawel	Rather R

CHENOPODIACEAE

Chenopodium vulvaria L.	Stinking Goosefoot	R. Chagford, 1929
C. album L.	Goosefoot	C
C. bonus-henricus L.	Good King Henry	Not C
Atriplex hastata L.		G

POLYGONACEAE

Polygonum convolvulus L.	Black Bindweed	C
P. aviculare L.	Knot Grass	C|
P. hydropiper L.	Water Pepper	C
P. mite Schrank		V R. Lustleigh
P. persicaria L.	Spotted Persicaria	G
P. lapathifolium L.	Pale Persicaria	G
P. bistorta L.	Bistort	Not uncommon
Rumex glomeratus Murr.	Sharp Dock	C
R. sanguineus L.	Wood Dock	C
R. pulcher L.	Fiddle Dock	G
R. obtusifolius L.	Broad-leaved Dock	C
R. crispus L.	Curled Dock	C
R. acetosa L.	Sorrel	C
R. acetosella L.	Sheep's Sorrel	A

EUPHORBIACEAE

Euphorbia helioscopia L.	Sun Spurge	Fairly C cultivation
E. amygdaloides L.	Wood Spurge	C
E. peplus L.	Petty Spurge	C
E. exigua L.	Dwarf Spurge	Fairly C
Mercurialis perennis L.	Dog's Mercury	C

ULMACEAE

Ulmus glabra Huds.	Wych Elm	G
U. procera Salisb.	Common Elm	C

CANNABINACEAE

Humulus lupulus L.	Hop	F

URTICACEAE

Urtica dioica L.	Stinging Nettle	A
U. urens L.	Small Stinging Nettle	Fairly C

MYRICACEAE

Myrica gale L.	Bog Myrtle	Not C

BETULACEAE

Betula pendula Roth.	Silver Birch	F
B. pubescens Ehrh.	Birch	Not C
Alnus glutinosa (L.) Gaertn.	Alder	C

CORYLACEAE

Carpinus betulus L.	Hornbeam	Fairly F
Corylus avellana L.	Hazel	C

FAGACEAE

Quercus robur L.	Oak	C
Q. petraea (Mattus.) Liebl.	Sessile Oak	Fairly F
Fagus sylvatica L.	Beech	Fairly C

SALICACEAE

Salix fragilis L.	Crack Willow	Not C. Chagford
S. purpurea L.	Purple Osier	R. Chagford
S. aurita L.	Auricled Sallow	G
S. caprea L.	Goat Willow	C
S. repens L.	Dwarf Willow	Northern Dartmoor only
Populus tremula L.	Aspen	Fairly C

EMPETRACEAE

Empetrum nigrum L.	Crowberry	Higher parts moor

ORCHIDACEAE

Epipactis purpurata Sm.		V R. Cornwood, 1854
E. helleborine (L.) Crantz		G
E. leptochila (Godf.) Godf.		V R. Cornwood
Listera cordata (L.) R. Br.	Lesser Twayblade	V R. Shipley Br.
L. ovata (L.) R. Br.	Twayblade	G

Neottia nidus-avis (L.) L. C. Rich.	Bird's Nest Orchid	R. Bovey Tracey Drum Bridge
Spiranthes spiralis (L.) Koch	Lady's Tresses	Locally plentiful
Hammarbya paludosa (L.) O. Kuntz	Bog Orchid	R
Coeloglossum viride (L.) Hartm.	Frog Orchid	R Peter Tavy, Tavy Cleave
Platanthera bifolia (L.) Rich.	Lesser Butterfly Orchid	L
Gymnadenia conopsea (L.) R. Br.		L
Anacamptis pyramidalis L. C. Rich.	Pyramid Orchid	Not uncommon
Orchis morio L.	Green-winged Orchid	C
O. mascula (L.) L.	Early Purple Orchid	C
O. latifolia L. sec. Pugsl.	Marsh Orchid	Not uncommon
O. praetermissa Druce	Marsh Orchid	C
O. pardalina Pugsl.	Marsh Orchid	Not uncommon
O. fuchsii Druce	Spotted Orchid	Not C Ashburton
O. ericetorum (E. S. Marshall)		C on heaths, esp. Dartmoor

IRIDACEAE

Iris pseudacorus L. (E. F. Lint.)	Yellow Flag	C

AMARYLLIDACEAE

Narcissus pseudo-narcissus L.	Lent Lily	Locally A
Galanthus nivalis L.	Snowdrop	Not C

DIOSCOREACEAE

Tamus communis L.	Black Bryony	G

LILIACEAE

Ruscus aculeatus L.	Butcher's Broom	O. North Bovey, Lydford
Polygonatum multiflorum (L.) All.	Solomon's Seal	O. Clifford Br., Shaugh Prior
Convallaria majalis L.	Lily of the Valley	V R. Shaugh Prior
Allium ursinum L.	Ramsons	C
Scilla non-scripta (L.) Hoffmgg. & Link	Bluebell	A
Colchicum autumnale L.	Meadow Saffron	R. Bovey Tracey
Narthecium ossifragum (L.) Huds.	Bog Asphodel	C bogs

JUNCACEAE

Juncus bufonius L.	Toad Rush	C
J. squarrosus L.	Heath Rush	C moor
J. compressus Jacq.		Not C

J. inflexus L.	Hard Rush	Fairly C
J. effusus L.	Soft Rush	C
J. conglomeratus L.	Common Rush	A
J. bulbosus L.	Lesser Jointed Rush	A. esp. moor
J. subnodulosus Schrank	Obtuse-flowered Rush	Not C
J. articulatus L.	Shiny Jointed Rush	C
J. acutiflorus Hoffm.	Greater Jointed Rush	Fairly C
Luzula forsteri (Sm.) DC.		Fairly C
L. pilosa (L.) Willd.		G
L. sylvatica (Huds.) Gaud.	Great Hairy Wood Rush	C
L. campestris (L.) DC.	Field Wood Rush	C
L. multiflora (Retz.) Lej.		C moors

SPARGANIACEAE

Sparganium simplex Huds.	Unbranched Bur-reed	Fairly C

ARACEAE

Arum maculatum L.	Lords and Ladies	C

LEMNACEAE

Lemna minor L.	Lesser Duckweed	C

ALISMATACEAE

Alisma plantago-aquatica L.	Water Plantain	G

POTAMOGETONACEAE

Potamogeton natans L.	Broad-leaved Pondweed	Not uncommon
P. polygonifolius Pourr.	Oblong-leaved Pondweed	C peaty ground
P. berchtoldii Fieb.	Small Pondweed	Not uncommon
P. pusillus L.		Very R. Meldon Quarry

ZANNICHELLIACEAE

Zannichellia palustris L.	Horned Pondweed	Not C

CYPERACEAE

Cyperus longus L.	Galingale	V R. Manaton intro.
Eleocharis acicularis (L.) Roem. & Schult.	Needle Club Rush	Not C
E. palustris (L.) Roem. & Schult.	Marsh Club Rush	C
E. multicaulis (Sm.) Sm.	Many-stalked Club Rush	Not uncommon
Scirpus pauciflorus Lightf.	Few-flowered Club Rush	Uncommon
S. caespitosus L.	Deer Grass	A
S. fluitans L.	Floating Club Rush	G southern Dartmoor
S. cernuus Vahl		Not C
S. setaceus L.	Bristle Club Rush	Fairly C
Eriophorum vaginatum L.	Hare's Tail Cotton Grass	C

E. angustifolium Honck.	Narrow-leaved Cotton Grass	V C bogs
E. latifolium Hoppe	Broad-leaved Cotton Grass	Rather R
Rhynchospora alba (L.) Vahl	White Beak Sedge	Locally C bogs
Schoenus nigricans L.	Black Bog Rush	Scarce, Heathfield
Carex dioica L.	Dioecious Sedge	V R. Heathfield, 1934
C. pulicaris L.	Flea Sedge	Fairly C
C. disticha Huds.	Soft Sedge	L & R
C. paniculata L.	Tussock Sedge	C
C. vulpina L.	Fox Sedge	C
C. pairaei F. Schultz		Fairly C
C. divulsa Stokes		Fairly C
C. echinata Murr.	Lesser Prickly Sedge	C. esp. bogs
C. remota L.		C
C. ovalis Good	Oval Sedge	C
C. nigra (L.) Reichard		V C
C. pilulifera L.		C
C. caryophyllea Latour.	Vernal Sedge	G
C. pallescens L.	Pale Sedge	Fairly C
C. panicea L.	Carnation Sedge	C
C. pendula L.	Great Pendulous Sedge	L. Widecombe
C. sylvatica Huds.	Wood Sedge	C
C. laevigata Sm.		G
C. binervis Sm.	Green-ribbed Sedge	C
C. distans L.	Distant-spiked Sedge	Fairly C
C. hostiana DC.	Tawny Sedge	L. Okehampton, Belstone
C. flava L. agg.		C
C. lepidocarpa Tausch		C
C. tumidicarpa Anderss.		Fairly C
C. hirta L.	Hairy Sedge	Fairly C
C. acutiformis Ehrh.	Lesser Pond Sedge	Not C. Heathfield
C. riparia Curt.	Great Pond Sedge	L. Princetown
C. rostrata Stokes	Bottle Sedge	Not C
C. vesicaria L.	Bladder Sedge	Not C. Tavistock

GRAMINEAE

Setaria viridis (L.) Beauv.	Green Bristle Grass	G
Phalaris arundinacea L.	Reed Grass	Not on high ground
Anthoxanthum odoratum L.	Vernal Grass	C
Alopecurus geniculatus L.	Fox-tail Grass	C, below 1,000 ft.
A. pratensis L.	Meadow Fox-tail Grass	C
Milium effusum L.	Wood Millet	Locally plentiful
Phleum pratense L.	Timothy Grass	C
Agrostis setacea Curt.	Heath Bent Grass	A
A. tenuis Sibth.	Fine Bent Grass	Not uncommon
A. canina L.	Brown Bent	C
Gastridium ventricosum (Gouan) Schinz. & Thell.	Nit Grass	Rather R. Cornwood
Aira caryophyllea L.	Silver Hair Grass	C locally

A. praecox L.	Early Hair Grass	G
Deschampsia caespitosa (L.) Beauv.	Tufted Hair Grass	G
D. flexuosa (L.) Trin.	Waved Hair Grass	C
Holcus mollis L.	Soft Grass	C
H. lanatus L.	Yorkshire Fog	C
Trisetum flavescens (L.) Beauv.	Yellow Oat	C
Helictotrichon pratense (L.) Pilger	Meadow Oat	R (calc.) Ashburton
Avena fatua L.	Wild Oat	Fairly C
Arrhenatherum elatius (L.) J. & C. Presl.	False Oat	C
Sieglingia decumbens (L.) Bernh.	Heath Grass	C
Phragmites communis Trin.	Reed	G
Cynosurus cristatus L.	Crested Dog's Tail	C
Koeleria gracilis Pers.		Uncommon, Ilsington
Molinia caerulea (L.) Moench.	Purple Moor Grass	C
Melica uniflora Retz.	Wood Melick	Locally A
Dactylis glomerata L.	Cocksfoot	C
Briza media L.	Quaker Grass	Not C. Widecombe
Poa annua L.	Annual Meadow Grass	A
P. nemoralis L.	Wood Meadow Grass	Not C
P. pratensis L.	Smooth-stalked Meadow Grass	C
P. trivialis L.	Rough Meadow Grass	C
Glyceria fluitans (L.) R. Br.	Floating Meadow Grass	Fairly C
G. plicata Fr.	Folded-leaved Meadow Grass	Uncommon, Ilsington
G. maxima (Hartn.) Holnb.	Reed Meadow Grass	R. Manaton, 1922
Scleropoa rigida (L.) Grisch.		C
Vulpia myuros (L.) Gmel.	Wall Fescue	Not C. Ilsington, Heathfield
V. bromoides (L.) S. F. Gray	Barren Fescue	C
Festuca ovina L. agg.	Sheep's Fescue	C
F. heterophylla Lan.		Uncommon, Heathfield
F. gigantea (L.) Mill.		Not uncommon
Bromus ramosus Huds.	Hairy Brome	W
B. erectus Huds.	Upright Brome	R. Holne
B. sterilis L.	Barren Brome	C
B. secalinus L.	Rye Brome	Not C. Manaton
B. racemosus L.		Not C. Ilsington, Moretonhampstead
B. hordeaceus. L.	Soft Brome	C
B. lepidus Holmb.		R. Belstone
Brachypodium sylvaticum (Huds.) Beauv.	False Brome	C

B. pinnatum (L.) Beauv.	Spiked False Brome	Ashburton (calc.)
Lolium perenne L.	Rye Grass	C
L. multiflorum Lam.	Italian Rye Grass	C
L. temulentum L.	Darnel	Scarce, Ilsington
Agropyron caninum (L.) Beauv.	Fibrous Couch Grass	Rather uncommon
A. repens (L.) Beauv.	Couch Grass	C
Nardus stricta L.	Mat Grass	C

PINACEAE

Pinus sylvestris L.	Scots Fir	C

HYMENOPHYLLACEAE

Hymenophyllum tunbridgense (L.) Sm.	Filmy Fern	Uncommon
H. peltatum (Poir.) Desv.	Wilson's Fern	Uncommon

POLYPODIACEAE

Pteridium aquilinum (L.) Kuhn	Bracken	A
Blechnum spicant (L.) Roth	Hard Fern	C
Asplenium obovatum Viv.	Lanceolate Spleenwort	L
A. adiantum-nigrum L.	Black Spleenwort	C
A. trichomanes L.	Maidenhair Spleenwort	C
A. ruta-muraria L.	Wall Rue	C
Athyrium filix-femina (L.) Roth	Lady Fern	C
Ceterach officinarum DC.	Rustyback	G
Phyllitis scolopendrium (L.) Newm.	Hart's Tongue	C
Cystopteris fragilis (L.) Bernh.	Brittle Bladder Fern	R. Cornwood, Tavistock
Polystichum aculeatum (L.) Roth	Hard Shield Fern	W
P. setiferum (Forsk.) Woyn.	Soft Shield Fern	C
Thelypteris oreopteris (Ehrh.) C. Chr.	Mountain Buckler Fern	Fairly C, esp. moor
T. polypodioides (L.) Sloss.	Beech Fern	L
Dryopteris filix-mas (L.) Schott	Male Fern	A
D. spinulosa (Müll.) Watt	Narrow Buckler Fern	R. Fingle Bridge
D. dilatata (Hoffm.) A. Gray	Broad Buckler Fern	C
D. aemula (Ait.) O. Kuntze	Hay-scented Buckler Fern	Not uncommon
Gymnocarpium dryopteris (L.) Newm.	Oak Fern	R. Manaton, Lydford
Polypodium vulgare L.	Common Polypody	C

OSMUNDACEAE

Osmunda regalis L.	Royal Fern	Not uncommon

OPHIOGLOSSACEAE

Ophioglossum vulgatum L.	Adder's Tongue	L. Holne
Botrychium lunaria (L.) Sw.	Moonwort	Uncommon

EQUISETACEAE

Equisetum telmateia Ehrh.	Great Horsetail	Fairly C
E. arvense L.	Common Horsetail	C
E. sylvaticum L.	Wood Horsetail	R. Holne Chase
E. palustre L.	Marsh Horsetail	Fairly C
E. fluviatile L.	Smooth Water Horsetail	G

LYCOPODIACEAE

Lycopodium selago L.	Fir Club-Moss	Thinly distributed
L. inundatum L.	Marsh Club-Moss	R & L. Heathfield
L. clavatum L.	Common Club-Moss	Fairly C
L. alpinum L.	Alpine Club-Moss	V R. Single records. Yes Tor, Chagford

ISOETACEAE

Isoetes fluviatile L.	Quillwort	R. Shaugh Prior, Cornwood

CHAROPHYTA

Chara delicatula Agardh	Locally plentiful, Manaton
C. vulgaris L.	Thinly distributed, Heathfield
Nitella translucens Agardh	R. Hennock
N. flexilis Agardh	R. Heathfield
N. opaca Agardh	Thinly distributed, Manaton

D.   Q

(B) VERTEBRATES
MAMMALIA

INSECTIVORA

TALPIDAE
Talpa europaea L. — Common Mole
SORICIDAE
Sorex araneus L. — Common Shrew
S. minutus L. — Pigmy Shrew
Neomys fodiens (Schreb.) — Water Shrew
ERINACEIDAE
Erinaceus europaeus L. — Hedgehog

CHIROPTERA

RHINOLOPHIDAE
Rhinolophus ferrum-equinum (Schreb.) — Greater Horseshoe Bat
R. hipposideros (Bechst.) — Lesser Horseshoe Bat
VESPERTILIONIDAE
Myotis mystacinus (Kuhl) — Whiskered Bat
M. nattereri (Kuhl) — Natterer's Bat
Pipistrellus pipistrellus (Schreb.) — Pipistrelle
Nyctalus noctula (Schreb.) — Noctule
N. leisleri (Kuhl) — Leisler's Bat
Plecotus auritus (L.) — Long-eared Bat

CARNIVORA FISSIPEDIA

CANIDAE
Vulpes vulpes (L.) — Fox
MUSTELIDAE
Meles meles (L.) — Badger
Lutra lutra (L.) — Otter
Martes martes (L.) — Pine Marten
Mustela erminea L. — Stoat
M. nivalis L. — Weasel
M. putorius L. — Polecat

RODENTIA

LEPORIDAE
Oryctolagus cuniculus (L.) — Rabbit
Lepus europaeus Pall. — Brown Hare
MUSCARDINIDAE
Muscardinus avellanarius (L.) — Dormouse

MURIDAE
Clethrionomys glareolus (Schreb.) — Bank Vole
Arvicola amphibius (L.) — Water Vole
Microtus arvensis (Bell) — Short-tailed Vole
Apodemus sylvaticus (L.) — Long-tailed Field Mouse
Micromys minutus (Pall.) — Harvest Mouse
Rattus norvegicus (Erxl.) — Brown Rat
Mus musculus (Bar.-Ham.) — House Mouse
SCIURIDAE
Sciurus vulgaris L. — Red Squirrel
S. carolinensis Gmelin — Grey Squirrel

ARTIODACTYLA

CERVIDAE
Cervus elaphus (L.) — Red Deer

AVES

PASSERIFORMES

CORVIDAE
Corvus corax L. — Raven — R F G
C. corone L. — Carrion-Crow — R A G
C. frugilegus L. — Rook — R A W
C. monedula L. — Jackdaw — R A W
Pica pica (L.) — Magpie — R C W
Garrulus glandarius L. — Jay — R C W
STURNIDAE
Sturnus vulgaris L. — Starling — R A G
ORIOLIDAE
Oriolus oriolus (L.) — Golden Oriole — T R O
FRINGILLIDAE
Coccothraustes coccothraustes (L.) — Hawfinch — R F L
Chloris chloris (L.) — Greenfinch — R C W
Carduelis carduelis (L.) — Goldfinch — R C W
C. spinus (L.) — Siskin — W V F O
C. flammea (L.) — Lesser Redpoll — W V F O
C. flavirostris (L.) — Twite — R R L
C. cannabina (L.) — Linnet — R C W
Pyrrhula pyrrhula (L.) — Bullfinch — R C W
Loxia curvirostra L. — Common Crossbill — T F O
Fringilla coelebs L. — Chaffinch — R C W
F. montifringilla L. — Brambling — W V F O
Emberiza citrinella L. — Yellow Bunting — R C W
E. cirlus L. — Cirl Bunting — R F L
E. schoeniclus (L.) — Reed-Bunting — R F L

Calcarius lapponicus (L.)	Lapland Bunting	T R O
Plectrophenax nivalis (L.)	Snow-Bunting	WV R L
PLOCEIDAE		
Passer domesticus (L.)	House-Sparrow	R C W
ALAUDIDAE		
Lullula arborea (L.)	Wood-Lark	R F W
Alauda arvensis L.	Skylark	R C G
MOTACILLIDAE		
Anthus trivialis (L.)	Tree-Pipit	SR F L
A. pratensis (L.)	Meadow-Pipit	R A G
A. spinoletta (L.)	Rock-Pipit	T R O
Motacilla flava (Blyth)	Yellow Wagtail	T F O
M. cinerea Tunst.	Grey Wagtail	R C W
M. alba yarrellii Gould	Pied Wagtail	R C W
CERTHIIDAE		
Certhia familiaris L.	Tree-Creeper	R C W
SITTIDAE		
Sitta europaea L.	Nuthatch	R C W
PARIDAE		
Parus major L.	Great Tit	R C W
P. caeruleus L.	Blue Tit	R A W
P. ater L.	Coal Tit	R C W
P. palustris L.	Marsh-Tit	R C W
P. atricapillus L.	Willow-Tit	R O
Aegithalos caudatus (L.)	Long-tailed Tit	R C W
LANIIDAE		
Lanius collurio L.	Red-backed Shrike	T R O
BOMBYCILLIDAE		
Bombycilla garrulus (L.)	Waxwing	T R O
MUSCICAPIDAE		
Muscicapa striata (Pall.)	Spotted Flycatcher	SR C W
M. hypoleuca (Pall.)	Pied Flycatcher	SR F L
REGULIDAE		
Regulus regulus (L.).	Goldcrest	R C W
SYLVIIDAE		
Phylloscopus collybita (Vieill.)	Chiffchaff	SR C W
P. trochilus (L.)	Willow-Warbler	SR A W
P. sibilatrix (Bechst.)	Wood-Warbler	SR C W
Locustella naevia (Bodd.)	Grasshopper-Warbler	SR F L
Acrocephalus scirpaceus (Herm.)	Reed-Warbler	T R O
A. schoenobaenus (L.)	Sedge-Warbler	SR F
Sylvia borin (Bodd.)	Garden-Warbler	SR C W
S. atricapilla (L.)	Blackcap	SR C W
S. communis Lath.	Whitethroat	SR C W
S. curruca (L.)	Lesser Whitethroat	SR R O
TURDIDAE		
Turdus dauma Lath.	White's Thrush	T R O

T. pilaris L.	Fieldfare	WV C W
T. viscivorus L.	Mistle Thrush	R C W
T. ericetorum Turton	Song-Thrush	R C W
T. musicus L.	Redwing	WV C W
T. eunomus Temm.	Dusky Thrush	T R O
T. torquatus L.	Ring-Ouzel	SR F L
T. merula L.	Blackbird	R A W
Oenanthe oenanthe (L.)	Wheatear	SR C W
Saxicola rubetra (L.)	Whinchat	SR F L
S. torquata (L.)	Stonechat	R F L
Phoenicurus phoenicurus (L.)	Redstart	SR F L
P. ochrurus (Gmel.)	Black Redstart	T F O
Luscinia megarhyncha Brehm	Nightingale	SR F O
Erithacus rubecula (L.)	Robin	R A W
PRUNELLIDAE		
Prunella modularis (L.)	Hedge-Sparrow	R A W
TROGLODYTIDAE		
Troglodytes troglodytes (L.)	Wren	R A W
CINCLIDAE		
Cinclus cinclus (L.)	Dipper	R C W
HIRUNDINIDAE		
Hirundo rustica L.	Swallow	SR C W
Delichon urbica (L.)	House-Martin	SR C L
Riparia riparia (L.)	Sand-Martin	SR C L

APODIFORMES

APODIDAE		
Apus apus (L.)	Swift	SR C G

CAPRIMULGIFORMES

CAPRIMULGIDAE		
Caprimulgus europaeus L.	Nightjar	SR F L

CORACIIFORMES

UPUPIDAE		
Upupa epops L.	Hoopoe	T F O
ALCEDINIDAE		
Alcedo atthis (L.)	Kingfisher	R C L

PICIFORMES

PICIDAE		
Picus viridis L.	Green Woodpecker	R C W
Dendrocopes major (L.)	Greater Spotted Woodpecker	R F W
D. minor (L.)	Lesser Spotted Woodpecker	R F L

CUCULIFORMES

CUCULIDAE
Cuculus canorus L.   Cuckoo   SR C W

STRIGIFORMES

STRIGIDAE
Nyctea scandaica (L.)   Snowy Owl   WV R O
Athene noctua (Scop)   Little Owl   R C W
Asio otus (L.)   Long-eared Owl   T R O
Strix aluco L.   Tawny Owl   R C W
Tyto alba (Scop.)   Barn-Owl   R C W

FALCONIFORMES

FALCONIDAE
Falco peregrinus Tunst.   Peregrine Falcon   R F O
F. subbuteo L.   Hobby   SR F O
F. columbarius L.   Merlin   R F W
F. tinnunculus L.   Kestrel   R C W
ACCIPITRIDAE
Buteo lagopus (Pontopp.)   Rough-legged Buzzard   WV R O
B. buteo (L.)   Common Buzzard   R C W
Circus aeruginosus (L.)   Marsh-Harrier   T R O
C. pygargus (L.)   Montagu's Harrier   SR F O
C. cyaneus (L.)   Hen-Harrier   WV R O
Accipiter nisus (L.)   Sparrow-Hawk   R C W
Milvus milvus (L.)   Kite   T R O
Haliaeetus albicilla (L.)   White-tailed Eagle   T F O
Pernis apivorus (L.)   Honey-Buzzard   T R O
PANDIONIDAE
Pandion haliaetus (L.)   Osprey   T R O

CICONIIFORMES

ARDEIDAE
Ardea cinerea L.   Common Heron   R C W
A. purpurea L.   Purple Heron   T R O
Botaurus stellaris (L.)   Bittern   T R O

ANSERIFORMES

ANATIDAE
Cygnus olor (Gm.)   Mute Swan   T F O
Tadorna tadorna (L.)   Sheld-Duck   R F O
Anas platyrhyncha L.   Mallard   R C W
A. crecca L.   Teal   R F L
A. penelope L.   Wigeon   WV R O
A. acuta L.   Pintail   T R O
Aythya ferina (L.)   Common Pochard   WV F O
A. fuligula (L.)   Tufted Duck   WV F O

Bucephala clangula (L.)	Goldeneye	WV F O
Clangula hyemalis (L.)	Long-tailed Duck	WV R O
Mergus merganser L.	Goosander	WV R O

PELECANIFORMES

PHALACROCORACIDAE
Phalacrocorax carbo (L.)	Cormorant	WV R O

PROCELLARIIFORMES

HYDROBATIDAE
Oceanodroma leucorrhoa (Vieill.)	Leach's Fork-tailed Petrel	T R O

PODICIPITIFORMES

PODICIPITIDAE
Podiceps ruficollis (Pall.)	Little Grebe	R F O

COLYMBIFORMES

COLYMBIDAE
Colymbus stellatus Pontopp.	Red-throated Diver	WV R O

COLUMBIFORMES

COLUMBIDAE
Columba palumbus L.	Wood-Pigeon	R A G
C. oenas L.	Stock-Dove	R C L
Streptopelia turtur (L.)	Turtle-Dove	SR F O

CHARADRIIFORMES

SCOLOPLACIDAE
Numenius arquata (L.)	Common Curlew	SR C L
N. phaeopus (L.)	Whimbrel	T F O
Scolopax rusticola L.	Woodcock	WV C W
Capella media (Lath.)	Great Snipe	T R O
C. gallinago (L.)	Common Snipe	R C W
Lymnocryptes minimus (Brünn.)	Jack Snipe	WV F W
Phalaropus fulicarius (L.)	Grey Phalarope	T R O
Calidris alpina (L.)	Dunlin	SR F L
Philomachus pugnax (L.)	Ruff	T R O
Tringa hypoleucos (L.)	Common Sandpiper	SR F I
T. ochropus L.	Green Sandpiper	T F O
T. totanus L.	Redshank	T F O

CHARADRIIDAE
Pluvialis apricaria (L.)	Golden Plover	WV C W
Charadrius morinellus (L.)	Dotterel	T R O
Vanellus vanellus (L.)	Lapwing	R C W

BURHINIDAE
Burhinus oedicnemus (L.)	Stone-Curlew	T R O

OTIDIDAE
Otis tarda L.	Great Bustard	T R O
O. tetrax L.	Little Bustard	T R O

LARIDAE
Larus ridibundus L.	Black-headed Gull	T F L
L. canus L.	Common Gull	T F L
L. argentatus Pont.	Herring-Gull	R C W
L. fuscus L.	Lesser Black-backed Gull	T F O
L. marinus L.	Great Black-backed Gull	R F O

RALLIFORMES

RALLIDAE
Crex crex (L.)	Corn-Crake	SR F W
Porzana porzana (L.)	Spotted Crake	T R O
Rallus aquaticus L.	Water-Rail	R F L
Gallinula chloropus (L.)	Moorhen	R C W
Fulica atra L.	Coot	R F L

GALLIFORMES

TETRAONIDAE
Lyrurus tetrix L.	Black Grouse	R F L
Lagopus scoticus (Lath.)	Red Grouse	R F L

PHASIANIDAE
Phasianus colchicus L.	Pheasant	R F W
Perdix perdix (L.)	Common Partridge	R F W

REPTILIA

Anguis fragilis L.	Slow-Worm
Lacerta vivipara Jacq.	Common Lizard
Natrix natrix (L.)	Grass-Snake
Vipera berus (L.)	Adder

AMPHIBIA

Rana temporaria L.	Common Frog
Bufo bufo (L.)	Common Toad
Triturus helveticus (Raz.)	Palmated Newt

FISHES

Lampetra fluviatilis L.	River Lamprey
Salmo salar L.	Salmon
S. trutta L.	Brown Trout
Thymallus thymallus (L.)	Grayling

Phoxinus phoxinus (L.)   Minnow
Nemacheilus barbatula (L.)   Loach
Anguilla anguilla (L.)   Common Eel
Gasterosteus aculeatus L.   Three-spined Stickleback

(C) INSECTS

ORTHOPTERA

ACRIDIDAE
Myrmeleotettix maculatus Thunb.   C. parallelus Zett.
Chorthippus bicolor Charp.

TETTIGONIIDAE
Leptophyes punctatissima Bosc.   Platycleis grisea (Fabr.)
Meconema thalassina (Fabr.)   Metrioptera brachyptera L.
Pholidoptera cinerea (L.)   Nemobius sylvestris L.

ODONATA

ZYGOPTERA

COENAGRIONIDAE
Pyrrhosoma nymphula (Sulz.)   Coenagrion pulchellum (v. d. Lind.)
Ischnura elegans (v. d. Lind.)   Ceriagrion tenellum (d. Vill)
                                                    (Requires confirmation)
Enallagma cyathigerum (Charp.)   C. puellum (L.)

AGRIIDAE
Agrion virgo (L.)   A. splendens (Harris)

ANISOPTERA

CORDULEGASTERIDAE
Cordulegaster boltonii (Don.)
AESCHNIDAE
Aeshna cyanea (Muell.)
CORDULIIDAE
Oxygastra curtisii (Dale)

LIBELLULIDAE
Orthetrum coerulescens (Fabr.)   S. flaveolum (L.)
O. cancellatum (L.)   S. sanguineum (Muell.)
Libellula depressa (L.)   S. scoticum (Leach)=danae (Sulz.)
Sympetrum striolatum (Charp.)

LEPIDOPTERA

HOMONEURA

HEPIALIDAE
Hepialus hectus (L.)   Gold Swift

H. lupulinus (L.)	Common Swift	
H. fusconebulosus (De G.)	Map-winged Swift	
H. humuli (L.)	Ghost	

HETERONEURA

ARCTIIDAE

Eilema lurideola (Zinck.)	Common Footman	
E. griseola (Huebn.)	Dingy Footman	Postbridge
Lithosia quadra (L.)	Four-spotted Footman	
Atolmis rubricollis (L.)	Red-necked Footman	
Cymbosia mesomella (L.)	Four-dotted Footman	
Comacla miniata (Forst.)	Rosy Footman	
Hypocrita jacobaeae (L.)	Cinnabar	
Phragmatobia fuliginosa (L.)	Ruby Tiger	
Cycnia mendica (Clerck)	Muslin	
Spilosoma lutea (Hufn.)	Buff Ermine	
S. lubricipeda (L.)	White Ermine	
Diacrisia sannio (L.)	Clouded Buff	
Arctia villaca (L.)	Cream-spot Tiger	
A. caja (L.)	Garden Tiger	
Parasemia plantaginis (L.)	Wood Tiger	

HYPSIDAE

Panaxia dominula (L.)	Scarlet Tiger

NOLIDAE

Roeselia confusalis (Herr.-Schaef.)

CYMBIDAE

Bena prasinana (L.)
Sarrothripus revayana (Scop.)

CARADRINIDAE

Apatele leporina (L.)	The Miller
A. alni (L.)	The Alder
A. tridens (Schiff.)	Dark Dagger
A. psi (L.)	Grey Dagger
A. megacephala (Schiff.)	Poplar Grey
A. rumicis (L.)	Knot Grass
Craniophora ligustri (Schiff.)	Coronet
Diphthera alpium (Osb.)	
Cryphia muralis (Forst.)	Marbled Green
C. perla (Schiff.)	Marbled Beauty
Stilbia anomala (Haw.)	Anomalous
Amphipyra pyramidea (L.)	Copper Underwing
A. tragopoginis (L.)	Mouse
Gortyna flavago (Schiff.)	Frosted Orange
Luperina testacea (Schiff.)	Flounced Rustic
Cosmia trapezina (L.)	Dun-bar
Caradrina clavipalpis (Scop.)	Pale Mottled Willow

C. morpheus (Hifn.)	Mottled Rustic
C. taraxaci (Huebn.)	Rustic
Mormo maura (L.)	Old Lady
Zenobia retusa (L.)	Double Kidney
Arenostola fluxa (Huebn.)	Mere Wainscot
A. pygmina (Haw.)	Small Wainscot
Meristis trigrammica (Hufn.)	Treble Lines
Phlogophora meticulosa (L.)	Angle Shades
Euplexia lucipara (L.)	Small Angle Shades
Xylophasia crenata (Hufn.)	Clouded-bordered Brindle
X. lithoxylea (Schiff.)	Light Arches
X. monoglypha (Hufn.)	Dark Arches
Apamea sordens (Hufn.)	Rustic Shoulder Knot
A. fissipuncta (Haw.)	
Celaena secalis (L.)	Common Rustic
Hydraecia oculea (L.)	Ear
Miana literosa (Haw.)	Rosy Minor
Procus strigilis (Clerck)	Marbled Minor
P. fasciunculus (Haw.)	Middle-barred Minor
Euxoa nigricans (L.)	Garden Dart
E. tritici (L.)	White-line Dart
Agrotis segetum (Schiff.)	Turnip
A. exclamationis (L.)	Heart and Dart
A. ypsilon (v. Rott.)	Dark Sword Grass
Peridromia saucia (Huebn.)	Pearly Underwing
Lycophotia porphyrea (Schiff.)	True Lover's Knot
Ochropleura plecta (L.)	Flame Shoulder
Amathes agathina (Dupon.)	Heath Rustic
A. castanea (Esper)	Neglected Rustic
A. c-nigrum (L.)	Setaceous Hebrew Character
A. ditrapezium (Borkh.)	Triple-spotted Clay
A. xanthographa (Schiff.)	Square Spot Rustic
A. glareosa (Esper)	Autumnal Rustic
A. depuncta (L.)	Plain Clay
A. baja (Schiff.)	Dotted Clay
Diarsia brunnea (Schiff.)	Purple Clay
D. festiva (Schiff.)	Ingrailed Clay
D. rubi (View.)	Small Square Spot
D. dahlii (Huebn.)	Barred Chestnut
Triphaena pronuba (L.)	Large Yellow Underwing
T. comes (Huebn.)	Lesser Yellow Underwing
T. janthina (Schiff.)	Lesser Broad Border
Axylia putris (L.)	Flame
Phalaena typica L.	Gothic
Cerastris rubricosa (Schiff.)	Red Chestnut
Anaplectoides prasina (Schiff.)	Green Arches

Aporophyla nigra (Haw.)	Black Rustic
Conistra ligula (Esper)	Dark Chestnut
C. vaccinii (L.)	Chestnut
Dasycampa rubiginea (Schiff.)	Dotted Chestnut
Atethmia centrago (Haw.)	Centre-barred Sallow
Jodea croceago (Schiff.)	Orange Upper Wing
Citria lutea (Stroem.)	Pink-barred Sallow
Cirrhia fulvago (L.)	Sallow
Agrochola lychnidis (Schiff.)	Beaded Chestnut
A. macilenta (Huebn.)	Yellow-line Quaker
A. lota (Clerck)	Red-line Quaker
Eupsilia transversa (Hufn.)	Satellite
Allophyes oxyacanthae (L.)	Green-brindled Crescent
Cucullia absinthii (L.)	Wormwood
C. chamomillae (Schiff.)	Chamomile Shark
C. umbratica (C.)	Shark
C. verbasci (L.)	Mullein
Xylena exoleta (L.)	Sword Grass
X. vetusta (Huebn.)	Red Sword Grass
Lithophane semi-brunnea (Haw.)	Tawny Pinion
Graptolitha ornitopus (Hufn.)	Grey Shoulder-knot
Xylocampa areola (Esper)	Early Grey
Griposia aprilina (L.)	Merveille du Jour
Antitype chi (L.)	Grey Chi
Bombycia viminalis (Fabr.)	Minor Shoulder-knot
Eumichtis adusta (Esper)	Dark Brocade
Dryobota protea (Schiff.)	Brindled Green
Leucenia pallens (L.)	Common Wainscot
L. lythargyria (Esper)	Clay
L. conigera (Schiff.)	Brown-line Bright-eye
Orthosia incerta (Hufn.)	Clouded Drab
O. gracilis (Schiff.)	Powdered Quaker
O stabilis (Schiff.)	Common Quaker
O. miniosa (Schiff.)	Blossom Underwing
O. munda (Schiff.)	Twin-spotted Quaker
O. gothica (L.)	Hebrew Character
Charaeas graminis (L.)	Antler
Tholera popularis (Fabr.)	Feathered Gothic
T. caespitis (Schiff.)	Hedge Rustic
Panolis griseovariegata (Goeze)	Pine Beauty
Hadena serena (Schiff.)	Broad-barred White
Diataraxia oleracea (L.)	Bright-line Brown-eye
Ceramica pisi (L.)	Broom
Polia nebulosa (Hufn.)	Grey Arches
Mamestra brassicae (L.)	Cabbage
Anarta myrtilli (L.)	Beautiful Yellow Underwing

PLUSIIDAE

Zanclognatha tarsipennalis (Treitsch.) — Fanfoot

Schrankia costaestrigalis Step. — Pinion-streaked Snout
Laspeyria flexula (Schiff.) — Beautiful Hook-tip
Scoliopteryx libatrix (L.) — Herald
Catocala promissa (Schiff.) — Light Crimson Underwing
Euclidimera mi (Clerck) — Mother Shipton
Ectypa glyphica (L.) — Burnet Companion
Jaspidia fasciana (L.) — Marbled White Spot
Eustrotia uncula (Clerck) — Silver Hook
Phytometra viridaria (Clerck) — Small Purple Barred
Polychrisia moneta (Fabr.) — Golden Plusia
Plusia chrysitis (L.) — Burnished Brass
P. festucae (L.) — Gold Spot
P. v-aureum (Huebn.) — Beautiful Golden Y
P. gamma (L.) — Silver Y
P. interrogationis (L.) — Scarce Silver Y
Abrostola tripartita (Hufn.) — Spectacle

LYMANTRIIDAE

Orgyia gonostigma (Fabr.) — Scarce Vapourer — Dartmeet
O. antiqua (L.) — Vapourer
Dasychira pudibunda (L.) — Pale Tussock
Lymantria monacha (L.) — Black Arches

STERRHIDAE

Sterrha sylvestraria (Huebn.) — Dotted Border Wave
S. fuscovenosa (Goeze) — Dwarf Cream Wave
S. trigeminata (Haw.) — Treble Brown Spot
Scopula remutaria (Huebn.) — Cream Wave
S. immutata L. — Lesser Cream Wave
S. imitaria (Huebn.) — Small Blood Vein
Cosymbia trilinearia (Borkh.) — Clay Triple Lines
C. punctaria (L.) — Maiden's Blush
Calothysanis amata (L.) — Blood Vein

GEOMETRIDAE

Chlorissa viridata (L.) — Small Grass Emerald
Geometra papilionaria (L.) — Large Emerald
Pseudoterpna pruinata (Hufn.) — Grass Emerald
Acasis viretata (Huebn.) — Yellow-barred Brindle
Chloroclystis coronata (Geyer) — V-Pug
C. rectangulata (L.) — Green Pug
C. debiliata (Huebn.) — Bilberry Pug
Gymnoscelis pumilata (Huebn.) — Double-striped Pug
Eupithecia expallidata Guen. — Bleached Pug

E. albipunctata (Haw.)	White-spotted Pug
E. castigata (Huebn.)	Grey Pug
E. laricata Frey.	Larch Pug
E. trisignaria Herr.-Schaef.	Triple-spotted Pug
E. abbreviata Step.	Brindled Pug
E. exiguata (Huebn.)	Mottled Pug
E. nanata (Huebn.)	Narrow-winged Pug
Chesias rufata (Fabr.)	Broom-tip
Calocalpe undulata (L.)	Scallop Shell
Lygris prunata (L.)	Phoenix
Eulype hastata (L.)	Argent and Sable
Thera firmata (Huebn.)	Pine Carpet
Cidaria fulvata (Forst.)	Barred Yellow
Ecliptoptera silaceata (Schiff.)	Small Phoenix
Lampropteryx suffumata (Schiff.)	Water Carpet
L. ostregiata Metc.	
Coenotephria derivata (Schiff.)	Streamer
Euphyia cuculata (Hufn.)	Royal Mantle
Euchoeca obliterata (Hufn.)	Dingy Shell
Hydrelia sylvata (Schiff.)	Waved Carpet
Xanthorhoe designata (Hufn.)	Flame Carpet
Calostigia salicata (Huebn.)	Striped Twin-spot Carpet

BREPHIDAE
Odezia atrata (L.)
Alsophila aescularia (Schiff.)
Brephos parthenias (L.)

SELIDOSEMIDAE

Semiothisa notata (L.)	Peacock
S. alternata (Schiff.)	Sharp-angled Peacock
S. liturata (Clerck)	Tawny-barred Angle
Ectropis luridata (Borkh.)	
E. consonaria (Huebn.)	
Cleora ribeata (Clerck)	Satin Carpet
C. lichenaria (Hufn.)	Brussels Lace
Biston strataria (Hufn.)	Oak Beauty
B. betularia (L.)	Peppered
Abraxas grossulariata (L.)	Magpie
Perconia strigillaria (Huebn.)	Grass Wave
Crocata gilvaria (Schiff.)	Straw Belle
C. ochrearia (Rossi)	Yellow Belle
Ellopia prosapiaria (L.)	Barred Red
Anagoga pulveraria (L.)	Barred Umber
Plagodis dolabraria (L.)	Scorched Wing
Angerona prunaria (L.)	Orange

Epione repandaria (Hufn.)	Bordered Beauty	
Selenia bilunaria (Esper)	Early Thorn	
S. lunaria (Schiff.)	Lunar Thorn	
S. tetralunaris (Hufn.)	Purple Thorn	
Deuteronomos alniaria (L.)	Canary-shouldered Thorn	
D. erosaria (Schiff.)	September Thorn	
D. fuscantaria (Haw.)	Dusky Thorn	
Ennomos autumnaria (Wern.)	Large Thorn	

POLYPLOCIDAE

Habrosyne derasa (L.)	Buff Arches
Thyatira batis (L.)	Peach Blossom
Tethea duplaris (L.)	Lesser Satin
Asphalia diluta (Schiff.)	Lesser Lutestring
Achlya flavicornis (L.)	Yellow Horned
Polyploca ridens (Fabr.)	Frosted Green

SPHINGIDAE

Hemaris fuciformis (L.)	Broad-bordered Bee Hawk
H. tityus (L.)	Narrow-bordered Bee Hawk
Macroglossa stellatarum (L.)	Humming-bird Hawk
Deilephila porcellus (L.)	Small Elephant
D. elpenor (L.)	Elephant
Sphinx ligustri (L.)	Privet Hawk
Acherontia atropos (L.)	Death's Head Hawk
Smerinthus ocellatus (L.)	Eyed Hawk
Dilina tilias (L.)	Lime Hawk
Celerio v. livornica (Esper)	Striped Hawk
Laothoe populi (L.)	Poplar Hawk

NOTODONTIDAE

Clostera curtula (L.)	Chocolate-tip	
Notodonta ziczac (L.)	Pebble Prominent	
N. dromedarius (L.)	Iron Prominent	
N. anceps (Goeze)	Great Prominent	
Drymonia ruficornis (Hufn.)	Lunar Marbled Brown	
Stauropus fagi (L.)	Lobster	Rare
Pterostoma palpina (L.)	Pale Prominent	
Lophopteryx capucina (L.)	Coxcomb Prominent	
Cerura vinula (L.)	Puss	
C. hermelina (Goeze)	Poplar Kitten	
C. furcula (Clerck)	Sallow Kitten	
Phalera bucephala (L.)	Buff-tip	

SATURNIIDAE

Saturnia pavonia (L.)	Emperor

PAPILIONOIDEA

SATYRIDAE
Pararge aegeria (L.)	Speckled Wood
Dira megera (L.)	Wall
Agapetes galathea (L.)	Marbled White
Eumenis semele (L.)	Grayling
Maniola tithonus (L.)	Gatekeeper
M. jurtina (L.)	Meadow Brown
Coenonympha pamphilus (L.)	Small Heath
Aphantopus hyperantus (L.)	Ringlet

NYMPHALIDAE
Argynnis selene (Schiff.)	Small Pearl-bordered Fritillary	
A. euphrosyne (L.)	Pearl-bordered Fritillary	
A. cydippe (L.)	High Brown Fritillary	
A. paphia (L.)	Silver-washed Fritillary	
A. aglaja (L.)	Dark Green Fritillary	
Euphydryas aurinia (v. Rott.)	Marsh Fritillary	
Vanessa atalanta (L.)	Red Admiral	
V. cardui (L.)	Painted Lady	
V. huntera Fabr.		Walkhampton 1942
Aglais urticae (L.)	Small Tortoiseshell	
Nymphalis polychloros (L.)	Large Tortoiseshell	
N. io (L.)	Peacock	
Polygonia c-album (L.)	Comma	

LYCAENIDAE
Lampides boeticus (L.)	Long-tailed Blue	Lydford 1945
Plebeius argus (L.)	Silver-studded Blue	
Aricia agestis (Schiff.)	Brown Argus	
Polyommatus icarus (v. Rott.)	Common Blue	
Lysandra bellargus (v. Rott.)	Adonis Blue	
Maculinea arion (L.)	Large Blue	2 weak colonies
Celastrina argiolus (L.)	Holly Blue	
Lycaena phlaeas (L.)	Small Copper	
Callophrys rubi (L.)	Green Hairstreak	
Thecla betulae (L.)	Brown Hairstreak	
T. quercus (L.)	Purple Hairstreak	
Strymon w-album (Knoch.)	White Letter Hairstreak	Ashburton, 1943-44

PIERIDAE
Leptidea sinapis (L.)	Wood White
Pieris brassicae (L.)	Large White
P. rapae (L.)	Small White
P. napi (L.)	Green-veined White
Euchloe cardamines (L.)	Orange-tip
Colias hyale (L.)	Pale Clouded Yellow

C. croceus (Geoffr.) — Clouded Yellow
Gonepteryx rhamni (L.) — Brimstone

HESPERIIDAE
Erynnis tages (L.) — Dingy Skipper
Pyrgus malvae (L.) — Grizzled Skipper
Thymelicus sylvestris (Poda.) — Small Skipper
Augiades venata (Brem. & Grey) — Large Skipper

DREPANOIDEA

DREPANIDAE
Cilix glaucata (Scop.) — Chinese Character
Drepana lacertinaria (L.) — Scalloped Hook-tip
D. falcataria (L.) — Pebble Hook-tip
D. binaria (Hufn.) — Oak Hook-tip

BOMBYCOIDEA

LASIOCAMPIDAE
Lasiocampa quercus (L.) and var.
　callunae Palm. — Northern Eggar
Poecilocampa populi (L.) — December
Eriogaster lanestri (L.) — Small Eggar
Macrothylacia rubi (L.) — Fox
Trichiura crataegi (L.) — Pale Oak Eggar
Malacosoma neustria (L.) — Lackey
Philudoria potatoria (L.) — Drinker
Gastropacha quercifolia (L.) — Lappet

PSYCHOIDEA

HETEROGENEIDAE
Heterogenea asella (Schiff.) — Triangle — **Old Records**

ZYGAENIDAE
Zygaena filipendulae (L.) — Six-spot Burnet
Z. trifolii (Esper) — Five-spot Burnet
Procris statices (L.) — Forester

COSSOIDEA

COSSIDAE
Cossus cossus (L.) — Goat

TINAEOIDEA

SESIIDAE
Aegeria formicaeformis (Esper) — Red-tipped Clearwing
A. tipuliformis (Clerck) — Currant Clearwing
Sesia apiformis (Clerck) — Hornet
Sphecia bembeciformis (Huebn.) — Lunar Hornet

D

R

COLEOPTERA

A small selection is listed including only the more interesting species.

Peculiar to the region

Carabus intricatus (L.)   In wooded valleys running south.

Characteristic of high regions

Pterostichus aethiops Panz.

Corymbites aeneus (L.)

Hypnoidus dermestoides (Herbst.)

Northern species

Oreodytes (Hydroporus) septentrionalis (Gyll)

Hydraena minutissima Step.

Barynotus v. schonherri (Zett.)

Coccinella quinquepunctata (L.)

Unusual species

Calosoma inquisitor (L.)

Agabus melanarius Aube

Hydrochus nitidicollis Muls.

Orectochilus villosus (Muell.)

Oxypoda spectabilis Maerk.

Gnypeta coerulea (Schlb.)

Calodera riparia Er.

Acidota crenata (Fabr.)

Metaxya islandica (Kraatz)

Quedius longicornis Kraatz

Q. auricomus Kies.

Cholera spadicea (Sturm.)

Corymbites siaelandicus (Muell.)

Hydrocyphon deflexicollis (Muell.)

Haplocnemus nigricornis (Fabr.)

Strangalia aurulenta (Fabr.)

Cis jacquemarti Mellie

Chrysolina fastuosa (Scop.)

Trachodes hispidus (L.)

HYMENOPTERA ACULEATA

CHRYSIDIDAE

Notozus constrictus Foerst

Omalus aeneus (Fabr.)

O. auratus (L.)

Hedychridium roseum (Rossi)

H. integrum (Dahlb.)

Spintharis neglecta (Shuck).

Chrysis cyanea (L.)

C. ignita (L.)

C. succincta (L.)

C. viridula (L.)

TIPHIIDAE

Tiphia femorata Fabr.

T. minuta V. d. Lind.

SAPYGIDAE

Sapyga quinquepunctata (Fabr.)

MYRMOSIDAE

Myrmosa atra (Panz.)

MUTILLIDAE

Mutilla europaea (L.)

FORMICIDAE

Myrmecina graminicola (Latr.)

Myrmica laevinodis Nyl.

M. ruginodis Nyl.

M. sulcinodis Nyl.

M. scabrinodis Nyl.

Leptothorax acervorum (Fabr.)

Lasius fuliginosus (Latr.)

L. niger (L.)

L. alienus (Foerst.)

L. flavus (Fabr.)

L. umbratus (Nyl.)

Formica rufa L.

L. nylanderi (Foerst.)
Tetramorium caespitum (**L.**)
Tapinoma erraticum (Latr.)

POMPILIDAE

Cryptocheilus affinis (V. d. Lind.)
Priocnemis perturbator (Harris)
P. coriaceus Dahlb.
P. minor (Zett.)
P. exaltatus (Febr.)
P. femoralis (Dahlb.)
P. pusillus Sch.
P. clementi Haupt.
Deuteragenia variegata (L.)

VESPIDAE

Eumenes coarctata (**L.**)
Odynerus spinipes (L.)
Ancistrocerus callosus (Thom.)
A. parietum (L.)
A. pictus (Curt.)
A. trimarginatus (Zett.)
A. parietinus (L.)
A. antilope (Panz.)
Symmorphus crassicornis (Panz)

SPHECIDAE

Astata boops (Schr.)
Tachysphex pompiliformis (Panz.)
Trypoxylon figulus (L.)
T. clavicerum Lep.
T. attenuatum Sm.
Ammophila sabulosa (L.)
Podalonia viatica (L.)
Spilomena troglodytes (V. d. Lind.)
Pemphredon lugubris (Fabr.)
Cemonus shuckardi Mor.
C. lethifer Shuck.
Diodontus minutus (Fabr.)
Passaloecus insignis (V. d. Lind.)
P. gracilis (Curt.)
P. monilicornis Dahlb.
Mimesa equestris (Fabr.)
M. rufa (Panz.)
Psenulus atratus (Fabr.)
P. concolor (Dahlb.)
Oxybelus uniglumis (L.)
Crabro cribrarius (L.)
C. peltarius (v. Schr.)

F. exsecta Nyl.
F. fusca L.

Pseudagenia carbonaria (**Scop.**)
Anoplius fuscus (L.)
A. nigerrimus (Scop.)
A. concinnus (Dahlb.)
Pompilus cinctellus Spin.
P. minutulus Dahlb.
P. spissus Sch.
P. trivialis Dahlb.
P. crassicornis Shuck.

S. elegans (Wesm.)
S. sinuatissimus Rich.
Vespa crabro L.
Vespula vulgaris (L.)
V. germanica (Fabr.)
V. rufa (L.)
V. austriaca (Panz.)
V. norvegica (Fabr.)

Ablepharipus podagricus (V. d. Lind.)
Crossocerus tarsatus (Shuck.)
C. varus Lep. & Bru.
C. anxius (Wesm.)
C. elongatulus (V. d. Lind.)
Blepharipus dimidiatus (Fabr.)
Hoplocrabro quadrimaculatus (Fabr.)
Clytochrysus zonatus (Panz.)
C. cavifrons (Thom.)
C. chrysotomus (Lep. & Bru.)
Solenius continuus (Fabr.)
Metacrabro lituratus (Panz.)
Corynopus coarctatus (Scop.)
Rhopalum clavipes (L.)
Lindenius albilabris (Fabr.)
Entomognathus brevis (V. d. Lind.)
Nysson spinosus (Forst.)
N. trimaculatus (Rossi)
N. dimidiatus Jur.
Gorytes mystaceus (L.)
Harpactus tumidus (Panz.)
Mellinus arvensis (L.)

Sphecidae

Coelocrabro leucostomoides Rich.
C. pubescens (Shuck.) **?**
C. cetratus (Shuck.)
C. capitosus (Shuck.)

Apidae

Colletes succincta (L.)
C. similis Sch.
C. daviesana Sm. F.
Prosopis communis (Nyl.)
P. hyalinata (Sm. F.)
P. confusa (Nyl.)
P. pictipes (Nyl.)
P. minutus Fabr.
Halictus rubicundus (Chr.)
H. xanthopus (Kirby)
H. laevigatus (Kirby)
H. zonulus Sm. F.
H. leucozonius (Schr.)
H. quadrinotatus (Kirby)
H. lativentris (Sch.)
H. calceatus (Scop.)
H. albipes (Fabr.)
H. fratellus Per.
H. villosulus (Kirby)
H. pauperatus (Br.)
H. punctatissimus (Sch.)
H. minutissimus (Kirby)
H. nitidiusculus (Kirby)
H. minutus (Schr.)
H. tumulorum (L.)
H. smeathmanellus (Kirby)
H. morio (Fabr.)
H. leucopus (Kirby)
Sphecodes spinulosus v. Hag.
S. gibbus (L.)
S. monilicornis (Kirby)
S. rubicundus v. Hag.
S. ephippius (L.)
S. puncticeps Thom.
S. hyalinatus v. Hag.
S. crassus Thom.
S. fasciatus (v. Hag.)
Andrena haemorrhoa (Fabr.)
A. carbonaria (L.)
A. bimaculata (Kirby)

Cerceris rybyensis (L.)
C. arenaria (L.)
C. cunicularia (Schr.)

A. minutuloides Perk.
A. minutula (Kirby)
A. subopaca Nyl.
A. ovatula (Kirby)
A. similus Sm. F.
A. wilkella (Kirby)
A. dorsata (Kirby)
Melitta leporina (Panz.)
M. tricincta Kirby
Panurgus banksianus (Kirby)
Anthophora acervorum (L.)
A. furcata (Panz.)
A. bimaculata (Panz.)
Eucera longicornis (L.)
Melecta punctata (Fabr.)
Epeolus variegatus (L.)
E. cruciger (Panz.)
Nomada germanica Panz.
N. armata Her.-Sch.
N. tormentillae Alfk.
N. rufipes Fabr.
N. flavopicta (Kirby)
N. goodeniana (Kirby)
N. marshamella (Kirby)
N. lineola (Panz.)
N. ruficornis (L.)
N. leucophthalma (Kirby)
N. hirtipes Per.
N. lava Panz.
N. fabriciana (L.)
N. flavoguttata (Kirby)
N. sheppardana (Kirby)
Megachile maritima (Kirby)
M. willughbiella (Kirby)
M. circumcincta (Kirby)
M. centuncularis (L.)
M. ligniscea (Kirby)
M. versicolor Sm. F.
Coelioxys rufescens Lep. & Ser.
C. elongata Lep.

APIDAE

A. *flavipes* Panz.
A. *thoracica* (Fabr.)
A. *pubescens* Oliv.
A. *nigroaenea* (Kirby)
A. *bicolor* (Fabr.)
A. *angustior* (Kirby)
A. *rosae* Panz.
A. *jacobi* Perk.
A. *trimmerana* (Kirby)
A. *fucata* Sm. F.
A. *lapponica* Zett.
A. *synadelpha* Perk.
A. *helvola* (L.)
A. *armata* (Gmel.)
A. *clarkella* (Kirby)
A. *apicata* Sm. F.
A. *praecox* (Scop.)
A. *fuscipes* (Kirby)
A. *nigriceps* (Kirby)
A. *denticulata* (Kirby)
A. *barbilabris* (Kirby)
A. *fulvago* (Chr.)
A. *labialis* (Kirby)
A. *humilis* Imh.
A. *coitana* (Kirby)
A. *tarsata* Nyl.
A. *hattorfiana* (Fabr.)
A. *marginata* Fabr.
A. *chrysosceles* (Kirby)
A. *labiata* Fabr.
A. *alfkenella* Perk.
A. *saundersella* Perk.
A. *falsifica* Perk.

C. *inermis* (Kirby)
Anthidium manicatum (L.)
Stelis punctatissima (Kirby)
S. *phaeoptera* (Kirby)
S. *ornatula* (Klug)
Osmia rufa (L.)
O. *coerulescens* (L.)
O. *leaiana* (Kirby)
O. *aurulenta* (Panz.)
O. *leucomelana* (Kirby)
Chelostoma florisomme (L.)
Bombus terrestris (L.)
B. *lucorum* (L.)
B. *lapidarius* (L.)
B. *pratorum* (L.)
B. *jonellus* (Kirby)
B. *lapponicus* (Fabr.)
B. *soröensis* (Fabr.)
B. *ruderatus* (Fabr.)
B. *hortorum* (L.)
B. *subterraneus* (L.)
B. *distenguendus* Mor.
B. *ruderarius* (Muell.)
B. *sylvarum* (L.)
B. *agrorum* (Fabr.)
B. *muscorum* (L.)
B. *humilis* (Ill.)
Psithyrus rupestris (Fabr.)
P. *vestalis* (Geoffr.)
P. *bohemicus* (Seidl)
P. *barbutellus* (Kirby)
P. *campestris* (Panz.)
P. *sylvestris* (Lep.)

HYMENOPTERA SYMPHYTA

PAMPHILIIDAE

Neurotoma saltuum (L.)
Pamphilius sylvarum (Step.)
P. *gyllenhali* (Dahlb.)
P. *vafer* (L.)

SIRICIDAE

Urocerus gigas (L.)

XIPHYDRIIDAE

Xiphydria camelus (L.)

P. *hortorum* (Klug)
P. *inanitus* (de Vill.)
P. *sylvaticus* (L.)

CEPHIDAE

Hartigia linearis (Schr.)
H. nigra (Harris)
Janus femoratus (Curt.)

ARGIDAE

Arge coerulescens (Geoffr.)
A. rustica (L.)
A. ustulata (L.)

CIMBICIDAE

Cimbex femorata (L.)
Trichiosoma lucorum (L.)
T. sorbi (Hart.)
Zaraea fasciata (L.)

DIPRIONIDAE

Diprion pini (L.)

TENTHREDINIDAE

Tenthredo maculata Geoffr.
T. mesomelas L.
T. temula Scop.
T. atra L.
T. moniliata Klug.
T. livida L.
T. ferruginea Schr.
T. balteata Klug.
T. colon Klug.
T. zona Klug.
T. scrophulariae L.
T. arcuata Forst.
T. schaefferi Klug
T. marginella Fabr.
T. olivacea Klug
T. viridis L.
T. punctulata Klug
T. picta Klug
Perineura rubi (Panz.)
Aglaostigma aucuparia (Klug)
A. fulvipes (Scop.)
Tenthredopsis nassata (L.)
T. litterata (Geoffr.)
Macrophyla punctum-album (L.)
M. albicincta (Schr.)
M. montana (Scop.)
M. ribis (Schr.)
M. duodecimpunctata (L.)
M. blanda (Fabr.)

Cephus pallipes (Klug.)
C. cultratus v. Eversm.

A. pagana (Panz.)
A. cyanocrocea (Forst.)

Abia sericea (L.)
A. candens (Kon.)
A. lonicerae (L.)

D. haematodes (Schr.)
D. nigratus (Muell.)
D. niger (L.)
D. aeneus Hart.
D. rugulosus Dal. Tor.
D. sanguinicollis (Klug) v. *fumosus* Step.
Monsoma pulverata (Retz.)
Monostegia abdominalis (Fabr.)
Eriocampa ovalis (L.)
Allantus togatus Panz.
Harpiphorus lepidus (Klug)
Emphytus rufocinctus (Retz.)
E. cinctus (L.)
E. cingulatus (Scop.)
Apethymus braccatus (Gmel.)
A. abdominalis (Lep.)
Protemphytus tener (Fall.)
P. pallipes (Spin.)
P. carpini (Hart.)
Ametastegia albipes (Thom.)
A. equiseti (Fall.)
A. glabrata (Fall.)
Empria immersa (Klug)
E. parvula (Kon.)
E. pumila (Kon.)
E. excisa (Thom.)
E. liturata (Gmel.)
E. tridens (Kon.)
Periclista albida (Klug)

Tenthredinidae

M. annulata (Geoffr.)
M. rapae (L.)
M. antennata (Klug)
Loderus eversmanni (Kirby)
L. vestigalis (Klug)
Dolerus pratensis (L.)
D. cothurnatus Lep.
D. aericeps Thom.
D. germanicus (Fabr.)
D. madidus (Klug)
D. ferrugatus Lep.
D. gonager (Fabr.)
D. puncticollis Thom.
D. ponsilensis Cam.
D. asper Zadd.
D. picipes (Klug.)
Athalia lineolata Lep.
A. glabricollis Thom.
A. lugens (Klug)
Stromboceros delicatulus (Fall).
Strongylogaster lineata (Chr.)
Brachythops flavens (Klug)
Selandria serva (Fabr.)
Aneugmenus temporalis (Thom.)
A. stramineipes (Klug)
A. fürstenbergensis (Kon.)
Melisandra cinereipes (Klug)
M. morio (Fabr.)
Scolioneura betuleti (Klug)
Metallus pumilus (Klug)
Profenusa pygmaea (Klug)
Messa nana (Klug)
Fenusa ulmi (Sund.)
F. dohrnii (Tisch.)
F. pusilla (Lep.)
Heterarthrus vagans (Fall.)
H. aceris (Mach.)
H. microcephalus (Klug)
Caliroa annulipes (Klug)
C. varipes (Klug)
Endelomyia aethiops (Fabr.)
Cladius pectinicornis (Geoffr.)
Priophorus ulmi (L.)
P. eradiatus (Hart.)
P. tener (Zadd.)

P. lineolata (Klug)
P. pubescens (Zadd.)
Ardis brunniventris (Hart.)
A. sulcata (Cam.)
Monophadnus pallescens (Gmel.)
Halidamia affinis (Fall.)
Blennocampna pusilla (Klug)
B. ruficruris (Brul.)
B. geniculata (Hart.)
B. alternipes (Klug)
B. tenuicornis (Klug)
B. waldheimii (Gimm.)
Tomostethus nigritus (Fabr.)
Entomostethus luteiventris (Klug)
E. punctatus (Kon.)
E. ephippium (Panz.)
P. proxima (Lep.)
Dineura virididorsata (Retz.)
D. stilata (Klug)
Nematus lucidus Panz.
Pteronidea compressicornis (Fabr.)
P. melanocephala (Hart.)
P. collina (Cam.)
P. ferruginea (Foerst.)
P. cadderensis (Cam.)
P. miliaris (Panz.)
P. fagi (Zadd. & Bris.)
P. flavescens (Step.)
P. pavida (Lep.)
P. bipartita (Lep.)
P. myosotidis (Fabr.)
P. viridescens (Cam.)
P. oligospila (Foerst.)
P. polyspila (Foerst.)
P. dispar (Zadd. & Bris.)
P. curtispina (Thom.)
P. capraea (L.)
Amauronematus histrio (Lep.)
A. fallax (Lep.)
A. humeralis (Lep.)
A. viduatus (Zett.)
A. tunicatus (Zadd.)
A. excellens Fors.
A. vittatus (Lep.)
A. amplus Kon.

TENTHREDINIDAE

P. varipes (Lep.)
Mesoneura opaca (Fabr.)
Hemichroa crocea (Geoffr.)
H. alni (L.)
Hoplocampa flava (L.)
H. chrysorrhoea (Klug)
H. pectoralis Thom.
H. crataegi (Klug)
H. alpina (Zett.)
H. rutilicornis (Klug)
Platycampus luridiventris (Fall.)
Croesus septentrionalis (L.)
C. varus (de Vill.)
Pontania leucosticta (Hart.)
P. leucaspis (Tischb.)
P. pedunculi (Hart.)

A. sagmarius Kon.
A. amentorum (Foerst.)
Nematinus acuminatus (Thom.)
N. fuscipennis (Lep.)
N. luteus (Panz.)
Pachynematus apicalis (Hart.)
P. clitellatus (Lep.)
P. rumicis (L.)
P. obductus (Hart.)
P. vagus (Fabr.)
Pristiphora fulvipes (Fall.)
P. melanocarpa (Hart.)
P. ruficornis (Oliv.)
P. pallidiventris (Fall.)
P. monogyniae (Hart.)
P. viridana Kon.

DIPTERA

ORTHORRHAPHA

NEMATOCERA

TIPULIDAE

Tipula (Acutipula) vittata Mg.
T. (Vestiplex) scripta Mg.
T. variipennis Mg.
T. marmorata Mg.
T. pabulina Mg.
T. lateralis Mg.
T. pagana Mg.
T. flavolineata Mg.
T. (Lunatipula) fascipennis Mg.
T. (L.) lunata L.
Nephrotoma dorsalis (Fabr.)
N. crocata (L.)
Dolichopeza albipes (Stroem.)
Dictenidia bimaculata (L.)
Ctenophora pectinicornis (L.)
Cylindrotoma distinctissima (Mg.)
Phalacrocera replicata (L.)
Limonia nubeculosa Mg.
L. macrostigma Schum.
L. didyma Mg.
L. modesta (Mg.)
Pedicea rivosa (L.)
P. littoralis (Mg.)

P. occulta (Mg.)
P. claripennis Verr.
P. immaculata (Mg.)
Dicranota pavida (Hal.)
Limnophila meigeni Verr.
L. dispar (Mg.)
L. lineola (Mg.)
L. fulvonervosa (Schum.)
L. aperta Verr.
L. ferruginea (Mg.)
L. lucorum (Mg.)
L. nemoralis (Mg.)
L. filata (Walk.)
Gonomyia tenella (Mg.)
Erioptera fuscipennis Mg.
E. trivialis Mg.
Ormosia nodulosa (Macq.)
O. varia (Mg.)
O. haemorrhoidalis (Zett.)
Molophilus griseus (Mg.)
M. appendiculatus (Staeg)
Tasiocera murina (Mg.)

TRICHOCERIDAE
Trichocera regelationis (L.)

ANISOPODIDAE
Anisopus fenestralis (Scop.)   *A. punctatus* (Fabr.)

CULICIDAE
Theobaldia morsitans (Theob.)

CHIRONOMIDAE
Anatopynia nebulosa (Mg.)   *H. gracilis* (Goetgh.)
Hydrobaenus leucopogon (Mg.)

SIMULIIDAE
Simulium ornatum Mg.   *S. costatum* Fried.
S. latipes (Mg.)

BIBIONIDAE
Bibio venosus (Mg.)   *B. laniger* Mg.
B. johannis (L.)

MYCETOPHILIDAE
Rhymosia fasciata (Mg.)   *Mycetophila fungorum* (de G.)
Allodia ornaticollis (Mg.)

BRACHYCERA

STRATIOMYIDAE
Beris chalybaeta (Forst.)   *G. flavipes* (Mg.)
Geosargus iridatus (Scop.)   *Chloromya formosa* (Scop.)
G. bipunctatus (Scop.)

RHAGIONIDAE
Xylophagus ater Mg.   *Rhagio tringaria* (L.)
Atherix ibis (Fabr.)   *R. lineola* Fabr.
A. marginata (Fabr.)   *Chrysophilus aureus* (Mg.)

TABANIDAE
Chrysops caecutiens (L.)   *T. bromius* L.
C. quadratus Mg.   *T. cordiger* Mg.
Haematopota pluvialis (L.)   *T. maculicornis* Zett.
H. crassicornis Wahlb.   *T. solstitialis* Mg.
Tabanus bovinus L.

BOMBYLIIDAE
Villa paniscus (Rossi)   *B. canescens* Mikan
Bombylius discolor Mikan

THEREVIDAE
Thereva nobilitata (Fabr.)

ASILIDAE

Isopogon brevirostris (Mg.)
Lasiopogon cinctus (Fabr.)
Dioctria atricapilla Mg.
D. oelandica (L.)
D. rufipes (de G.)
D. baumhaueri Mg.
D. linearis (Fabr.)

Laphria marginata (L.)
Asilus crabroniformis (L.)
Dysmachus trigonus (Mg.)
Machimus atricapillus (Fall.)
Epitriptus cingulatus (Fabr.)
Neoitamus cynaurus (Loew.)

EMPIDIDAE

Platypalpus agilis (Mg.)
P. pallipes (Fall.)
Empis stercorea L.
E. punctata Mg.
E. femorata Fabr.

E. pennaria (Fall.)
E. chioptera (Mg.)
Rhamphomyia tarsata (Mg.)
Trichopeza longicornis (Mg.)
Clinocera bipunctata (Hal.)

DOLICHOPODIIDAE

Dolichopus atratus Mg.
Liancalus virens (Scop.)

Argyra diaphana (Fabr.)
A. leucocephala (Mg.)

CYCLORRHAPHA

ASCHIZA

DORILAIDAE

Dorilas varipes (Mg.)

D. ater (Mg.)

SYRPHIDAE

Paragopsis sabulonum (Fall.)
Myathropa florea (L.)
Eristalinus sepulchralis (L.)
Tubifera cryptarum (Fabr.)
T. pertinax (Scop.)
Ferdinandea cuprea (Scop.)
Zelima segnis (L.)
Z. sylvarum (L.)
Penthesilea berberina (Fabr.)
P. oxyacanthae (Mg.)
P. floccosa (Mg.)
Arctophila fulva (Har.)
Cinxia silentis (Har.)
C. lappona (L.)
Brachyopa bicolor (Fall.)
Rhingia macrocephala (Har.)
Microdon mutabilis (L.)
Volucella inanis (L.)
V. inflata (Fabr.)
V. bombylans (L.)
Neoascia podagrica (Fabr.)
N. dispar (Mg.)

C. solstitialis (Fall.)
Cheilosia granditarsa (Forst.)
C. rosarum (Fabr.)
Platycheirus manicatus (Mg.)
P. discimanus Loew.
P. clypeatus (Mg.)
P. angustatus (Zett.)
P. sticticus (Mg.)
Stenosyrphus compositarum (Verr.)
S. lasiophthalmus (Zett.)
Mesosyrphus punctulatus (Verr.)
M. annulatus (Zett.)
Sphaerophoria menthrasti (L.)
Episyrphus guttatus (Fall.)
E. auricollis (Mg.)
E. cinctus (Fall.)
E. cinctellus (Zett.)
E. balteatus (de G.)
Ischnyrosyrphus glaucius (L.)
I. laternarius (Müll.)
Epistrophe elegans (Har.)
E. grossulariae (Mg.)

SYRPHIDAE

Sphegina clavipes (Fall.)
Baccha elongata (Fabr.)
Chilomyia illustrata (Har.)
C. funebris (Har.)
C. intonsa (Loew.)
C. corydon (Har.)
C. nebulosa (Verr.)
C. albipila (Mg.)
C. fraterna (Mg.)
C. impressa (Loew.)
C. vernalis (Fall.)
Cartosyrphus antiquus (Mg.)
C. scutellatus (Fall.)
C. soror (Zett.)
C. paganus (Mg.)
Orthoneura nobilis (Fall.)
O. splendens (Mg.)
Chrysogaster hirtella Loew.

Pipiza noctiluca (L.)
P. lugubris (Fabr.)
Chrysotoxum cautum (Har.)
C. festivum (L.)
C. bicinctum (L.)
Xanthogramma pedissequum (Har.)
Didea fasciata Macq.
Scaeva pyrastri (L.)
S. selenitica (Mg.)
Metasyrphus latifasciatus (Macq.)
M. nitens (Zett.)
Syrphella albostriata (Fall.)
S. tricincta (Fall.)
S. venusta (Mg.)
Syrphus lucorum (L.)
Syrphidis ribesii (L.)
S. vitripennis (Mg.)
S. nitidicollis (Mg.)

SCHIZOPHORA

ACALYPTERAE

CONOPIDAE
Conops flavipes L.
Physocephala rufipes (Fabr.)

Myopa buccata (L.)
M. testacea (L.)

OTITIDAE
Herina frondescentiae (L.)

PALLOPTERIDAE
Palloptera angelicae v. Ras.

DRYOMYZIDAE
Dryomyza flaveola (Fabr.)

Neuroctena anilis (Fall.)

TRYPETIDAE
Vidalia cornuta (Scop.)
Trypeta cylindrica (R.-D.)
T. tussilaginis (Fabr.)

Xyphosia miliaria (Schrank)
Tephritis vespertina (Loew.)

LAUXANIIDAE
Calliopium aeneum (Fall.)
Minettia longipennis (Fabr.)

Prorhaphochaeta inusta (Mg.)
Cnemacantha pallidiventris (Fall.)

PSILIDAE
Loxocera sylvatica Mg.

Psila fimetaria (L.)

SEPSIDAE
Nemopoda nitidula (Fall.)

SCIOMYZIDAE
Pelidnoptera nigripennis (Fabr.)
Tetanocera elata (Fabr.)
T. ferruginea Fall.
T. robusta Loew.

CHAMAEMYIIDAE
Leucopis griseola (Fall.)

OPOMYZIDAE
Opomyza germinationis (L.)

Lunigera chaerophylli (Fabr.)
Trypetoptera punctulata (Scop.)
Ilione albiseta (Scop.)

CALYPTERAE

CORDILURIDAE
Scopeuma stercorarium (L.)

LARVAEVORIDAE
Brachicheta strigata (Mg.)
Exorista simulans (Mg.)
Crocuta geniculata (De G.)
Ernestia rudis (Fall.)
Varichaeta radicum (Fabr.)
Lypha dubia (Fall.)
Gymnocheta viridis (Fall.)
Linnaemya vulpina (Fall.)
Bithea spreta (Mg.)
Larvaevora grossa (L.)
L. ferox (Panz.)
Servillia lurida (Fabr.)

CALLIPHORIDAE
Sarcophaga carnaria (L.)
Metopia argyrocephala (Mg.)
Hypoderma lineatum (de Vill.)
H. bovis (L.)

MUSCIDAE
Pyrellia cyanicolor Zett.
Graphomya maculata (Scop.)
Mesembrina meridiana (L.)
Morellia hortorum (Fall.)

S. squalidum (Mg.)

S. ursina (Mg.)
Anthoica inanis (Fall.)
Thelaira leucozons (Panz.)
Pelatachina tibialis (Fall.)
Macquartia flavipes (Mg.)
Cleonice grisea (Fall.)
Dexiosoma caninum (Fabr.)
Myocera carinifrons (Fall.)
Dexia vacua (Fall.)
D. rustica (Fabr.)
Alophora hemiptera (Fabr.)

Calliphora erythrocephala (Mg.)
C. vomitoria (L.)
Onesia biseta Villen.

M. simplex (Loew.)
Haematobia stimulans (Mg.)
Fannia hamata (Macq.)

GLOSSARY

A FEW TECHNICAL and local terms, the meanings of which it has been considered inconvenient to incorporate into the text, are defined below.

ANCIENT TENEMENTS   There are 35 of these on Dartmoor. They are farms of great antiquity, probably antedating the " Perambulations." They are not owned by the Duchy of Cornwall (except by subsequent purchase), being held by Copy of Court Roll, and carrying various privileges and obligations.

BIOTITE   One of the micas. A silicate of aluminium, potassium, magnesium and iron. Dark brown to black in colour, most of the tiny black scales in granite being this mineral. When hydrated it alters to form chlorite.

BRECCIA   A sedimentary rock made of angular fragments cemented together. Usually formed as a result of deposition of fragments eroded by wind and weather, and therefore not water-worn.

CARINATION   In pottery, a raised keel or shoulder angle on the surface of a vessel.

CHLORITE   See Biotite. A hydrated silicate of aluminium and magnesium (and iron), produced commonly as an alteration product of biotite. Usually green in colour.

FELSPARS   Silicates of aluminium and potassium, sodium or calcium. Clear and colourless when fresh, but usually altered and cloudy after exposure. They form the large, cream or pink, crystals so prominent in many granites, especially on Dartmoor.

FERRULE   A bronze protector for the base of a spear shaft.

HAEMATITE   A red, brown or blackish iron oxide.

IGNEOUS ROCKS   Crystalline rocks produced directly by the cooling of molten material from the earth's interior.

IN-COUNTRY   The name by which the inhabitants of Dartmoor refer to the cultivated lands off the Moor.

LYNCHET   Cultivation terraces on the sides of hills, usually regarded as of pre-historic date.

MAGMA   The hot molten material within parts of the earth's crust, which on cooling crystallises as igneous rock.

METAMORPHIC AUREOLE   The belt of rock surrounding a block of igneous rock

255

	intruded from below. The great pressure and heat exerted by the intrusion compresses and bakes the strata into which it is exuded, and they are correspondingly altered through thicknesses of three-quarters of a mile or more.
NEWTAKE	Originally a right of holders of Ancient Tenements to enclose eight acres of land (exclusive of bog and rock) if the father and grandfather of the tenant had held the land successively. Latterly, abused by " squatters " and nowadays no longer exercised.
OROGENIC ACTIVITY	Movements of the earth's crust which result in the upfolding of mountain ranges.
PALSTAVE	A type of Bronze axe.
PNEUMATOLYSIS	A complex process whereby rocks become hydrated and so altered in mineral content and structure.
SEDIMENTARY ROCKS	Rocks formed by the deposition of water—or wind-borne fragments, usually cemented together by infiltrated material. Examples are sandstones, chalk, slates and shales.
TIN-STREAMING	The old method of extracting tin ore by placing gravel on an inclined plane and stirring while water from a stream flows rapidly over it. The lighter refuse is swept away and the heavy ore left behind.
TOURMALINE	A boro-silicate of aluminium with either magnesium, iron or alkali metals. Usually brown or very dark green. A constituent of certain types of granite.
VOLCANIC TRAP	A dark rock, usually columnar in structure, formed as a result of eruption of molten magma at the earth's surface.

BIBLIOGRAPHY

THE LIST of works appended does not pretend to be fully comprehensive. It includes, however, most of the books and papers which are readily accessible and which the interested reader may wish to consult.

SECTION I.   General and historical works.

CARRINGTON, N. T. (1826). Dartmoor. London, Hatchard & Son.
CROSSING, W. (1914). Guide to Dartmoor. Plymouth, Western Morning News.
DAVIES, E. W. L. (1863). Dartmoor Days. London, Longman, Green, Longman, Roberts & Green.
FALCON, T. A. (1900). Dartmoor Illustrated. Exeter, James G. Commin.
FOX, AILEEN (1954). Excavations at Kestor, an Early Iron Age Settlement near Chagford, Devon. Trans. Devons. Assn. 86, 21-62.
FOX, AILEEN (1957). Excavations on Dean Moor, in the Avon Valley, 1954-1956. The Late Bronze Age Settlement. ibid 89, 18-77.
GORDON, DOUGLAS (1931). Dartmoor in all its Moods. London, John Murray.
GORDON, D. St. LEGER- (1950). Devonshire. London, Robert Hale.
GOULD, S. BARING (1900). A Book of Dartmoor. London, Methuen & Co.
HOSKINS, W. G. (Ed.) (1957). Dartmoor National Park. National Park Guides No.1. London, H.M. Stationery Office.
MOORE, T. (1829). The History of Devonshire. London, Robert Jennings.
PAGE, J. L. W. (1889). An Exploration of Dartmoor. London, Seeley & Co.
PAGE, J. L. W. (1893). The Rivers of Devon. London, Seeley & Co.
PAGE, W. (1906). A History of Devonshire (Victoria History of the Counties of England), Vol. I. London, Constable & Son.
PARISH, C. W. (1947). The Creation of an Industry. London (Printed privately).
POLWHELE, R. (1797). History of Devonshire. London, Trewman & Son.
RISDON, T. (c. 1620). The Chorographical Description or Survey of the County of Devon. Reprinted 1811. London, Rees & Curtis.
ROWE, SAMUEL (1896). Perambulation of the Antient and Royal Forest of Dartmoor. (3rd Ed.). Exeter, James G. Commin.
THOMPSON, W. H. (1932). Devon, a Survey of it, Coasts, Moors and Rivers. London, University of London Press.
(1945). Report on National Parks in England and Wales. Cmd. 6628. (The Dower Report). London, H.M. Stationery Office.
(1947). Report of the National Parks Committee, England and Wales. Cmd. 7121. London, H.M. Stationery Office.

(1947). Conservation of Nature in England and Wales. Cmd. 7122. London. H.M. Stationery Office.

(1947). Needs of the Armed Forces for Land for Training and Other Purposes. Cmd. 7278. London, H.M. Stationery Office.

WORTH, R. H. (1953). Dartmoor, Plymouth.

WORTH, R. N. (1886). History of Devon, London. Elliot Stock.

SECTION II. Geology, Climate and Topography.

ANON. (1947). Devon and Cornwall, a Preliminary Survey. Exeter, Wheaton & Co.

ANON. (1946-47). The Joint-Mitnor Cave. Trans. & Proc. Torquay Nat. Hist. Soc. X: 1-2.

BRAMMALL, A. (1926). The Dartmoor Granite. Proc. Geol. Ass. Lond. 37: 251-77.

(1912) Dartmoor. Mem. Geol. Surv. U.K.

(1913) Newton Abbot. Mem. Geol. Surv. U.K.

STAMP, L. D. (1941). The Land of Britain; Devonshire. Land. Util. Surv. 92.

STAMP, L. D. (1946). Britain's Structure and Scenery. London, Collins.

USHER, W. A. E. (1906). Geology; in Page, A History of Devonshire (*vide antea*).

SECTION III. Natural History.

BURR, M. (1936). British Grasshoppers and their Allies. London. Philip Allen & Co.

CHRISTY, M. & WORTH, R. H. (1922). Ancient Dwarfed Oak Woods of Dartmoor. Trans. Devons. Ass. 54: 291-342.

CLAPHAM, A. R. (1946). Check-list of British Vascular Plants. J. Ecol. 33: 308.

CLAPHAM, A. R., TUTIN, T. G. & WARBURG, E. F. (1952). Flora of the British Isles. Cambridge University Press.

CLARK, E. J. (1948). Studies in the Ecology of British Grasshoppers. Trans. Roy. Entom. Soc. 99: 173-222.

DEVON (1929-52). Ann. Rep. Devon Bird Watching and Preserv. Soc. Exeter.

DIXON, H. N. (1924). Student's Handbook of British Mosses.

D'URBAN, W. S. M. & MATHEW, M.A. (1895). The Birds of Devon. (2nd Ed.). London. R. H. Porter.

GODWIN, (H. 1934). Pollen Analysis, I & II. New Phytol. 33: 278-305.

GODWIN, H., CONOLLY, A. P. & MEGAW, E. M. (1950). Late Glacial Deposits in Cornwall. Phil. Trans. Rog. Soc. B. 234: 399-469.

GOOD, R. (1947). The Geography of Flowering Plants. London, Longman.

HARPER, J. H. D. (1951). Bat Banding in Devonshire. Trans. Devons. Ass. 83: 272-277.

HARRIS, G. T. (1921). Ecological Notes on Wistman's Wood and Black Tor Copse. Trans. Devons. Ass. 53: 232-45.

HARRIS, G. T. (1938). An Ecological Reconnaissance of Dartmoor. Trans. Devons. Ass. 70: 37-55.

LACK, D. (1933). Habitat Selection in Birds. J. Anim. Ecol. 2: 239-62.

LACK, D. (1935). The Breeding Bird Population of British Heaths and Moorland. J. Anim. Ecol. 4: 43-51.

LACK, D. (1939). Further Changes in the Breckland Avifauna caused by Afforestation. J. Anim. Ecol. 8: 277-85.

LACK, D. & VENABLES, L. S. V. (1939). The Habitat Distribution of British Woodland Birds. J. Anim. Ecol. 8: 39-71.

MARTIN, W. K. & FRASER, G. T. (1939). Flora of Devon. Arbroath, T. Buncle & Co.

NEAL, E. G. (1948). The Badger. London, Collins.

RAISTRICK, A. (1931). The Glacial Maximum and Retreat. Trans. Nth. Nat. Un.

RICHARDS, T. J. (1952). *Nemobius Sylvestris* in S. Devon, (1st part) Entomol. 85: 83-87.

STIDSTON, S. T. (1952). A list of Lepidoptera of Devon. Part I. and Introduction, Torquay, Torquay Times and Devonshire Press.

TANSLEY, A. G. (1939). The British Islands and their Vegetation. Cambridge, Cambridge University Press.

WATSON, W. (1932). The Bryophytes and Lichens of Moorland. J. Ecol. 20: 284-313.

The Victoria County History (1906) contains exhaustive lists of the fauna and flora of Devon as then known. In some instances localities have been mentioned, but for the most part occurrence within the County alone is recorded.

The Transactions of the Devonshire Association constitute a mine of information on the history, natural history and archæology of Dartmoor. In particular the annual reports of Sections, Committees and the like should be consulted; also numerous papers by the Worths, father and son (R. N. and R. H.). Pickard and others on archæology, and by C. A. Briggs, L. M. Blackmore, C. W. Bracken, E. Parfitt, R. C. L. Perkins and others on natural history.

Other papers on archæological matters may be found in the files of Antiquity and of the Proceedings of the Devon Archæological Exploration Society.

D.   S

INDEX

Figures in heavy type refer to pages opposite which illustrations will appear.